RECREATING

THE AMERICAN

LONGRIFLE

FIFTH EDITION

by
William Buchele
George Shumway
Peter A. Alexander

GEORGE SHUMWAY PUBLISHER

York · Pennsylvania

*The elegant design above and the title page border have been taken from the work of
Johann Georg Schwandner, first published in 1756. His extensive work provides
many similar designs that can be an inspiration to those designing flintlock firearms.*

Copyright © 1970 by George Shumway
under the title RECREATING THE KENTUCKY RIFLE
Copyright © 1999 by George Shumway
ISBN 0 - 87387 - 107 - 3

Library of Congress Catalog Card No. 97 – 66234
This FIFTH EDITION published 1999.
Printed and bound by The Maple-Vail Book Manufacturing
Group, York, PA

GEORGE SHUMWAY PUBLISHER
3900 Deep Run Lane * York * PA 17402 – 8314
(717) 755-1196

The American muzzle-loading rifle, when regarded simply as a shooting device or gun, became obsolete at the close of the Civil War more than 130 years ago. Today, however, tens of thousands of people are interested in these rifles. They study them, read about them, collect them, shoot them, go hunting with them, and they make them. The National Muzzle Loading Rifle Association has about 25,000 members at present, and there are tens of thousands of others with an active interest.

During the decades of the 1960s and 1970s there was a mushrooming of interest in making or recreating the longrifle. Dillin's well-known book, THE KENTUCKY RIFLE, has been around since 1924, but it was not until 1960 that an important new light was brought to the subject through the publication of two books, Kindig's THOUGHTS ON THE KENTUCKY RIFLE IN ITS GOLDEN AGE, and Kauffman's PENNSYLVANIA-KENTUCKY RIFLE. Kindig's book treats the rifle as a work of art, and for the first time brings this art together in a way that it can be seen, studied, and compared. The conclusion to be drawn from Kindig's book, which of course the author points out, is that the art of the longrifle is one of the most important and finest forms of early American art.

The longrifle, then, is not just a gun that shoots, and not merely an important tool of the frontier American, which we appreciate today because of its part in the romantic past. If designed with taste, and made with skill, it can exist solely as an object of beauty – a complex sculpture of three-dimensional art with two-dimensional art superimposed, made from beautiful wood in combination with iron, brass, silver, and ivory or bone. Some, if not many, of the finer longrifles being made today will be preserved for their esthetic aspects and not be put to use for shooting. But these are exceptions. Nevertheless, they show that it can be well worthwhile to build a fine rifle, even if it never will be shot.

However, the longrifle is basically a shooting device – a dynamic instrument as well as a static object – and to be fully appreciated it needs to be handled, loaded, shot, hunted with, and cleaned, as well as being looked at. I believe that any rifle made today should first of all be a practical firearm, rugged enough to withstand the rigors of a wet winter week in the woods, a fall on a slippery hillside, and a fifty-shot day at a shooting match. But it should be a thing of beauty too.

This book is an attempt to help others through the steps of building a rifle. It all began in 1966 when Bill Buchele wrote, illustrated, and published the First Edition, consisting of 500 copies. The following year the work was turned over to me to distribute and sell, and by 1969 the stock was gone. A Second Edition was needed, enlarged and revised, so I went to work on it with Bill's help. He provided some additional text, and some additional drawings. I added three beginning chapters, contributed some new drawings, and did some editing to tie the parts together. In 1976 I prepared a Third Edition, adding more text and illustrations.

The field of rifle building continued to expand, and as the Third Edition stock ran low it became desirable to revise and enlarge the text and illustrations once again for a Fourth Edition. Peter Alexander worked with me on it. He had conducted classes in rifle building at Prescott, Ontario. In these classes he made use of the Third Edition of this book, and thereby learned some of the many questions not answered by it that arise in the minds of those building their first rifles. Furthermore, there were new developments in the rifle-building field that deserved mention. The Fourth Edition of 1983 now is out of print, and its continuation is this Fifth Edition.

This book is a composite of ideas from William Buchele, Peter Alexander, and me. All of us have contributed both written words and drawings, but in the end it has been my responsibility to do the final writing and editing, and to tie it all together.

It is hoped that a person electing to make a rifle has some imagination as well as some ability working with wood and metal. These will see him or her through the lesser details not treated here. One need not be a skilled machinist or a skilled woodworker to build a rifle, and one need not have a shop full of machine tools. The old timers did their work with hand tools only, and so can the craftsperson of today.

George Shumway   30 May 1998

PREFACE II

It was a pleasure to be asked to work on the previous, or Fourth Edition, of this book with Dr. Shumway in 1982. As he points out, I used the Third Edition as a textbook for my classes in longrifle building, because years before I had learned how to build rifles from the Second Edition and had found it the best book available. When students asked a lot of questions that were not answered by the book, I found it necessary to write out and mimeograph a great deal of additional information for them. So the Fourth Edition, now out of print, and now this Fifth Edition, are attempts to answer the basic questions beginners have when they build their first rifles. We have concentrated on showing as precisely as possible how to accomplish the most important and difficult steps in building a longrifle. More drawings, and photographs of old original, as well as modern, longrifles have been added, to aid the visual reader. The Bibliography should prove useful, as the books listed there are essential to me.

I've been building longrifles since 1971, thanks to the impression Walt Disney's Davy Crockett made on a child many years before. There are few American longrifles of any quality in Canada, so like many across North America, I had to learn what I could from photographs in books. But I knew there was much I couldn't see in pictures, and consequently my guns were never quite right.

I began to travel to the States. I will never forget the moment when I held a fine original – a John Armstrong rifle – in my hands for the first time. The owner must have been amused and amazed at my drooling and babbling enthusiasm. No photographs could capture the incredible beauty of that rifle. And I didn't have a camera either. But the owner allowed me to take the lines off the gun, to sketch and measure, and take rubbings of the inlays. I returned home determined to make an exact duplicate.

That gun was a quantum leap ahead of what I had been doing, but it still wasn't quite right. Each time I came down to the States and examined more originals, I learned a little more, and came a little closer to my goal, which is to make a rifle that is perfect – that no one who knows the American longrifle can fault. I haven't done it yet, but I'm getting there. Gradually I'm moving from exacting recreation toward interpretation. And I can see, some distance in the future, creating my own style entirely. But there is such a great deal to learn.

But that's the excitement of making these longrifles. Each gun is an artistic statement that marks a point in a progress of endless development. The study of the fine originals, and the medium from which they came, also serves as a defense against an increasingly mundane and plastic world which works against the individual.

So, my experience in creating the American longrifle has been particularly wonderful. Apart from the guns themselves, it has brought me into contact with some of the finest people in the world, whom I count friends. These friends made it possible for me to examine many fine original rifles and taught me how to look at them from the maker's point of view. I am grateful also to the modern makers who willingly shared their techniques and knowledge with a fumbling beginner, and even more important, their criticisms of my attempts. I wish there were space here to recognize all these people, but instead I will share with you their techniques and ideas, which is more useful.

This edition, then, is a composite of the thoughts of William Buchele, George Shumway, and everything I've learned. I'm particularly grateful to George Shumway, first for the opportunity to try my hand at this project, and second, for his unfailing patience and humor, which overcame many periods of frustration. In addition, the many discussions we've had have added greatly to my knowledge of the longrifle. And lastly, my thanks to Dorothy Shumway, whose encouragement, Texas brand of humor, and typing skills are in no small measure responsible for the Fourth Edition, and now this Fifth Edition.

Peter A. Alexander

Written 28 January 1983 and slightly modified for this new Fifth Edition - 30 April 1998

WILLIAM M. BUCHELE
(1895 - 1977)

"A thing of beauty
is a joy forever."
This ancient phrase
aptly describes the
flintlock rifles made
by William M. Buchele,
the original author of this
book. In the recently published book
by Robert Weil titled CONTEMPORARY
MAKERS OF MUZZLE LOADING FIREARMS,
William Buchele is acknowledged as one of
the 31 important contemporary rifle makers
whose work is shown there.

One might ask how did Buchele acquire these
skills? Was he apprenticed to a master? In searching
through the facts available to me concerning his life it is
evident that these questions have some answers. Bill Buchele
was a friend of mine, and I knew him for over 15 years.

LaDow "Doc" Johnston, a great friend and admirer of Buchele, wrote of him in an article that appeared in the mag-
azine MUZZLE BLASTS for June 1978: "William Buchele was born in Louisville, Kentucky in 1895, and died in 1977.
He attended schools in Toledo, Ohio. He joined the infantry in World War I. He was trained at Camp Sherman, Ohio.
His infantry training included rifle shooting. Here Buchele showed his first proficiency in using the rifle by having the
highest score and winning his first trophy. After the war he studied art and became very proficient in painting with oils.
He was not situated financially to continue in the artistic field as a full-time avocation. He studied evenings at the Toledo
Museum of Art in design and painting.

In 1930 he became interested in astronomy and he built by himself a six-inch telescope for celestial observation.
Later he constructed a twenty-inch lens and built all the actuating parts for its operation. His proficiency in building
these instruments gained him far reaching fame for his engineering skill and the grinding of precision lenses. During World
War II, Buchele was asked to leave Toledo and superintend an optical plant in Binghamton, New York. His abilities were
recognized by government and industry, and later he built his own factory to produce optical equipment. He was very
successful, yet all during his optical producing experience he had a secret desire to create the art of carving on gun stocks
that would equal or better those of the 16th and 17th century European masters. To accomplish this he turned over the
optical business to his son to operate so that he could concentrate on art and gun stock carving.

In a very few years Buchele became one of the most artistic and capable gunstock carvers in the country, and in the
opinion of knowledgeable persons, better.

One of Buchele's other hobbies was bicycle racing. He became the Ohio champion racer, and in 1974, at the age of
78, became the oldest cyclist to complete the 210 mile trip from Columbus to Portsmouth, Ohio. In 1972 Buchele, on
his bicycle, was involved in a car collision which hospitalized him in intensive care for 30 days. He completely recovered
from this accident."

In May 1974, THE AMERICAN RIFLEMAN magazine featured an article by Ashley Halsey, Jr., titled "The Best Kentuckies—Old or New?" Pictured with descriptions were five of the finest original Kentuckies made by N. Beyer, George
Schroyer and Christian Beck, along with contemporary examples by William Buchele, Carl Pippert, Robert Ditchburn,
Wallace Gusler and George Stanford. This national publicity made him famous. When viewed in perspective, these modern replicas of the 18th century master gunsmiths causes one to excaim with pride. We still can duplicate the old masters.

In searching for information concerning Buchele's life, I came upon some experiences and contacts from existing gunsmiths who knew him well. For example, from Jerry Gutches, Toledo, Ohio:

"He was quite a guy. I wish I had known him years sooner. When I first started making and restoring Kentucky rifles,
Bill always had some advice and encouragement for me. He was the toughest character I ever met (physically). People
who thought he was tough after recuperating from getting hit by a car on his bicycle should have seen what he was doing
physically about two weeks before he went to "talk shop" with one of his fellow gunsmiths, Frederick Sell.

He called me to come over and to buy the last of his gunstock wood. When I got there he had a big patch of surgical
dressing on his forehead. He had at this time quit working in the basement shop, as he had been "blacking out" and had
fallen down the steps a number of times. This was after he had sold most of his tools and had quit working on guns.

William Buchele

I asked him if he had fallen again, and cut his head. He said no, and would show me. We went downstairs where he had hauled a huge tree limb that came down in a storm, and was using an electric chain saw to cut it up. He was losing so much strength that he could not hold the saw up, and it had hit the floor and bounced up and hit him in the head. Even after this he cut up the limb. I asked him what wood he had to sell, as he had already sold some of it. He replied that he always thought that any day they would find a cure for cancer, and that he would again be healed, and if that happened he would need some wood to get started again. So he rat-holed eight pieces of super-fine curly maple for that purpose. Then he realized how weak he was and he said he wanted me to have the wood. Knowing he had little time to live, he said he still had things to do. He was picking hairs from the back of his hand to make some fine brushes, as he wanted to do some miniature paintings on ivory if his eyes would permit him to do so."

George Shumway, who was a friend of Buchele's for about 15 years, paid him a last visit about two weeks before his death. He was told that Buchele's early gun stock work was on cartridge rifles, but that he turned to making muzzle-loading arms in part because the customers there were more willing to pay suitably for the work. Buchele also stated that he had served as a sniper during World War I and had seen active service at the front.

In summation, William M. Buchele was a man with many skills and talents who was accomplished both in the world of art and in the world of mechanics. He gladly shared his knowledge with others.

Samuel E. Dyke   June 1982

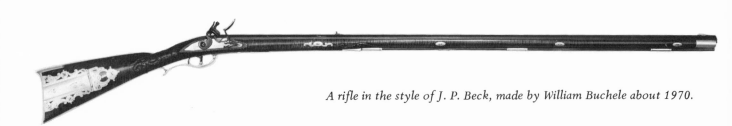

A rifle in the style of J. P. Beck, made by William Buchele about 1970.

ACKNOWLEDGEMENT

It is with deep appreciation that I acknowledge indebtedness to my many friends, without whose unstinting help and encouragement this book might never have been written.

I am also grateful to my understanding wife Wilma, and Daughter Jeanne, who helped in many ways to put this book together.

W. B.

CONTENTS

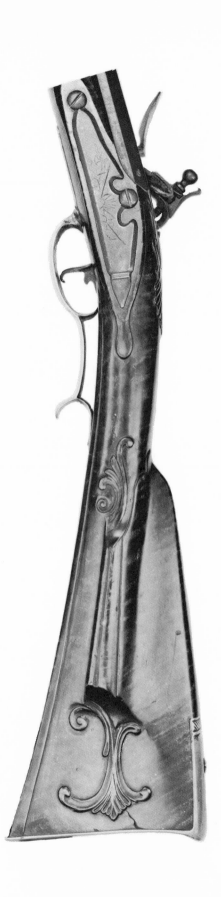
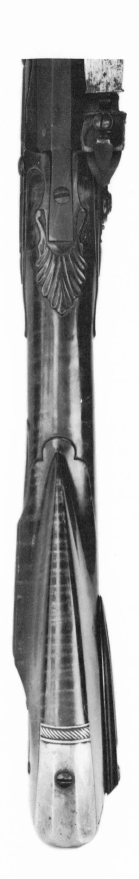
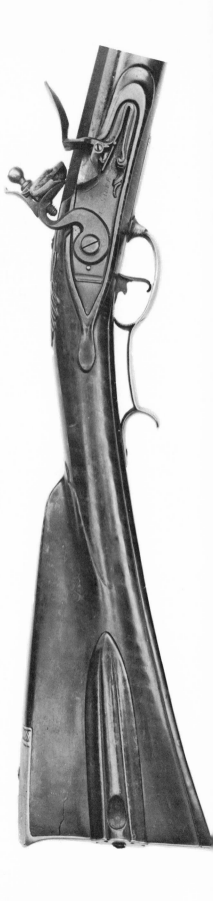

C. E. Siler built this rifle in 1965, and it is the first rifle that he made. It is an outstanding example of creative thought and careful planning for a first rifle. It is styled to the period 1770-1785, and purposely was designed to reflect English influence in the carving, the engraved arms on the iron side-plate, and the architecture, especially the extension of the wrist far down the butt. Siler lives in North Carolina and this was his idea of a rifle that might have been made there during the Revolutionary War period; it is not a copy of any existing rifle.

CHAPTER 1

SOME THOUGHTS ON BUILDING A RIFLE

It is well to give a good deal of thought to the *kind* of rifle one intends to build before plunging in with saw, rasp, and gouge. There are so many things to take into consideration that even a man with many years of experience as a shooter and collector may find it difficult to specify exactly what he wants in the way of design and dimensions. One of the great delights of working with muzzle loading rifles is the freedom one has to combine variables in a creative way, to produce a result that can best meet the needs of the creator. In this beginning chapter the more important of these variables are discussed briefly and a bit of philosophy is thrown in gratuitously.

What kind of rifle should you make? If you are not an old hand at shooting and collecting you may feel that you want one *exactly* like an old one that you own or have seen or at least have seen pictures. A more experienced hand who finds an old one of just the right shape for him will readily compromise on certain details, knowing that the conditions under which a rifle is used today differ somewhat from those conditions of 150 or 200 years ago.

Excluding the heavier rifles (of more than 14 pounds) intended chiefly for target use, the typical rifle of today gets used in three ways, for shooting at targets at shooting matches, for hunting and for plinking. Today's rifle shooter may spend most of his shooting time at matches, and the remainder hunting and plinking. If he takes his match shooting seriously, he would find himself handicapped if his rifle were an exact replica of a typical old one. The old rifle can be typified as having a caliber of about .42, very low open sights, a worm-equipped ramrod, and a muzzle-end too heavy.

Today's match shooter frequently encounters offhand matches and probably would have a rifle that he can handle in that position. The shooter of olden times probably did much less offhand shooting, taking his hunting shots from rest as much as possible and doing his match shooting from the traditional old log. For the shooter of old, the small caliber of his rifle was a practical economy when lead and powder were costly items. For the shooter of today the costs of lead and powder are small enough to be of no practical concern. How the shooter of old got by with his low open sights is a mystery. Today's shooter finds that for serious target competition his sights need to be higher above the barrel, to minimize thermal effects on the air near the top of the barrel. The shooter of old cleaned his rifle by means of tow (unspun flax waste) attached to a worm at the end of his ramrod. Today's shooter often tries to minimize fouling by running a cloth patch down the bore after each shot, and this calls for a ramrod equipped not with a worm but instead with a jag to hold the cloth patch.

Considering the question of caliber and accepting the necessity of meeting today's needs on sight height and ramrod end, there are other compromises and decisions to be made. The caliber is an important item to settle, and calls for compromise. The small calibers, in the range .32 to .42, are ideal for plinking and small game hunting but are a bit light for deer hunting and target shooting yet pleasant to shoot.

What kind of a rifle would you make? Perhaps you want a special rifle for a special need. Some typical examples are as follows:

A) A light rifle for plinking, for a woman or child to use, or for taking with you for squirrel shooting on a fall canoe trip down a river. This would call for a light caliber, between .32 and .42 and a tapered barrel probably 38 to 40 inches long.

B) A general purpose rifle for match shooting, hunting, and plinking. A caliber of .45 or .50 or .54 would be best, with a barrel between 36 and 44 inches long.

C) A rifle for big game hunting in the West. This might be a plains-type rifle, though not necessarily percussion and not necessarily half-stocked. A heavy caliber, between .50 and .60 would be called for, and the barrel well might be short, between 36 and 40 inches in length.

D) A rifle for match shooting from rest. Probably 60 caliber, the barrel as long and as heavy as one can get.

Pause to consider what style of rifle you should make. Having decided to what purposes your rifle will be put, and from this having determined the general dimensions, it remains to decide what style of architecture and decoration suits your needs and desires. A great variety of possibilities exist. You can design your own from scratch without regard to traditional styling or, at the other extreme, you can make a Chinese copy of an existing old rifle. Probably, though, you will find that the rifles of some particular school of gunsmithing, and perhaps even the work of some particular old time gunsmith, suit you best.

In the early days rifles were made from Maine to Georgia and from the coastal states to the Mississippi Valley. Rifles were built differently in different regions. There were differences from state to state, and within states there were differences from county to county and even from town to town within a county. The term *school of gunsmithing* is used to refer to the activities of the gunsmiths of a particular region where certain distinguishing architectural and design features were used. Such a great variety of styles exist among the dozens of known gunsmithing schools that almost anyone's needs can be met through one school or another.

It is completely beyond the scope of this book to treat the design characteristics of the various schools of gunsmithing. The bibliography at the end of this work lists a number of titles that provide help in this field.

What is presented here are the basic techniques used to make a longrifle that is both functional and of appropriate and attractive design. Function is basic and primary, of course, but even a barrel on a log will shoot. Appearance is of great importance also. The person who holds a really fine rifle in his hands will use it to better advantage than an ill-shaped piece.

A simple tool for copying the profile of an old rifle. It consists of a block of wood 1 1/4 inches thick, 3 1/4 Inches high and 6 1/2 inches long, with an inclined hole for a pencil. A rubber band attached to the pencil and to a dowel retracts the pencil when finger pressure is removed from the pencil end. The leading edge of the block is vertical, and is slightly rounded, and it is in line with the point of the pencil when it is in contact with the paper.

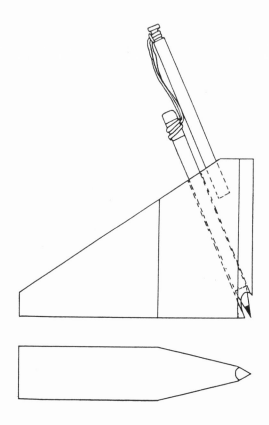

CHAPTER 2

DESIGNING THE RIFLE

Paper, pencils and the time needed to sketch, draw, and design a rifle are cheap in the long run. There are many subtle points about the structure and architecture of a rifle that come to light in the course of scale drawing. Basically, if the design looks good on paper, then it probably will work out well in the wood. If you make such drawings, including inlays and carving, you will have a fair approximation of what your rifle will finally look like. You can take these plans to knowledgeable friends for criticism. Changes are more cheaply made on paper than on wood. Besides, drawing is good practice for the artwork you will eventually incorporate into your gun.

Of course, full-scale drawings are not possible until you have the basic hardware, which consists of barrel, lock, butt-plate and trigger-guard. These parts are discussed in the next chapter. But before you buy your hardware, decide upon a basic design.

A lot can be learned about building a longrifle by examining as many originals as you can. But look at them critically. You will lose some of your innocence. You will learn that some rifles, but not nearly as many as you thought, are designed to perfection, as far as the architecture is concerned. You will discover that many pieces, which at first glance seemed near perfect, have faults in design, which you could correct if you were to build the rifle. And you would find that to hold and aim some of them would be pretty awkward. Two hundred years ago, comparatively few people built rifles, and those who did, did so after extensive training. If an original does not fit you, that doesn't mean it wasn't perfect for the original customer.

In designing your own rifle, the problems of creating your own work versus copying the work of an original gunsmith will arise. Your rifle will be your own creation whether you attempt a close copy of an original or do your own thing totally. But, as you are going to invest some $250 to $400 in parts as well as many valuable hours in the making, deciding your goal before you start is worthwhile.

In the book CONTEMPORARY MAKERS OF MUZZLE LOADING FIRE ARMS by Robert Weil, John Bivins, Jr., has written an excellent introduction. John divides contemporary makers into four often overlapping groups: Documentarians, Interpreters, New School, and Modernists.

The documentarians are basically copyists. Their goal is exacting recreations of the work of the early masters. By an extensive study of the original guns, they try to climb into the mind of an early artisan. If you wish to join this group, you would, for example, study as many rifles by J. P. Beck as possible, asking yourself precisely how he created his rifles, before making your own.

The Interpreters are freer than the Documentarians in that they interpret the early designs and often develop them beyond the intent or even capability of the original gunsmiths. Their work shows a strong recognition of existing early rifles, but they seek a combination of details that represent the best of the early period. So, you might buy a J. P. Beck butt plate and trigger guard, and take the lines from a Beck rifle, but from there, go on to create your own art and decoration, which while not specifically the style of Beck, still falls within what might have been created in Lebanon County, Pennsylvania. This is nothing new. Nicholas Beyer, was at least 20 years younger than his master, J. P. Beck, yet used the same hardware and often the same stock pattern. But he created his own work and did not copy that of the master.

Interpreters often cross the boundaries of different traditional schools of gunsmithing, but they have enough knowledge to pick the right combination of motifs which fit together harmoniously. In the past, some members of the Sheets family of Northern Virginia used the same stock pattern as that used by George Schreyer of Hanover, Pennsylvania, but went on to create their own beautiful work. You also can do this kind of interpretation, but do it with discretion.

Some schools of gunsmithing used certain very distinct and unique design features, each of which is beautiful in its own place. But it is poor taste to pluck some of these features out of their artistic context and use them indiscriminately on a composite rifle. As an example, one could envision a rifle

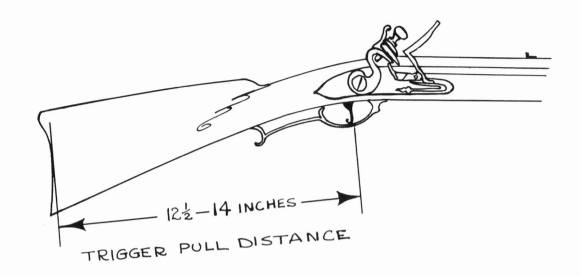

12½–14 INCHES

TRIGGER PULL DISTANCE

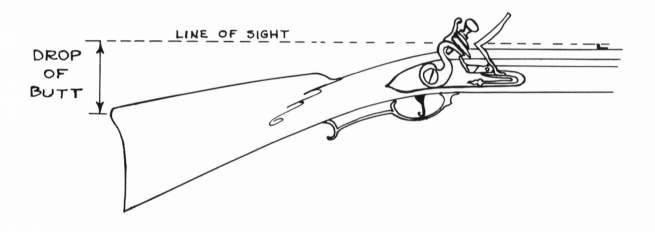

LINE OF SIGHT

DROP
OF
BUTT

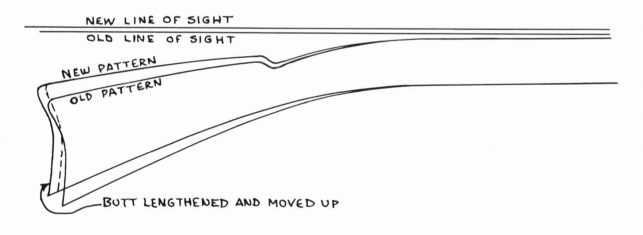

NEW LINE OF SIGHT

OLD LINE OF SIGHT

NEW PATTERN

OLD PATTERN

BUTT LENGTHENED AND MOVED UP

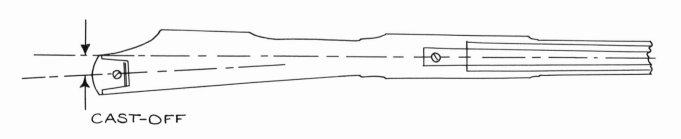

CAST-OFF

with a Roman nose butt-stock as made in the Lehigh Valley, equipped with a narrow-bowed Bedford County type trigger guard, a Lancaster daisy patchbox, a Virginia doubly-pierced side plate and a silver diamond on the cheek piece, and a North Carolina incised comb line. Since the parts are not in harmony, no matter how well a skilled maker might carry it out, it wouldn't be right.

The New School makers have an enormous knowledge of traditional gun design and decoration which frees them to concentrate on the general ideals of the period. They do not restrict themselves to any particular traditional school of gunsmithing, but create new and exciting combinations of motifs. You can join this group, but it takes a great deal of study to create a totally original work of art which through its architecture and decoration relates to a specific time period.

The Modernists focus on functional and mechanical efficiency, and often bypass traditional design. Their goal is accuracy in shooting above all else. This approach is a most valid one, of course. Those who take it must deal with the same fundamentals as those with the other approaches.

Every rifle is an artistic statement, even those produced by the Modernists, so before you plunge into the making, decide what you want to say.

DESIGN DIMENSIONS

The rifle you build is intended for yourself or for some other particular individual. It's the difference between having a suit custom-tailored for you, or buying one off the rack. Therefore there are some key dimensions to be considered in designing your rifle.

Trigger-reach is the distance between the trigger and the curve of the butt plate. For a man 5'8" or more in height, the trigger-reach should be about 13 ½ inches, but for the 6-foot crowd it may need to be 13 ¾ or 14 inches. Good fit is important. The easiest method to find your trigger-reach is to take the measurement from a gun that really feels good. Another method is to measure the distance from the crook of your elbow to the spot on your index finger that would press a trigger, with your finger slightly crooked. A third method is to make a "try stock" by cutting a butt shape out of plywood. Use a nail for a trigger and fool around. A trigger-reach too long can be quite uncomfortable as you strain to fit the rifle to your shoulder, and one too short can cause your thumb to jam against your nose. Thus, trigger-reach and drop must be considered together when designing a rifle. This is the purpose of the plywood "try stock." Fool around until you have designed a comfortable stock.

Drop is a measure of the vertical distance that the heel of the butt lies below the line of the sights. It affects not only how the rifle must be held but also how the cheek is positioned so that the eye can line up the sights with ease.

The drop of the butt on old rifles varies greatly. Rifles from Pennsylvania east of the Susquehanna River have a relatively small drop. The usual range being between 2 and 3 ½ to 6 inches. Rifles from Bedford, Huntington, Cambria, and Somerset counties in south-central Pennsylvania, typically have an exaggerated drop to the butt also of between 4 and 6 inches. Sometimes the drop of the butt is so extreme that the rifle is just plain awkward to hold. But if one of these rifles is otherwise much to your liking, do not hesitate to make one similar with a straighter stock.

If you are taking the lines off an old rifle but feel that the trigger-reach is a little short, you will of course lengthen the butt. But this will drop the position of your cheek with respect to the line of sight. If at the same time you expect to have the sights a bit higher off the barrel, say ¼ inch above the old sights, then your cheek will be left hanging in the air unless you compensate by straightening the stock a bit. Raising the heel of the butt about ½ inch should be close to the order of correction.

Recoil is a force to consider when designing the trigger-pull and drop. Rifles of .54, .58, and .69 caliber can be comfortable to shoot all day if the rifle is properly designed for the shooter. Most shooters will sight-in their rifles from a bench, so a design with a lot of drop that may feel good in the offhand position may be uncomfortable when shot from the bench.

There is another important factor to keep in mind and allow for, which might be called the hunting-coat factor. The rifle that fits so nicely when you try it out in your shirt sleeves in the summer or in the warmth of your home may catch under your armpit and never get to your shoulder if you throw it into position on a cold December day, when you have on three shirts, a sweater, and a hunting coat. This is a serious problem, and one to be reckoned with. The most practical solution is to make the trigger-reach a little shorter than might be ideal for shirt-sleeve use, say ¼ to ½ inch. Or to have two rifles.

One thing to consider when lengthening a butt to a trigger-reach that suits you, is the butt-plate casting you buy. As you lengthen the trigger-reach, the distance from the heel to the toe of the butt-plate must increase, so that the butt-stock retains the same relative dimensions as the original. It is a small matter, but one more reason to make a scale drawing of the rifle.

Cast-off is a measure of the distance that the center-line of the butt lies from a vertical plane passing through the axis of the barrel, measured at the heel of the butt, when the rifle is held in its usual position. It is the third matter of importance in laying out the butt-stock. You never may have examined old rifles for cast-off, but if you start looking for it, you surely will find it on some rifles. Generally, rifle butts are cast-off about ¼ inch. *Cast-on* is the comparable term used when the butt is bent toward the shooter. The purpose of cast-off or cast-on is to help the shooter line up the sights.

If you think of the stock as a piece of wood attached to the barrel, then you will realize that the barrel determines most of the stock dimensions. Barrels come in different sizes, so you should know the external dimensions of your barrel before designing your stock. Below the barrel is a thin web of wood, and then a hole for the ramrod, and then (to the rear of the rear ramrod pipe) more wood.

Commercial hickory ramrods come in at least five diameters, ¼ (.25), 5/16 (.313), 3/8 (.375), 7/16 (.438), and ½ (.50) inches. To minimize breakage, the ramrod should be as large as possible, but to make a slender fore-stock, the ramrod should be of modest diameter, particularly where it enters the lower fore-stock. Rifles with a caliber between .32 and .38 would utilize a 5/16-inch rod. Rifles with a caliber between .40 and .50 would utilize rods of 3/8-inch size, and those of .54 caliber a 3/8 or 7/16-inch rod. However, gunsmiths often taper a rod to fit a smaller diameter hole in the lower fore-stock, for example a 3/8 inch rod tapered to fit a 5/16-inch fore-stock hole.

Whatever the choice of barrel and ramrod size, major considerations must be given to the thickness of wood left between the bottom of the barrel channel, and the ramrod groove and hole. This is called the *web*. Too thin a web and there is not room enough for the transverse screws that hold the lock in place. Too thick a web and the rifle may take on a heavy or clumsy look. The optimum thickness is more or less determined by the wood that would lie above a straight line running from a point 1/8 inch below the barrel at the muzzle, to a point 3/16 inch below the barrel at the breech end. The diagram below shows how to lay out the wood around the barrel. The extra wood above the barrel and below the ramrod give a little room for adjustments, and may be removed when the barrel is inletted and the ramrod hole is drilled successfully.

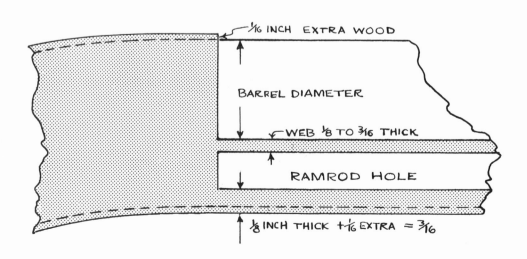

Now the butt-stock can be drawn. Using a piece of paper about 24 inches square, draw the illustration on page 14, using the breech diameter of your particular barrel. Locate the breech end of the barrel 6 inches to the left of the right side of the paper. Draw the top line of the barrel 2 inches below, and parallel to the top of the sheet. Draw a line parallel with the top of the paper and ¼ inch above the top line of the barrel. This line represents the line of sight, as shown on page 12. Now draw a line, also horizontal, at the mid-point of the barrel height. This line represents the top of the side-wall of the stock forward of the breech, and it shows where the top surface of the pan of the lock should lie.

After reading through Chapters 10 and 36, and probably disassembling part of the lock, place the lock-plate on the drawing in proper position, and trace around it. Assume that the touch-hole will be located about 1/8 inch forward of the front end of the breech-plug. With reference to Chapter 15, determine where the trigger will be located, if a single trigger, or the front trigger for a double-set trigger, and draw it in. Draw in also the rear trigger of a double-set system.

The next step is to measure for your trigger-reach distance, 12 to 15 inches to the left of the trigger, and mark it on the paper. Directly above is the sight line. Mark down from it the drop of the butt, probably between 2 and 3 inches. This marks the top of the heel of the butt-plate. Place the butt-plate casting in position and sketch a line marking the top of the comb toward the breech. The direction taken by this top profile line, and the corresponding bottom profile line, determine much about the shape of the butt-stock. If you are recreating a stock with photographs of the original piece, it can be helpful to enlarge the photos to full-size by copy machine, and use these as a guide for your drawing.

To complete the drawing of the butt-stock by putting in the lines of the wrist may seem a simple matter, but it is not. Of particular importance is the top profile line running from the top of the barrel tang to the front of the comb. The old-time gunsmith master of York County, Pennsylvania, George Schreyer, usually got it right. His younger associate, Frederick Sell, also a master, often did not drop the profile line steeply enough in the region of the barrel tang, yielding wrist tops that appear slightly humped.

Another design matter concerns the location of the front end of the comb. On most well-designed longrifles the comb terminates on the top directly opposite the rear spur of the trigger-guard below the wrist. Therefore, place the trigger-guard on the drawing, noticing that the front post enters the stock typically about where the front screw of the lock-plate is located (see p. 62). Sketch the guard in its position and then draw the front end of the comb opposite the rear spur of the guard.

The wrist at the rear end of the lock panel and side-plate panel typically is almost circular in cross section, but its width decreases toward the front end of the comb where its cross-section becomes elliptical, i.e. less wide than high. At the front end of the comb the height of the wrist typically is between 1 ¼ and 1 ½ inches.

With the paper plan complete to your satisfaction, transfer the butt-stock profile to a piece of plywood, or even better, a piece of ¾ in. thick board, that is long enough to include the whole rifle, and cut to the outline.

It can be very helpful also to make another drawing, top view. This will determine where the barrel channel is to be located on top of the stock blank. Of even greater importance, it will show how best to locate the stock relative to the sides of the blank. Stock blanks usually are not overly thick, and a generously proportioned butt-stock, with 2 inch butt-plate, high cheek-piece, and cast-off, must be positioned carefully to take best advantage of the thickness available. Looking down from the top on a rifle with no cast-off, it is apparent that the cheek-piece projects further than any other part of the left side. To have enough wood to make an adequate cheek-piece, it probably will be necessary to have the centerline somewhat to the right of the centerline of the blank.

If cast-off is to be built into the stock, then this must be allowed for also. With cast-off and a wide cheek-piece, it may be desirable to have a layout in which the axis of the barrel is not parallel to the side of the blank but instead points off to the right a bit.

The cheek-pieces on old rifles rarely projected more than ½ inch from the left side of the butt. Viewed from above, the left side of the butt would be defined by a line running from the left side of the butt-plate at its widest point, to the side of the wrist. More often the cheek-piece projects ¼ to 3/8 inch beyond this line, and it projects more at the rear than at the front end.

From the basic pattern it is an easy matter to determine the minimum width of the stock blank that will be needed. Using the paper pattern showing the right side of the rifle, cut out a silhouette of the stock including the barrel from a piece of plywood, hardboard, or other suitable material. This will help in choosing a stock blank, laying out the pattern on the blank, and in deciding on the trigger-pull distance.

Ron Griffie of Denton, Md., who has been supplying gun stock blanks to muzzle-loading rifle makers for years, also prepares pre-carved stocks. In positioning the wood blanks in his carving machine he makes use of the following calculation, which might be of use in thinking about and laying out the gun on the top surface of the blank for those who would shape the stock by hand. However, this calculation assumes that the axis of the barrel is parallel with the side of the stock.

Let A be the width of the butt-plate at its widest point, and B be the diameter of the barrel across the flats at the breech. Let P be the thickness of the lock and side-plate panels, measured from the barrel to the outer surface. Let C be the amount of cast-off, and E be the amount of excess wood between the right side-panel and the right side of the stock blank. Then in the simple case with no cast-off, $E = A/2 - (B/2 + P)$. This assumes that the right edge of the butt-plate is held against the right side of the stock blank, and is valid as long as E does not come out a negative number. And if E is a negative number because of a narrow butt-plate, then it is the right-side, or lock panel that lies along the right side of the blank, not the butt-plate.

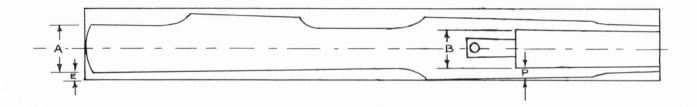

If cast-off is involved, then the more general equation applies: $E = A/2 - (B/2 + P) + C$. For example, if A = 2 inches, B = 1, and P = .33 (a generous figure), then $E = 1 - (.5 + .33) + .25 = .42$ inches.

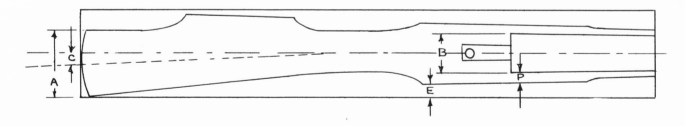

CHAPTER 3

ASSEMBLING PARTS AND RAW MATERIAL

So many muzzle-loading rifles are being built at present that it is relatively easy to find suppliers eager to sell all the parts and supplies needed. The best opportunity to learn about the great variety of parts available and to purchase them is to walk the aisles of commercial row at the range of the National Muzzle Loading Rifle Association at Friendship, Indiana, during the major shooting matches held there, typically mid-June and mid-September. At the larger gun shows held across the country parts are always available. Most suppliers advertise in the magazines listed in the back of this book, and most have catalogs and literature available illustrating and describing the parts.

Parts vary in dimension, quality, and price. Having a pretty good idea of the kind of rifle you want to make, it is well to look over the field before buying the first parts that you come across. Good raw materials and parts are not cheap, but they aren't expensive either. Generally they are offered at very fair prices, and you will not get swindled if you buy the better quality materials.
Typical late 1990s prices for the materials and parts needed to build a longrifle are as follows:

Price Range	Typical Cost	
$180-210	$185	Barrel, tapered & flared, with breech plug
$80-135	$90	Flintlock
$40-125	$80	Stock blank, curly maple
$8-24	$15	Butt-plate
$8-20	$15	Trigger-guard
$10-20	$15	Sheet brass for ramrod pipes & patchbox
$2-10	$10	Screws, pins, small pieces of steel
$2-3	$2	Ramrod, hickory
	$412	

The column headed "Typical Cost" is an attempt to give typical prices, but it is possible to find good or fine quality materials at lesser prices. Inflation raises costs as time goes by. The two parts on which it is best not to skimp are the barrel and the lock. A good lock should be obtained, and a barrel with a swamped, tapered, or octagon-to-round exterior configuration is well worth the cost.

LOCKS, FLINT AND PERCUSSION

Locks and their tuning are discussed extensively in Chapter 36, LOCK NOTES, but a few comments are worthwhile here. The flintlock is by no means a simple mechanism. In the old days it was not economical to make them in America with its shortage of labor whereas in England and in continental Europe cheap labor was available. Consequently, most locks on old American flint rifles are of English or continental origin.

Today a number of good serviceable locks are available to the prospective buyer. In quality, these range from satisfactory to excellent. The choice of styles is considerable. At the present time there are a number of locks styled after the continental or German type of the late 18th century, which often were used on longrifles of the 1770-1810 period. Also available are round-tailed English-pattern locks of simple design such as were produced in quantity in Birmingham, England, and sold by American hardware dealers between 1800 and 1840. In addition, some locks of Bedford County, PA., styling are available. Basically, the lock you choose should be one that could have been used on a gun of the period that you are recreating.

Most locks produced today are equipped with a fly on the tumbler. The fly is a little piece that prevents the sear from falling into the half-cock notch as the hammer falls, possibly resulting in a broken sear or broken notch, and in any case a miss-fire. The fly is essential when the lock is used with universal triggers. The fly is not essential when used with a simple single trigger.

A number of different percussion locks are available for purchase. Some of today's makers provide flint and percussion locks made with the same internal parts and having plates of the same size and shape. This makes it possible to provide a gun with interchangeable flint and percussion locks.

This is a feature that is sound in principle, but rarely done, as most shooters tend to prefer one ignition over the other. As with flintlocks, percussion locks should be purchased with quality in mind.

BARRELS

The barrel, of course, is the heart of the muzzle-loading rifle. Basically, the rifle *is* a barrel, with some attached parts that help in firing it. The stock attaches to the barrel, rather than the other way around. A variety of barrels of new manufacture are available today, some offered in certain fixed lengths, external diameters, and calibers. Considering the work involved in making a rifled barrel, the prices of today's products are cheap.

Barrels are made from solid bars of mild low-carbon steel. Precision machines drill the holes through the centers of the bars and other machines cut the spiral grooves. Production barrels start with octagon stock, through which the hole is bored, reamed and rifled. While the hole is straight, it may not be equidistant from the outside flats of the barrel at the breech end. This condition is known as "run-out". Custom made barrels, on the other hand, start with round stock, and after the hole is drilled, reamed, and rifled, the flats are milled equidistant from the bore. Custom barrels are more expensive, and generally are well worth the extra cost.

Whatever caliber you choose, the second internal factor to consider is the pitch of the rifling, which traditionally is measured by the number of inches of barrel length needed for one full twist of the grooves. Barrels old as well as new usually have a pitch lying between one turn in 48 inches and one turn in 72 inches. While no definitive study showing the optimum pitches for round balls of various sizes and speeds has been made, the latest tests suggest that the *slower* pitch (i.e. one turn in 66 inches) is less critical. In other words, the slower twist will tend to place balls in a tight group equally well with a variety of large powder charges, while the faster twist rifling (less than one turn in 48 inches) may give best results in a particular powder charge range. However, the beginner will not be wrong in buying a barrel with a pitch or twist in the range between one turn in 48 inches, and one turn in 72 inches. The common twist rate today is one turn in 66 inches for barrels of .50 or .54 caliber.

A barrel's length is the distance from the front face of the muzzle to the rear face of the barrel at the breech end. It does not include the tang. It is an external measurement. The length of the bore is shorter than the barrel length by the length of the breech-plug screw, i.e. the bore length is the distance from the front face of the breech-plug screw inside the barrel to the front face of the barrel at the muzzle.

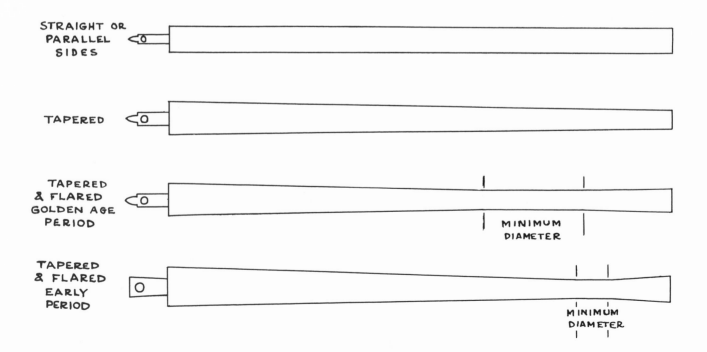

STRAIGHT OR PARALLEL SIDES

TAPERED

TAPERED & FLARED GOLDEN AGE PERIOD — MINIMUM DIAMETER

TAPERED & FLARED EARLY PERIOD — MINIMUM DIAMETER

A properly made breech plug is an essential part of a rifle barrel. Some barrel makers sell their barrels with breech plugs properly installed, but others do not. Barrels generally come with threaded breeches, and you may have to buy a breech plug and fit it by hand, as discussed in Chapter 7. Tangs of different sizes and shapes are available. For rifles of 18th century styling a short flared tang is best. For Golden Age rifles a parallel-sided tang of short or medium length is appropriate. An extra long tang is called for in making a rifle of southern Appalachian styling.

The external size and shape of the barrel is of considerable importance. Barrels come in four shapes: *parallel-sided, straight-tapered, swamped or tapered-and-flared,* and *octagon-to-round straight-tapered.*

Parallel-sided barrels generally are found on late-flint and percussion period guns. Some makers of very fine Golden Age rifles, like John Armstrong of Emmitsburg, Maryland, used parallel-sided barrels. The problem with parallel-sided barrels is weight, and rifles made with them often are muzzle-heavy. If a parallel-sided barrel must be used, avoid lengths of more than 42 inches, and diameters too large or, for safety's sake, too small. A well made .45 caliber barrel measuring 13/16 inch across the flats is generally regarded as safe, but this is minimum size, and a barrel of 7/8 or 15/16 in. diameter is preferable.

Straight-tapered barrels sometimes were used on old rifles, and they are available today. By providing a breech diameter larger than the muzzle diameter they yield rifles with much better balance and with an added safety factor.

Tapered-and-flared, or swamped barrels are largest at the breech, and taper to a minimum diameter 6 to 10 inches behind the muzzle, then flare out somewhat to the muzzle. Barrels of this type not only balance the best in a rifle, but they also look the best. German flintlock rifles of the 18th century almost always had barrels of this type. The flare, or enlargement, at the muzzle is aesthetically pleasing, it provides a higher base for the front sight than a straight-tapered barrel would provide, and it adds a little mass at the end of the barrel, which is an aid in shooting.

Another advantage of the tapered-and-flared barrel is that it provides for a subtle slendering of the stock from breech to muzzle, which adds to the beauty of the rifle. It also aids in making a wrist region that is architecturally pleasing. It is a fact that almost all of the old rifles of the flintlock period had swamped barrels, though on many of the later ones it was a minor feature.

Octagon-to-round barrels are barrels that taper also. They have an octagonal section for about 12 inches forward of the breech, then change to round for the rest of their length. In old Pennsylvania, some rifles, and most "smooth-rifles" had such long slender barrels, which were very light at the muzzle.

With such a wide choice of barrels on the market today, you can well build any type of gun you want. However, do heft as many different barrels as possible to gauge balance and weight before buying.

Recommendation: Having done our author's duty to mention the barrel choices available, we close this portion of the chapter with a recommendation that we feel strongly about, and we urge you to follow, particularly if you are making your first rifle: buy a barrel that is tapered and flared, either of early period style, or golden age style. Let it be 38 to 42 inches long, and .45, .50 or .54 caliber, with breech-end diameter across the flats 1 in. (.45 cal), or 1 1/16 in. or 1 1/8 in. (.50 and .54 cal.).

WOOD FOR STOCKS

Wood for longrifle stocks is relatively easy to buy today thanks to the many suppliers who have risen to meet the demand. The traditional wood is curly maple, prized for its beauty and cussed for its wavy grain. But in addition, stock blanks of cherry and black walnut often are available, and occasionally curly ash. Cherry is regarded as a fine American wood for gunstocks, being hard, strong, and particularly stable. Old guns of all sorts from New England generally were stocked in cherry. Maple was the usual stock wood for rifles and other guns made in Pennsylvania, Maryland, Virginia, North Carolina and Ohio. Gunsmiths of the sourthern Appalachian Mountains often used black walnut for their iron mounted rifles. In the pre-Revolutionary War period, black walnut and cherry more frequently were used in the south than in later years, and they saw some use in Pennsylvania.

The hardness of these woods varies from tree to tree, depending upon the environmental conditions under which they grow, and the species of tree. Silver maple, for example, often is quite soft, and in general should be voided. The best maple for stocks comes from the red maple and sugar maple. A good maple stock blank should be hard enough to resist denting with a fingernail, adequately seasoned, of suitable thickness for an ample cheek-piece, probably 2 ¼ inches minimum, should have ample wood in the region of the comb for whatever butt design is chosen, and the overall grain direction should be favorable throughout, with grain direction at the wrist more or less parallel with the direction of the wrist. It is a matter of choice whether the grain is not curled, slightly curled, heavily or tightly curled, or birdseye.

Thoroughly seasoned wood, of course, is most desirable to have for building a rifle. Green wood shrinks and warps as it dries, causing much difficulty to the person trying to use it. Stocks that have been seasoned by air drying are best. The drying process can be accelerated by kiln drying, but it is best that the wood be air dried for a year or more before using the kiln.

Ron Griffie, who has been supplying gunstocks for years, points out that green maple wood has a moisture content of about 33%. It is seasoned and ready to use when the moisture content lies between 6% and 13.4% depending upon the area in which you live. Thus, a person living in the southwest might find his stock stabilizing at around 6% moisture content, while a citizen of Mississippi would have a seasoned stock of 13% to 16% moisture content. Ron recommends that you let your stock rest in your workshop for about a month before working on it, to harmonize with the moisture content of the air in your locality. But above all, buy your wood from a reliable source.

Wood for longrifles is available today in two basic shapes: the stock blank, and the pre-carved stock. The stock blank is simply a plank which has been planed and cut to a vague shape, such that almost any gun can be made from it. The pre-carved stock, of course, is more expensive because the barrel channel has been cut out, the ramrod groove made, the hole drilled, and the butt area roughly shaped to a particular school of gunsmithing. The barrel channels of most pre-carved stocks are cut for straight-sided barrels. Barrel channels for tapered or swamped barrels can be cut, but this generally is done on a custom basis.

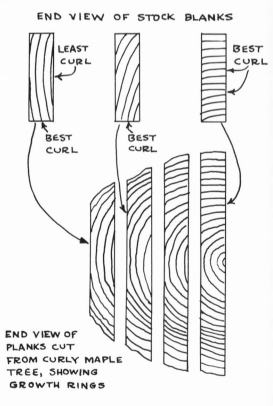

END VIEW OF STOCK BLANKS

END VIEW OF PLANKS CUT FROM CURLY MAPLE TREE, SHOWING GROWTH RINGS

The main difficulty in making a stock is to drill the ramrod hole so that its inner end, located 12 to 14 inches inside the lower fore-stock, ends up in the right place. To save time and avoid waste, some producers of partially finished stocks take a ball-end router bit and cut a groove in the bottom of the barrel channel from the breech almost to the rear ramrod entry, at a depth equal to the ramrod hole depth. Thus it is only necessary to drill an inch or two to complete the ramrod hole. The lack of a web seriously weakens the lower fore-stock and these stocks should be avoided.

The stock blank is considerably less expensive that the pre-carved stock. It entails much more work, but this is not necessarily bad. Of greatest importance, it allows the builder the opportunity to create his own design. The price of maple stock blanks varies considerably. Premium prices are charged for blanks that have an extra fine curl, but they are little different otherwise from the plainer pieces that usually sell at very reasonable prices. The beginner would do well to avoid the fancy wood, choosing a blank with modest curl, or even a relatively plain piece. Many fine old rifles were made with wood having little or no curl.

BUTT PLATES AND TRIGGER GUARDS

Cast brass butt-plates and trigger-guards in a variety of shapes and sizes are available from many suppliers. They come as rough castings that must be finished by filing and polishing. There are two casting methods. Sand casting, the traditional method, produces a rough product out of yellow brass. Investment castings, made out of a yellow bronze, come almost finished pieces, but are somewhat more expensive. At any rate, try to inspect the casting for flaws before buying. Some castings in German silver are also available for late flint and percussion period guns. Also you can buy some furniture cast in steel by the investment process.

The important thing about furniture is to buy parts that are appropriately designed for the style of rifle to be built. A number of schools of rifle design used uniquely shaped parts, and reproductions of these parts are relatively common. Because the butt-plate and trigger-guard determine a number of essential stock dimensions, it is important to buy the right furniture. It is beyond the scope of this book to treat these different designs, but the bibliography lists a number of fine books to assist the reader.

Butt-plates vary greatly in the amount of curvature they have. Early rifles have butt-plates with little or no curvature. In the late flint and percussion period the butt-plate curvature was considerable and frequently extreme. Butt-plates with extreme curvature are found on old rifles designed to be shot from the biceps not the shoulder. Such butt-plates are to be avoided for their impracticability. They are all but impossible to use for anything but offhand shooting. A particularly good butt-plate design was used by the gunsmiths J. B. Beck and Nicholas Beyer of Lebanon, Pennsylvania. Good reproductions of these are readily available today. Beck butt-plates and trigger-guards would be appropriate for recreations of guns from such schools as Lebanon, Dauphin, Lancaster, and York, but would be glaring faults on reproductions styled to Bedford, Huntingdon, and Emmitsburg schools. Whatever butt-plate you choose, make sure to buy a trigger-guard appropriate to the same school of maker.

Trigger-guards generally come in two sizes, one designed for a single trigger, and the other, somewhat larger in the bow, for double set triggers. It is a good idea to decide whether you are going to use a single trigger, or double set triggers, in your gun before buying your trigger-guard.

TRIGGERS, SINGLE AND DOUBLE-SET

The making of triggers is treated quite fully in Chapter 15. Of course, dealers have a wide variety of triggers for sale, from rough castings for single triggers, to complete units of double-set triggers. The choice of making or buying is up to you, but on the whole it is better to make your own. For one thing, it is cheaper. For another, it is easier to make your trigger fit your trigger-guard and gun, than to fiddle with your trigger-guard to make it fit commercial triggers.

ADDITIONAL PARTS AND SUPPLIES

Suppliers of muzzle loading parts now offer most of the additional things needed to complete the rifle. Brass and German silver sheet stock of varying thickness, or complete patch boxes, ramrod pipes, fore-end caps, ribs for half-stock rifle barrels, screws, side-plates, front and rear sights, barrel loops, cap boxes, pre-shaped inlays of brass, German silver, and silver, ramrod tips, and more are available.

But the whole thrust of this book is to make your own gun, so restrain yourself. Some parts should never be bought, such as the fore-end cap, as this needs to be made to fit the rifle, not the rifle made to fit the cap. And why buy a stamped or cast side plate, which may not fit the panel when you shape it some months down the road, and which you can easily make cheaper and better yourself?

Jeweler's supply houses are a good source for silver in many thicknesses, silver wire for making pins to fasten inlays to the stock, jeweler's saws, engraving and chasing tools and other related supplies. Welding supply houses sell silver solder and flux. Small optical screws in German silver are available from optometrists. By designing your gun before you rush out to buy, you can make up a list of materials and proceed to shop around for only what you need, and at the best prices.

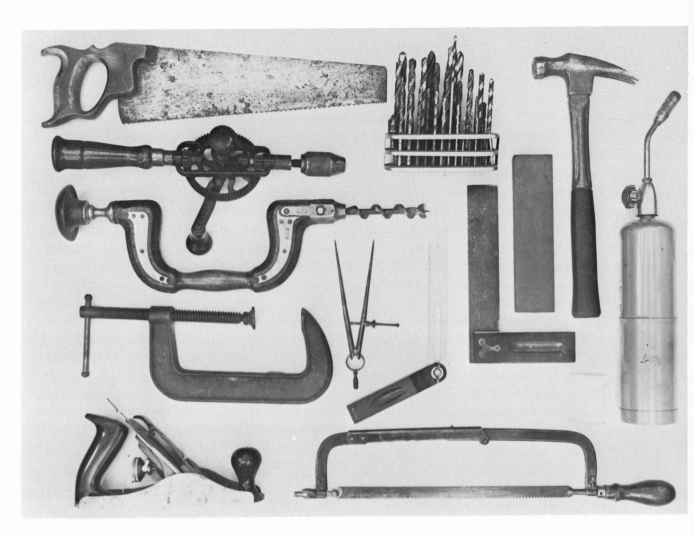

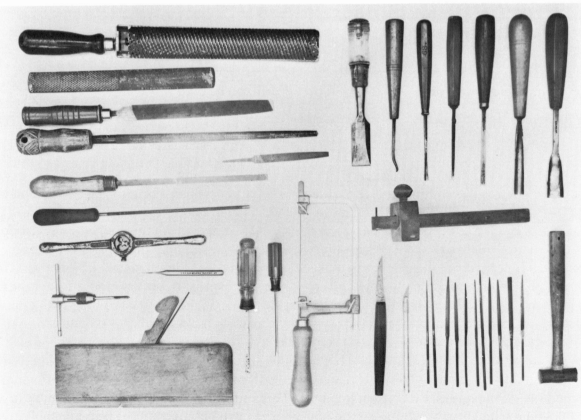

Typical hand tools used for building a longrifle.

CHAPTER 4

TOOLS AND A PLACE TO WORK

The rifle cannot be built overnight, or even over a long weekend. Typically it takes the beginner a number of months of part-time work to complete. It is of course desirable that an adequate workbench be available for the work, having a good mechanic's vise at one end, and being well illuminated. But if it were necessary, a rifle could be built in an apartment on a kitchen table. The workbench needs to be solid, firm, and adequately large, but the details of its construction are not important.

Good light is essential. In the early days, before electricity, a workbench was placed so that there was a window behind it, which provided a back light that was about the only light a craftsman had to work with. Today a similar arrangement can be an advantage, too, but electric lights are a necessity if one is to work at night and at other times when prime daylight is not available. One or more fixed lights shining down on the bench and located toward the rear of the bench to provide backlighting are desirable. In addition, it is most desirable to have one, or possibly two, moveable lights to provide the directional light so often needed while doing exacting work.

A good vise attached to the workbench is a necessity. Preferably it should have a swivel base, and ideally one of the two jaws should be on a pivot to better hold the non-parallel sides of the gunstock. A second vise which can be clamped to the bench in various locations can be useful also. A selection of C-clamps are handy to have also.

The gunsmiths of old had only hand tools to work with, and did a remarkable job using them. Today's rifle maker likewise can get along without power tools, but where he can put them to good advantage he might as well use them if they are available. It is well to bear in mind that although the old time gunsmith had no power tools, he did have an assortment of hand tools specially made to perform certain tasks difficult to do with the more common hand tools. The old timer was a full time professional who had served an apprenticeship of a number of years duration to learn his trade. Knowing exactly how to proceed and having specialized tools available, he worked rapidly and skillfully. As an apprentice he observed on many occasions the procedures of his master, and participated in various parts of the rifle making process for a year or two or three before he was allowed to make a complete rifle.

Of the various power tools that might be put to use in building a rifle, the drill press is the most important. There are a few operations in which a drill press gives a decided advantage over a hand drill or a hand-held power drill. A hand-held power drill can be used to advantage also, not only as a drill, but also as a lathe of sorts for holding screws and other round parts so that they can be shaped with files, and later polished. It may be possible to use a router to clear wood out of a barrel channel, but if the barrel is tapered-and-flared, the difficulties of guiding the router are considerable and it probably is safer to stick to hand tools. An electric grinder has a multitude of shop uses. A metal lathe can be used to make tips for ramrods and some other small parts, and to face off the ends of rifle barrels. A lathe with or without a milling attachment can be useful but is not essential.

As a source of heat the old time gunsmith had a forge available that served him in many ways. Today's rifle builder can get along without one, but will need some source of high heat. A simple propane torch will serve adequately, and of course an oxy-acetylene rig is the ultimate.

Probably the most widely used tool in the old time gun shop was the file. A good selection of them is essential. A good hand with a file can do most of the things a power tool can do, and a few that it can't do, and surprisingly often, just as fast. Take care of your files, using a file card to clear clogged material from the teeth, and avoid piling them on top of each other. For flat filing on small parts the four-inch mill file is particularly good, for its small size allows you to feel what you are doing. Larger mill files, half-round files, rat tails, and triangular files are all needed. A set of needle files is of particular importance, and sets usually contain 8 to 12 different types.

Wood rasps are necessary too. Coarse-toothed flats and half-rounds can take wood away in a hurry when the initial rough shaping is being done. Some particularly efficient rasp-like tools are

A simple vise to hold a rifle on a drill press, made from scrap wood. The faces of the vise are metal, and the front face is tapped ¼-20 to accept carriage bolts with T-handles.

A swivel base bench vise can serve most rifle building needs. With The aid of a hand-vise, work can be held at almost any angle. The adjustable light behind the work provides the kind of illumination needed for good filing.

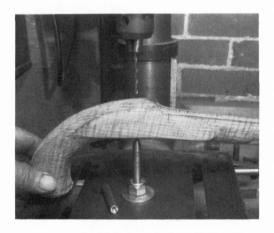

A pointed rod securely fastened in line with the center of the drill bit can be used to drill accurately the tang screw hole. To use, drill halfway through, then reverse the wood and complete the hole.

Antique post vises still can be obtained at moderate cost. Also shown are a bench anvil and a breech-plug wrench.

This mid-20th century vise is particularly versatile, and can be positioned on the support post as shown or vertically.

Two supports of equal height, and a center clamp, make a useful jig to drill lock-plate holes perpendicular to the metal surfaces.

available from the Stanley Tool Company and sold under the name of Surform™. They are made more or less like a cheese grater and the teeth stay free from clogging. Flat, half-round, and full round blades are available.

A sharp hand saw is useful for the initial shaping of the stock blank, and a hacksaw is essential for general metalwork. An important tool for the gunsmith is the jeweler's saw, available from some muzzle-loading parts suppliers, from jewelry supply houses, and tool supply stores. A jeweler's saw has an adjustable frame, somewhat like a hacksaw, which holds a very slender fine-toothed saw blade in tension. The blade is held in the frame so that the teeth point toward the handle, thus a jeweler's saw cuts on the pull stroke. Jeweler's saw blades are made of hardened steel, and will cut steel, iron, brass, silver, and wood. The blades are fragile and frequently break, so it is well to have a few dozen on hand. Fortunately, they are inexpensive. Number 8 blades are a good all-around size. Lubricate them with a bit of beeswax. When cutting sheet metal, always have the blade more or less perpendicular to the sheet. When piercing in sheet metal is intended, as for example in the finial or side-plates of a patchbox, a hole is first drilled and then the blade is mounted through it. At the end of long cuts in sheet metal it is best to disengage the blade from the frame rather than attempting to back the blade out of the cut.

A wood plane can be used to advantage in shaping certain portions of the stock, but it is not an essential tool for building a rifle. The typical plane has a blade width of 2 inches, and the flat of the plane is about 9 to 10 inches long. For use on curly maple it must be kept very sharp. In use, the plane is moved down the wood with the blade held at an angle of perhaps as much as 45° to the direction of the wood grain, and very thin cuts are made.

Chisels and gouges are essential for gun stocking. The number of chisels you need is directly related to the amount of gun making you do. There is nothing sacred about a chisel as it comes from the store. Grind it to whatever shape suits your needs, making sure to keep it cool by dunking often in water. It's good to keep a finger on the steel close to the region being ground, so that when the metal gets hot to the touch it can be dunked. Flat chisels new from the store usually have too great an angle on the front bevel, and need to be ground so that this bevel angle is between 10° and 15°.

When buying chisels, buy the best quality pieces that you can find. A basic chisel to have is a flat chisel 1-in. wide. Good quality pieces are available of U.S. manufacture. For the smaller chisels intended for wood carving, it is best to seek out pieces made in Germany, Switzerland or Scandinavia. Many fine old chisels can be found in the antique marketplace, and these usually are either of German or English manufacture. The pieces useful for inletting work have blades between 1/8 and ½ in. wide.

One or more sharp knives are essential for stock carving. Almost any narrow-bladed knife will do, provided it has good steel in the blade. The readily available Exacto knife is a most useful tool, with its inexpensive and replaceable blades. Tightwads and other prudent craftspeople know that these thin blades can be resharpened just like any other knife.

Knives, chisels and plane blades must be kept sharp with medium and fine-grit carborundum stones, but to put a fine edge on them for finished carving and stock shaping it is well to have a very fine-grained Arkansas stone or modern ceramic stone. As a lubricant for these stones use auto engine oil thinned with kerosene.

Some specialized hammers are needed too. A ball peen hammer is used to shape metal. A wooden mallet drives chisels. A chasing hammer drives gravers. You can make the mallet from a piece of hardwood, and though chasing hammers usually are made of metal, it is possible to make one of wood.

Common screwdrivers of various sizes are needed. In addition, screwdrivers with tapered blades to work in tapered screw slots of early type may be desired.

There are, in addition, a few specialized tools needed for various tasks. These are discussed along with their use in later chapters. But keep in mind that the only tools you need are the ones you are going to use. Part of the fun of hand-crafting a rifle is making special tools that you will use.

CHAPTER 5

ORDER OF PROCEDURE

The complexities of building a rifle make it necessary to follow an order of procedure. Certain steps must be done before others or it will be almost impossible to end up with a functioning rifle. The beginner, in particular, needs a sequence of steps to follow. The outline below, which is reflected in the order that chapters are presented, will lead the beginner through the maze. Not all experienced gun makers follow this order exactly, but the order for performing the major operations of inletting the barrel, making the ramrod groove and hole, and inletting the lock, is standard procedure. The order for some of the lesser operations is arbitrary, and this will be apparent when one gets to them. For example, it makes no difference whether one installs the ramrod pipes before the trigger-guard, or afterward; they are at opposite ends of the stock and are not dependent on each other in any way. Also, as soon as the ramrod groove is completed, and the basic shaping of the fore-stock is done, it is a security measure to have a ramrod shaped to go in the lower fore-stock hole. This will help to protect the sides of the ramrod groove while other work continues. Finishing the ramrod can be done later.

1   Draw on paper the full-size pattern of rifle as viewed from right side and from top.
2   Plane smooth top and right side of stock blank, draw outline of stock on right side.
3   Saw stock blank as per stock outline.
4   Draw top view of stock on wood and lay out barrel position.
5   Inlet barrel without breech-plug in it.
6   Make ramrod groove and drill entry hole.
7   Install lock and drill stock for lock screws.
8   Shape and inlet barrel tang.
9   Install butt-plate.
10 Begin shaping lock region and wrist.
11 Shape the butt-stock.
12 Make trigger.
13 Inlet trigger and trigger-guard.
14 Make and install barrel loops.
15 Make barrel loop keys.
16 Make and install ramrod pipes.
17 Shape fore-stock.
18 Make and install muzzle-cap.
19 Make side-plate.
20 Make lower butt moulding.
21 Make and install patchbox and cover.
22 Make and install toe-plate.
23 Make and install metal inlays.
24 Engrave metal inlays.
25 Carve the stock.
26 Install wire inlay.
27 Finish stock surface.
28 Make and install sights.
29 Make touch-hole.
30 Blue or brown the barrel.
31 Make ramrod.

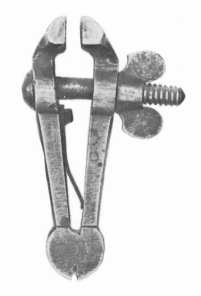

The hand vise was widely used in the old days. It can be handy today, particularly when used in combination with a bench vise to hold small parts.

CHAPTER 6

LAYING OUT THE RIFLE ON THE STOCK BLANK

It is best to have a rifle designed on paper, and a pattern of hardboard or plywood made, before buying a stock blank. By laying the pattern on various blanks, one can determine that the pattern will fit and that the grain direction in the region of the wrist is favorable. Stock blanks almost invariably are sold with the two sides planed smooth so that grain direction and grain figure, or curl, can be seen to best advantage. The first job is to plane the sides of the blank if they already are not smooth.

Then lay the pattern on the right side of the blank and mark around it. Mark well the position of the breech end of the barrel. For the initial cutting it is well to leave an extra ½ inch of wood at the butt end, and an extra 1/8 to 1/4 inch of wood on the underside of the lower fore-stock from the trigger region to the rear ramrod entry (for now, about 14 inches forward of the breech end of the barrel). The finished profile line of the upper fore-stock will be at about the mid-point of the ramrod, but for the initial cutting provide about 3/16 inch extra wood.

Cutting the blank to shape can be done with a handsaw, aided by a 1-inch chisel and a plane and a rasp, always cutting to the outside of the layout lines. If a bandsaw is available, it is a great time saver and muscle saver. Using a bandsaw is the fastest and easiest way to do a number of wood removal operations, so if one is available, make use of it. But proceed with caution unless you are skilled in its use.

After cutting to shape, take a plane and/or various rasps and files, and trim the newly cut surfaces to the layout lines, keeping them square with the faces of the blank. It is particularly important in building a right-handed rifle that the top surface of the blank lies perpendicular to the right side. The steps that follow call for a square stock.

Using the top-view drawing of the rifle, trace or otherwise lay out the outline of the rifle on the top surface of the stock. Establish the position of the barrel carefully, particularly at the breech end, and mark a vertical line on the front end of the stock where the centerline of the barrel intersects the front end of the stock.

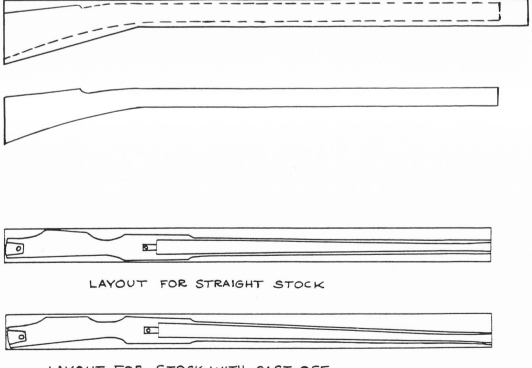

LAYOUT FOR STRAIGHT STOCK

LAYOUT FOR STOCK WITH CAST-OFF

CHAPTER 7

INSTALLING THE BREECH PLUG IN THE BARREL

In the early days, the threaded screw that closed the breech end of the barrel was called the *breech pin*. Today we call it a breech plug. Many of the gun barrels sold to gun makers today come with the breech plug already fitted and installed. This usually is the case with custom-made barrels that are tapered-and-flared, or that have some other specific outside configuration. Production barrels, which usually are of constant exterior dimension from one end to the other, almost always have the breech end properly threaded to accept one of the standard size breech plugs that are commercially available.

If your barrel has the breech plug already installed it would be well to check it out to make certain that it is properly installed. And if the barrel has no plug, then you will have to get or make a suitable one, and install it. In either case there are lessons to be learned.

The depth of the threaded portion of the barrel breech, and therefore the length of the breech plug is a matter of concern. Old barrels typically had a very coarse thread and usually the length of the thread was a mere 3/8 inch. In recent years the makers of rifle barrels have determined through tests that a properly fitted breech plug of ½ inch length is suitable for a barrel of almost any caliber.

Unfortunately, most flintlocks sold today are patterned after 18th and 19th century locks where the fence-to-pan-center distance was about 3/8 inch. This makes it impossible to have the fence line up with the rear end of the barrel, which is the ideal. There is at least one notable exception, an English-style lock offered by Jim Chambers with a fence-to-pan center distance of about ½ inch.

A breech plug longer than ½ inch yields a touch hole position that forces the lock to be too far forward, which may cause difficulty in locating the rear lock screw properly. Also, the fence of the lock will end up too far forward. Ideally the fence should line up with the rear end of the barrel.

In buying a breech plug for your barrel there are three considerations to deal with. First, the threaded plug must fit snugly into the breech threads. For any nominal thread size, different taps and different dies will provide fits between the two parts ranging from too-sloppy-to-use, to too-tight-to-put-together. If a trial plug screwed half way in can be made to wobble from side to side, it is too loose and should be rejected. A good snug fit is desired, and this means that you probably can screw it almost all the way in by hand, but not necessarily with two fingers. Minor burrs left in the threading process may call for the plug to be run in and out a few times with the help of a wrench. But in any case, the plug is brought to its final position with the help of a wrench.

The second thing to consider in buying a breech plug is the shape of the tang. Barrels for rifles of Golden Age style usually had tangs that were relatively short (between 2 and 3 inches) and that were equal in width to the width of the top flat of the barrel. Barrels for rifles of earlier styling, i.e. the pre-Revolutionary and Revolutionary periods, typically had tangs that flared out at the rear end and were of about the same length. Iron-mounted rifles of Southern Appalachian Mountain style typically had very long tangs extending to the front end of the comb. Half-stock plains rifles, including those of Hawken style, typically had long tangs also, as an important means of strengthening the wrist of the stock. You can purchase breech plugs with any of these tang styles. In choosing a short tang, get a flared one if possible. It also is possible, and structurally sound, to cut off a tang from a breech plug and to affix by means of silver solder, brazing, or welding, another tang of desired shape.

The third consideration is that the distance from the axis of the breech plug to the top surface of the tang is equal to, or slightly greater than, half the barrel diameter at the breech, i.e. the top surface of the tang should be flush with the top flat of the barrel, or slightly higher. If it is a little higher, it can be filed down at a later time. If the tang is too low, it is possible, and structurally sound, to remove it and replace it with a piece of appropriate size and, perhaps, of more appropriate shape. This new tang can be attached to the breech plug lug by silver-soldering, brazing, or welding.

No matter what the situation, the tang should be no thinner than 1/8 inch. It is preferable for it to be 3/16 or ¼ inch thick, and at this stage is still straight. Later, after the stock wrist profile is determined, it will be bent to conform to it, and still later filed flush with the adjacent wood.

Another problem that arises in fitting a breech plug to a production barrel concerns run-out at the breech, which is a measure of how far the axis of the bore deviates from the center of the octagon barrel at the breech end. A production barrel with moderate run-out may shoot just as accurately, and be just as safe as a custom barrel with no run-out. But in setting up the rifle, the barrel flat that lies closest to the run-out should be placed either at the top, or at the bottom, and of these two possibilities, it probably is best to place it at the top. If it is placed at one side then it will be necessary to offset the rear sight, or at least the rear sight notch. Fortunately, some barrel makers stamp their names and marks on the flat with the least or most run-out. It is traditional for barrel makers to use the bottom flat for their marks, so the barrel flat positioning may already be determined for you.

For a breech plug to fit properly, the lug at the rear end, which includes the front face of the tang, must meet and come up tight against the rear face of the barrel. At the same time, the front end of the threaded part of the plug must come up tight against the shoulder where the threaded part of the breech meets the bore of the barrel. If the plug is a bit long, then it needs to be cut off to fit. If the plug is a bit short, then the rear face of the barrel needs to be cut back.

To fit the plug it is necessary to use a marking paint, preferably a machinist's blue, which is a kind of non-drying Prussian blue paint. This is dabbed around the shoulder of the barrel breech, if the plug is too long, and the plug screwed in tightly, with the aid of a wrench. When it is removed, blue should show on the face of the plug where contact was made. With a mill file remove a small amount of metal as indicated by the blue on the end of the plug. Repeated cuts and tries are made, the final cuts being very light ones. Try to maintain the same torque on the wrench each time. If the rear face of the barrel needs to be cut back, the job can be done with a file – carefully. However, a lathe with a headstock hole large enough to accept the barrel is the preferred tool to use if it is available.

In using a wrench on the lug at the end of a breech plug care must be taken not to damage the top edges of the tang. The sides of the lug are tapered, not parallel, so the lug is widest at the top. If the sides of the lug are parallel, they should be tapered before the lug and tang are let into the stock.

After the breech plug has been fitted perfectly, clean out the breech. Then make up a mixture of powdered graphite and petroleum jelly, coat the threads with this black guck, and screw the plug into place. It should come out easily in the future, even after months of firing the rifle.

The table below shows typical breech plug thread sizes in relation to barrel diameters and bore sizes.

Barrel diameter across flats, inches	Thread size	Calibers
13/16	9/16 x 18	.32 .36 .40 .45
7/8	9/16 x 18	.32 .36 .40 .45
	5/8 x 18	.40 .45 .50
15/16	5/8 x 18	.40 .45 .50
11/16	11/16 x 16	.50 .54
3/4	3/4 x 16	.50 .54
1	5/8 x 18	.40 .45 .50
	11/16 x 16	.50 .54
	3/4 x 16	.58
1 1/16	5/8 x 18	.45 .50
	11/16 x 16	.50 .54
	3/4 x 16	.50 .54 .58
	7/8 x 14	.69 .72
1 1/8	5/8 x 18	.45 .50
	11/16 x 16	.50 .54
	3/4 x 16	.50 .54 .58 .62
	7/8 x 14	.69 .72

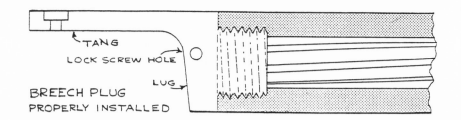

TANG

LOCK SCREW HOLE

LUG

BREECH PLUG
PROPERLY INSTALLED

TOP FLAT

BARREL WITH
RUN-OUT AT
BREECH END

PROPER ORIENTATION
OF BARREL, WITH
THINNEST WALL
AT TOP

BARREL WITH CENTERED
BORE - SELECT PRO-
DUCTION BARREL OR
CUSTOM BARREL

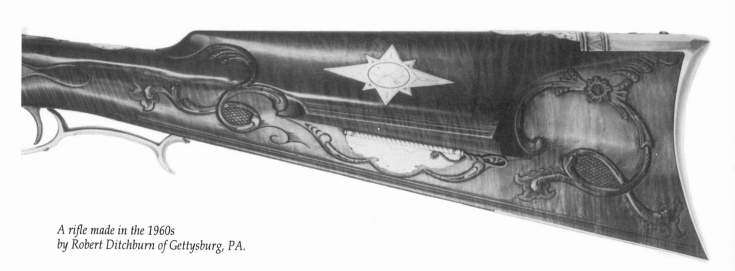

A rifle made in the 1960s
by Robert Ditchburn of Gettysburg, PA.

CHAPTER 8

CUTTING THE BARREL CHANNEL

To fit a long octagonal rifle barrel properly into a gun stock calls for hard work and determination. Basically it is a matter of cutting and trying, cutting and trying, until the job is done. A straight-sided non-tapered barrel can be easier to inlet than a tapered or swamped barrel, but that should not be a criterion for choosing the straight-sided barrel in favor of the other types.

The straight-sided barrel channel can be cut in part, or almost completely, with the aid of power tools, but in the end there may be as much time and effort put into using them as it takes to do it all by hand. The problem comes in guiding the tools accurately. It is possible to use a shaper if blades are specially ground to the shape of the bottom of the channel, but sometimes the stocks shatter and fly apart. A router also can be used to advantage for removing the wood on the straight sides and the bottom, provided that a way can be figured out to guide it accurately. A simple table saw also can be used to cut the sides and the bottom of the channel, but the finishing must be done by hand anyway.

The channel for a tapered barrel, or for a swamped barrel, of necessity must be cut by hand, or by a very sophisticated modern wood-carving machine. But the general approach to rifle building suggested by this book is on a middle ground where inletting the barrel and drilling the ramrod hole are at the heart of the matter, and should be experienced by anyone new to rifle building.

If one takes the modern wood-carving machine one step farther beyond inletting the barrel and drilling the ramrod hole, to shaping the stock and inletting for specific pieces of furniture, then one essentially has a kit. This comment is not made to denigrate rifles made using machine-shaped stocks, for some of these stocks, or kits, are very carefully designed using stock patterns and furniture designs based upon particularly good rifles made by old masters. Excellent rifles can be made working with these pre-carved stocks, and in many ways this book also can be an aid to those using this approach.

Some old-time gunmakers simply rounded the bottom of the barrel channel to speed the inletting, a cheap and less strong solution not recommended here.

So, for most situations, it is best to go at the task with hand tools, determination, and patience. The illustrations on the following page show the step-by-step procedure for making the barrel channel and doing some preliminary wood removal on the fore-stock. After planing the top of the stock blank smooth, straight, and square with the sides, mark the position of the breech end of the barrel. Make a second transverse mark 5/8 inch forward of the breech mark. Then, on each side of the blank, mark where the axis or mid-line of the barrel will be when inlet with the top flat at the muzzle even with the top surface of the wood, and the top flat at the breech end is 1/16 inch below the top surface of the wood. Then on each side mark a line 1/8 inch above the mid-line of the barrel. This last line is the limit for initial wood removal, and it must stop at the line that is 5/8 inch forward of the breech.

Remove the wood to the line drawn, and on the left side near the breech end remove the projecting corner to leave a neat upward-turned curve that ends 1/16 inch forward of the breech end of the barrel.

To begin the barrel inletting, remove the breech plug from the barrel. After the barrel is completely inlet, then the plug and tang are let into the wood. To get the wood out of a barrel channel by hand as rapidly and easily as possible calls for the use of drills, chisels, gouges, and special planes. But prior to beginning with these it is best to drill a series of closely-spaced holes. A good sharp bit in a hand-brace can work wonders in a hurry. The lower part of the holes should be of smaller diameter, no greater than the width of the bottom flat of the barrel. Narrow antique wood-planes with convex blades ¼ to ½ inch wide are particularly helpful. Finished cuts are made with flat chisels, files, rasps. It is particularly important that the vertical sides of the wood fit snugly against the barrel, not only for appearance, but also because the finished wall thickness may be reduced to about 3/32 inch.

An important aid in fitting the barrel is a transfer color that is put on the barrel each time it is forced into the channel. This can be almost any greasy material, with some colored pigment added, such as cup grease and burnt umber pigment. Lipstick can be used. Vaseline thinly applied and blackened by smoke from a candle will do. At the Williamsburg gun shop a mixture of soot and olive

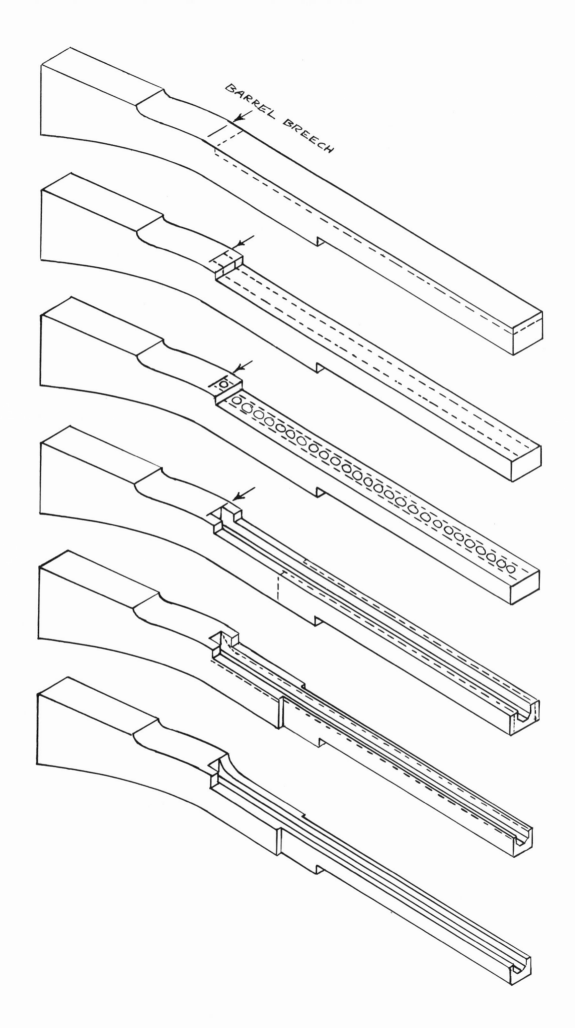

BARREL BREECH

oil is used. Lamp black from a candle flame will serve, without applying grease. More expensive preparations can be bought – but the spirit of muzzle-loading calls for the use of things free and easy to get whenever possible. Transfer color is best used only on the three lower barrel flats. Its use on the side flats can be misleading, for color on the sides of a snugly fitting barrel will suggest wood removal where none is needed. Instead, look for shiny spots on the wood from repeated contact.

Every once in a while, check that the top flat of the barrel is square with the sides of the stock, as it must be. Also, make sure that the breech end of the barrel is in solid and complete contact with the wood behind it. The barrel channel has been brought to proper depth when the top flat of the barrel at the breech end is 1/16 inch below the wood immediately behind it.

Cutting the barrel channel by hand is the toughest of all the tasks of stocking a rifle. Many hours of work are required, and the first-timer may get a bit discouraged by it. But it must be done, and for a good rifle it should be done carefully so that a close fit is achieved.

With the barrel channel completed, some excess wood should be removed from the sides of the fore-stock. Beginning about 2 inches in front of the forward end of the lock, the sides should be trimmed to a thickness of about 3/16 inch measured from the inside wall of the barrel channel. Some experienced gunsmiths who favor slender fore-stocks immediately reduce the side walls of the barrel channel to a thickness of 1/8 inch, but the beginner could well use the extra 1/16 inch. Keep the sides of the fore-stock flat and square with the top and bottom of the stock, as an aid in holding the fore-stock in a vise.

The next thing to do to the fore-stock is to reduce the upper surface of the wood on either side of the barrel to its final level, which is the mid-line of the side flats of the barrel. Be certain that the barrel is held tightly to the bottom of the barrel channel when doing the marking and cutting. And remember that the upper surface of the side wall on the left side near the breech must curve upward, beginning ½ to ¾ inch in front of the breech end of the barrel. For illustrations of this, see p. 94.

On the right side, the flat upper surface of the side wall is for now carried back to within about ½ inch from the breech end of the barrel. When the lock-plate is let into the wood, its shape will determine how much additional cutting will be needed.

It is most likely that the barrel bedding, and initial fore-stock trimming, will not be done all in one day. To prevent the possibility of warping of the wood as a result of moisture changes and/or the release of stresses in the wood, keep the barrel clamped in the wood when not being worked upon.

After the barrel inletting chores are completed, you have every reason to congratulate yourself, for some of the hardest work now is out of the way.

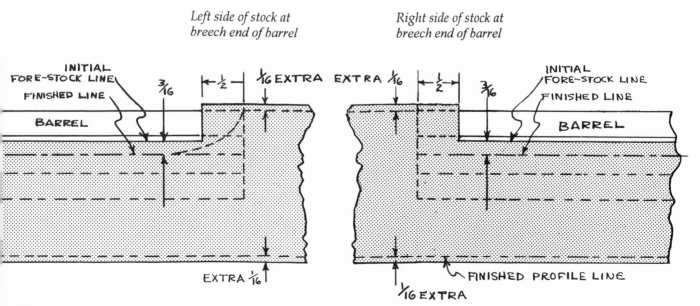

Left side of stock at breech end of barrel   *Right side of stock at breech end of barrel*

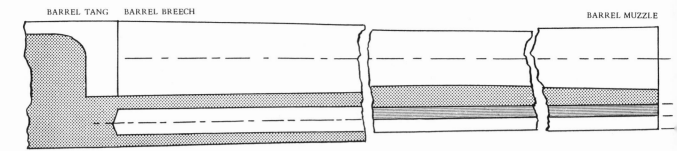

BARREL TANG   BARREL BREECH   BARREL MUZZLE

Line B marks lower limit of sidewall for ramrod groove on upper forestock, also ramrod hole axis.

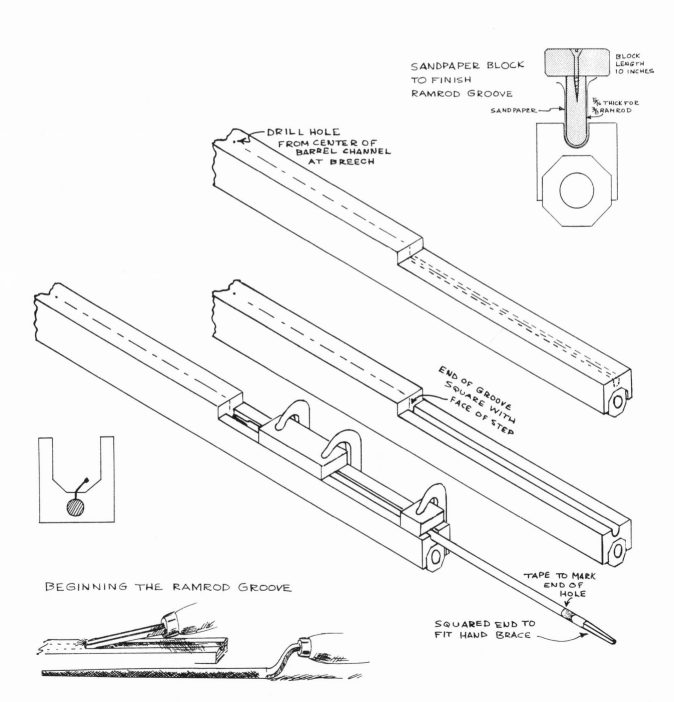

SANDPAPER BLOCK TO FINISH RAMROD GROOVE

BLOCK LENGTH 10 INCHES

SANDPAPER

5/16 THICK FOR 3/8 RAMROD

DRILL HOLE FROM CENTER OF BARREL CHANNEL AT BREECH

END OF GROOVE SQUARE WITH FACE OF STEP

TAPE TO MARK END OF HOLE

SQUARED END TO FIT HAND BRACE

BEGINNING THE RAMROD GROOVE

34

CHAPTER 9

MAKING THE RAMROD GROOVE AND HOLE

The big problem with drilling the ramrod hole is to get it to come out in the right place. This calls for drilling a straight hole about 14 inches deep and having it end up within about 1/16 of an inch of the desired location. Down below the breech end of the barrel there isn't much excess wood to play around with. The forward lock screw must pass transversely between the barrel and the ramrod. Ideally there will be just enough wood between the bottom of the barrel channel and the ramrod hole for the screw to pass through – about 3/16 inch. If the ramrod hole ends up too low it does not interfere with the screw but it will limit how much wood can be trimmed away between trigger and rear ramrod pipe. If the hole ends up too high it may leave little or no room for the screw, though usually it is possible to cut a groove across the underside of the barrel sufficiently deep to allow the screw to pass.

Ramrod sizes were mentioned and discussed briefly in Chapter 2. The size of the ramrod and of the ramrod hole in the lower fore-stock remains a matter of concern. Assuming that your barrel is of .45 or .50 or .54 caliber, there is the choice of having a ramrod of uniform diameter for its whole length, or of having a rod that tapers slightly where it enters the hole in the lower fore-stock. For the beginner it probably is best to use a rod of uniform diameter, which for any of these calibers would be a 3/8 inch rod. A long 3/8 inch drill rod is reasonably stiff, and is less subject to wandering than a 5/16 inch rod.

Before drilling the ramrod hole, it is necessary to form the groove, or channel in which the ramrod will lie. This must be done accurately because it determines the direction of the ramrod hole. When laying out the lines of your groove, make sure your groove is directly centered on the barrel, otherwise your drill may go too far toward the lock mortise, or to the side-plate panel.

On a fine rifle it is surprising how little wood remains between the ramrod groove and the bottom of the barrel channel. As pointed out earlier, it lies between 1/8 and 3/16 of an inch. If this *web* is much thicker, the fore-stock begins to take on a thick and heavy look. And if it is thinner there is not much to hold the two sides of the fore-stock together.

Layout lines must be drawn accurately. On each side of the stock draw a line (A) that starts 3/16 inch below the bottom flat of the barrel at the muzzle. The other end of each line should be 3/16 inch below the position of the bottom flat of the barrel at the breech end. This line represents the top of the ramrod groove and hole, as viewed from the side, with the barrel horizontal and the top flat up.

Now, below each line, and parallel to it, draw a second line (B) that represents the center, or axis, of the ramrod, and ramrod hole, from the muzzle through the entry position to the breech end of the barrel. It also represents the lower limit for the upper fore-stock wood from the muzzle end to the ramrod entry position. Now draw a third line (C) parallel to the axis line (B), and below it, to represent the lower limit of the ramrod, as shown by the drawing opposite.

The next concern is the length of the ramrod hole in the lower fore-stock. On a typical longrifle it is between 10 and 12 inches, but on very slender long-barreled rifles it could be as much as 14 inches. The exact position of the entry hole, measured from the breech end of the barrel, is determined by the balance point of the rifle. The balance point is the position along the fore-stock where the fully equipped rifle balances, as when held horizontal by one hand.

The balance point is very important, because in bringing the rifle to the shoulder, the left hand should be at the balance point. Also, when the rifle is carried by the right hand alone, it is gripped at the balance point. It works best for the balance point to lie 2 to 3 inches to the rear of the entry hole. For a long and heavy barrel with little or no taper, perhaps 1 inch across the flats and 44 to 48 inches long, the balance point may be well down the barrel, 14 or 15 inches. For a tapered and flared barrel 42 inches long, with the weight well toward the breech, the entry hole can be 12 or 13 inches from the breech. For a shorter barrel, not heavy at the front end, the entry hole can be closer to the breech, between 10 and 12 inches. Germanic jaeger rifles of the 18th century, with short barrels between 24 and 30 inches in length, typically have a length of about 9 or 9 ½ inches for the ramrod hole.

At this stage it is difficult to know where the balance point will be, and it is practical simply to make the ramrod hole 14 inches long, with the expectation that it will be shortened later.

The ramrod groove is easily cut with hand tools, and there is no need to attempt the use of power tools. A rough groove can be formed with gouge and mallet. A rat-tail file smaller in diameter than the intended groove diameter can be used to good advantage, provided that the tang of the file is bent upward to take a small wooden handle. To insure that the groove is as straight as possible it is well to do the final shaping with sandpaper wrapped around the rounded edge of a board. This board can be about 24 inches long, 3 inches wide, and ½ or ¾ inches thick, with one edge tapered to about 5/16 inch thickness, and rounded, for a 3/8 inch groove. Throughout the process it is particularly important to keep checking the depth, straightness and direction of the groove.

A special drill must be prepared to make the ramrod hole. There are various ways to make this drill, and all seem to do the job. One method is to begin with a common, or preferably long-shank, twist drill, and to join it to the end of a piece of cold rolled steel rod of the same diameter. The rear end of the drill shank is annealed, turned to a smaller diameter, and threaded. The end of the long rod is drilled and tapped, and the two pieces screwed together. The joint is silver soldered for permanency. Or the two rods simply can be welded together. Be certain that the long rod is not larger in diameter than the drill or it will bind in the hole.

Another drill that will do the job, and probably the easiest to prepare, is made from a 36 inch piece of tool steel drill rod. The cheaper water-hardening variety will do. With a grinder or milling machine, the sides are cut away for a distance of about 1 or 1 ½ inches back from the point, leaving a blade between 1/8 and 3/16 inches wide. If the blade is thinner near the center of the rod than at the outer edge it is advantageous. A high angle point can be put on the rod with a lathe prior to cutting the sides, or the point can be filed to shape afterward. This drill works well and has no tendency to wander. This drill rod is hard enough as purchased to be used without hardening, but of course it can be heated and quenched if desired. This drill will have to be lengthened. Probably the easiest way is to drill and tap the end for a ¼ -20 screw, and then to cut threads on a piece of ¼ inch rod and screw the two together.

Another drill that can be used is a gun barrel drill. This is less easy to procure and more expensive, but can be used to advantage if available.

In drilling the hole it is necessary to make one or two grooved blocks that are clamped over the drill to hold it tightly in the ramrod groove. A bit of soap will help as a lubricant. The end of the groove where the drill enters the wood should be square so that the drill gets off to a good start.

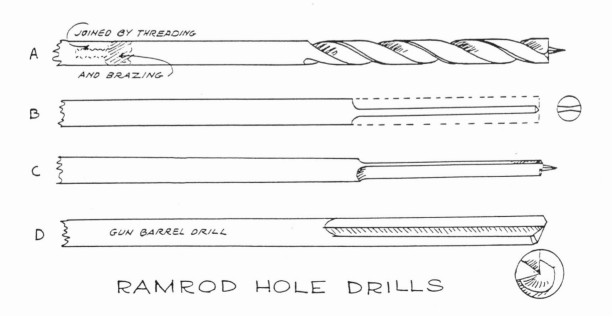

RAMROD HOLE DRILLS

Clamp the barrel in the stock for rigidity. Lay the long drill on the bottom of the stock so that the cutting tip is about 1 inch past the breech end of the barrel, and wrap a bit of tape around the shank even with the muzzle. This will indicate when the hole is deep enough. Place the drill in the groove, and clamp it down with C-clamps holding the grooved blocks of wood in order to hold the drill firmly in the groove. It is best to do the drilling by hand, using a carpenter's brace instead of an electric drill. The first inch or two is the most important, so use care in starting. As a rule the drill is advanced about ½ inch with each cutting, after which it is withdrawn and the chips removed. It will be noticed that the drill turns harder as the hole gets deeper. It can be made to turn easier if a bit of paste wax is placed inside the hole. Continue drilling by ½ inch stages until the tape you wrapped about the shank is 1 inch from the muzzle of the barrel.

If you are curious about the exact location of the ramrod hole (and who is not?) a simple thing can be done to find out. Drill two 1/8 inch holes in the center of the bottom of the barrel channel, one at the breech end, and one just to the rear of the ramrod entry. By wrapping a piece of masking tape around the drill shank, the bottom of the hole can be marked first on the drill, then transferred to the side of the stock. A line drawn between these two points will indicate the bottom of the hole, and show whether it has wandered up or down. This line also will show how much slenderizing may be done underneath the stock between trigger and ramrod entry. By placing the barrel channel under a strong light which shines through the 1/8 inch holes, you can, by looking down the ramrod groove, see whether your drill wandered to the right or left.

If, despite every care, your drill wandered and broke through the underside of the stock, you may well curse. But don't discard the stock. This defect can be covered by a long brass inlay in front of the trigger guard. In the old days it happened in the building of more than one fine old rifle.

If the drill wanders upward and breaks through into the barrel channel, a repair can be made and the blank saved. Cut a channel as long as necessary and as wide as the bottom flat of the barrel with chisels and gouges. Make this deep enough to receive the ramrod or the drill. Cut a piece of matching wood with the underside cut out to receive the ramrod, and carefully fitted to the hole in the barrel channel. Wrap a piece of paper around the ramrod drill and insert it into the hole. Glue the wood patch in place, and after the glue has hardened, re-run the drill in the hole to round it out if necessary. If you have done a neat job, the stock will be almost as strong as ever, and only you will know what has been done to salvage it.

With the ramrod groove made and the hole drilled, the sides of the groove can be reduced to their final level, which is half the ramrod diameter. So for a 3/8 inch ramrod, the sides of the groove will be 3/16 inch high. For a really slim upper fore-stock, the sides of the groove can be reduced later to about 1/8 inch, but that is a matter for judgment and further thought.

When the sides of the groove are close to their final level, you can make a simple tool to insure that the sides are of uniform height and are level. Take a block of wood about 8 inches long and 2 inches wide. Take a piece of ramrod and carefully plane away or otherwise cut away one half, to make a piece 8 inches long and half-round in cross section. Lay a piece of fine sandpaper on the block and fasten the half-round rod to the block over the sandpaper, using small brads. By moving this sandpaper block up and down the stock the sides of the groove are easily brought to uniform height.

Now the lower surface of the fore-stock, between the trigger and the ramrod entry, can be brought to its appropriate position. This is determined by drawing a line on the side of the stock beginning 1/8 inch below the ramrod hole at the entry position, and ending at a point 3/16 inch below the ramrod hole at the breech end of the barrel.

CHAPTER 10

INSTALLING THE LOCK

It is desirable to install the lock, and to partially shape the lock region next, prior to inletting the barrel tang. The stock in the region of the lock and wrist contains certain fixed dimensional factors that radiate from it. To work from both ends towards the center, or lock and wrist area, could be disastrous.

Before proceeding to lay out the lock mortise, remove the internal parts of the lock. It is best to have a mainspring vise to remove the mainspring. If you don't have one, bend the mainspring very carefully in your vise-grip pliers, handvise, or bench vise. Watch out for the *fly* (détente)! This is a tiny piece of metal inserted in the tumblers of some locks, and it has the habit of falling out and getting lost. When you disassemble the lock, place the fly in a safe and secure place (which you won't forget) and leave it there until you finally re-assemble the lock. Never snap a lock without the fly in it as it may tend to damage or break off the half-cock notch.

Make certain that the edges of the lock-plate, all around, except the region of the pan and bolster, have a slight inward bevel. This helps in getting a tight and neat metal-to-wood fit. With a file, smooth the cast edges of the plate, being sure to preserve the bevel, or the create one if there is none.

With the lock prepared, the next step is to prepare the flat area of the stock into which the lock will be mortised. This flat wood area that surrounds the lock-plate is called the lock panel, and the corresponding area on the opposite side of the stock that surrounds the side-plate is the side-plate panel. Make certain that the lock panel surface is flat, and at 90° to the top flat of the barrel, and sand it smooth.

A carefully made sheet metal copy of the lock-plate shape, including the holes for the retaining screws is well worth making as an aid for lock location.

In positioning the lock, there are four things of importance to consider. The most important is the relationship of the pan to the touch-hole. The center of the touch-hole never should lie at the bottom of the pan, for the powder then has to burn downward to reach it. The touch-hole should be positioned above the bottom of the pan by a distance of between 3/32 and 5/32 in., and of course it should lie on or close to the centerline of the pan. A touch-hole in this zone receives the effect of the burning pan of powder as well as possible, and ignites the main charge almost instantaneously, if the touch-hole is correctly made. Locate the lock so that the top surface of the bolster adjacent to the pan meets the barrel along the centerline of the side flat, or better, is slightly below it by no more than 1/16 in.

For more complete treatment of the touch-hole, see Chapter 33. Basically, the touch-hole should be centered on the side flat of the barrel, or better, lie slightly below it by no more than 1/16 inch, and be forward of the breech-plug face by about 3/16 inch. If a touch-hole liner is to be used, the hole center should be positioned so that its threaded exterior does not interfere with the breech plug, which typically puts it 5/32 to 3/16 inch ahead of the breech plug face. If no liner is to be used, a distance of 3/16 inch is suitable. Mark the position of the touch-hole lightly with a center punch. When the lock has been inlet it may end up slightly off the intended position, and minor adjustments in the final touch-hole location can be made.

The second most important thing determining the lock position is the forward lock screw that passes between the barrel and ramrod, through the web of wood. On the right side of the stock it is a good idea to draw the position of the web of wood lying between the bottom of the barrel channel and the top of the ramrod hole. First mark the position of the bottom of the barrel channel. At the ramrod entry the bottom hole drilled in the bottom of the barrel channel at the breech end allows a smaller bit with a piece of masking tape wrapped around it, or simply a small stick, to be used to determine the total distance from the bottom of the barrel to the bottom of the ramrod groove, and therefore the thickness of the web. Ideally, the forward lock screw should pass through the center of the web and not touch either the bottom of the barrel or the ramrod hole.

If the web ended up rather thin, say 3/32 inch or less, it will be necessary to cut a small notch in the underside of the barrel to allow room for the lock screw to pass. If the web is adequately thick there may be a little room for vertical adjustment of the screw hole location. Additional vertical adjustment for the front end of the lock-plate is provided by the fact that the screw hole at the nose of the lock-plate does not have to be exactly centered, and typically it could lie as much as 3/32 inch above or below the center of the nose of the plate.

The third consideration is that the tail at the rear end of the lock ideally should center on the wrist. Deviations from this may be necessary, depending on the geometry, but they should be minimized. The position of the lock tail relative to the wrist is primarily a matter of appearance, not of function.

The fourth matter to consider is the relationship of the fence along the back edge of the pan and the breech end of the barrel. In the old days, in England and America, properly made guns and pistols almost invariably had the back of the fence in line with the breech end of the barrel. But today, if the plug is long and the touch-hole liner is installed in front of the plug, it may be necessary to place the lock forward of the ideal position. The problem arises today because modern barrel makers have lengthened the plug to ½ inch for safety considerations, as opposed to antique plugs which typically were 3/8 inch long. At the same time, locks made today usually are replicas of old locks. A proper fence/breech alignment can be achieved with some of the larger locks available today, most notably Chamber's Round Plate English Lock.

With the above factors as a guide, determine the exact position of the lock-plate, hold it in place, and mark lightly around the lock, and mark well the position of the bolster. Inlet the bolster, taking care to get a neat cut, for the top edge behind the fence will be part of the finished mortise. This initial cut should be just deep enough to allow the lock-plate to lie flat against the stock. Do not remove any more wood than is necessary along the bottom edge of the bolster. With the plate positioned exactly as desired, use a sharp thin knife blade to scribe the outline of the lock, keeping the line as close to the plate as possible. Then proceed to inlet the plate, taking great care to do it well, for a very tight fit. Constantly use the square to ensure that the lock-plate is square with the top of the barrel, and that when finished it lies fully flush against the side flat.

The illustration shows some exaggerated results of inattention when inletting. The bolster must end up tight against the barrel, or powder from the flash pan may get in the crack, build up in quantity, and eventually blow the lock off. It has happened. And if the lock-plate is tilted slightly, so that the bottom is farther out than the top, the frizzen may scrape the barrel as it opens.

Great care must be taken that there are no gaps between the lock-plate edge and the wood, as this will show as an obvious fault. So take time, and use transfer color liberally to do the job well.

What if, despite every care taken, the lock-plate is improperly inlet? There are basically two choices: The first is to find a matching piece of wood, carefully glue it into the mortise and start all over again.

A much simpler solution is to bed the lock in epoxy cement. Buy some burnt umber paint pigment or tempera paint powder. Mix the epoxy and add the powder until it turns a dark brown. Avoid the rapid-setting epoxy cements. Put the glue all around the edge of the lock mortise. Now, coat the lock-plate with Vaseline – in every conceivable and inconceivable place the glue could possibly flow. Also, coat the barrel with Vaseline in the lock area. Insert the lock into the mortise, and clamp it to the barrel. Leave it 24 hours and then remove it.

With the lock-plate installed, mark the position in the mortise of the tumbler, bridle, and sear screws, and the mainspring lug by scribing through the holes in the plate. With the lock-plate removed, take the bridle and lay it on your marks in your mortise, then cut out that area. When you have cut fairly close to final depth, install the bridle on the lock-plate, and by use of transfer color, inlet to final depth. The bridle is removed, the tumbler replaced in the lick, the bridle replaced, and, with transfer color, the tumbler inlet so that it moves freely. In the same manner, the sear-spring can be inlet.

Next is the sear. If a large lock is used with a small barrel, the arm of the sear may be longer than necessary. The sear arm should not penetrate much more than half the thickness of the stock, so if it seems long, carefully measure it in relation to the lock-plate, and cut off any excess length. The location in the mortise of the sear arm is determined, and the hole into which it goes is drilled with a 5/16 drill, making sure not to touch the edge of the lock mortise in that area.

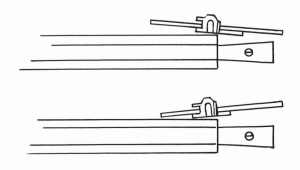

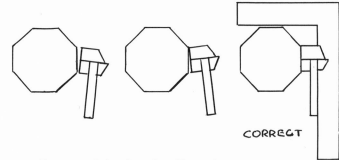

CORRECT

Exaggerated sketches of problems that can arise when inletting a lock-plate. Make certain it is square with the barrel.

POSITIONING THE LOCK

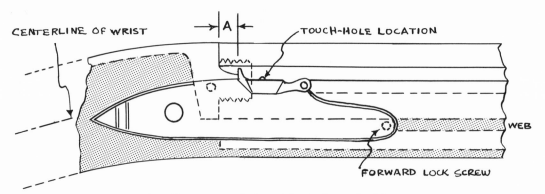

CENTERLINE OF WRIST

A

TOUCH-HOLE LOCATION

WEB

FORWARD LOCK SCREW

In order of importance, lock position is determined by:
1. *Touch-hole location.*
2. *Forward lock screw location.*
3. *Lock tail location relative to wrist centerline.*
4. *Relationship of barrel end to rear surface of fence on pan (A). Ideally the two should be in line, but with a touch-hole 9/16 inch or more from the barrel end, this may not be possible.*

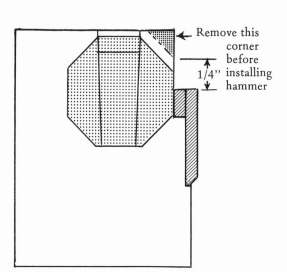

→ Remove this corner before installing hammer

1/4"

Scale drawing of a transverse section through the stock of a rifle at the position of the rear lock-screw. This gun is a smooth-rifle, made c. 1775 by Isaac Berlin at Easton, PA. The drawing is presented at 135% of actual size, looking forward from the breech end.

Of particular importance is the rear lock-screw that slopes downward, emerging on the left side about 3/16 inch lower than a screw sunk normal to the lock-plate. This makes it possible to slope the wood on the left side of the tang at almost 45°, almost in line with the left oblique flat of the barrel.

As with the other parts, use transfer color to help inlet the sear. Try it with the tumbler in its various positions. Do not inlet the mainspring at this time, for the hammer must be installed first.

When the hammer is installed on the plate (see next page), it will be necessary to cut a notch in the edge of the wood panel above the plate for the arresting shoulder on the back of the hammer. To make as small a notch as possible, some removal of wood between where the barrel tang will be, and the upper edge of the lock-plate, will be necessary at this time. With the tang not yet inlet, it will suffice to mark its location and shape on the wood where it will be inlet.

The upper edge of the flat panel in which the lock-plate is mortised, i.e. the lock-plate panel, should be drawn on the wood, beginning ¼ inch above the edge of the lock at the fence. For now, this should increase to 5/16 inch at a distance of 2 inches back from the fence. For a more complete account of lock panels, see Chapter 13. Most of the wood between the top of the lock-plate panel and the upper edge of the tang is removed, having essentially a flat surface that stops short of the tang edge by about 3/16 inch. Refer to the illustration opposite (p.40).

Dealers today sell lock and tang screws of suitable shape and size, so it generally is not worth the time and trouble of making them. The rear lock screw usually is of 10-32 size for medium and large locks, but screws of 8-32 size are adequate. For the 10-32 screw a #11 drill is needed for the body of the screw, and a #21 drill for the tapped hole. For the 8-32 screw the body drill is #19, and the tap drill #29.

The location of the screws takes a little thought. The forward screw location is determined by existing relationships. The hole, of course, must pass ahead of the mainspring. If the web is so thin that a transverse groove must be made in the bottom of the barrel for the screw to pass, then let the drill at first only mark the barrel, but remove the barrel to complete the hole, which may have to be done by filing.

The rear screw goes through the bolster of the lock near its back end, and usually passes through the lug of the breech-plug. But where the hole emerges from the wood on the left side of the stock is of considerable importance in the shaping of the wood in the surrounding region. The problem is that if the rear lock-screw hole is drilled (and tapped) perpendicular to the lock-plate, the hole emerges on the left side of the stock too high, and it determines the location of the side-plate and side-plate panel, which in turn determines the architecture of the entire left side of the stock in the lock region.

The solution is simple, and the old-time gunmakers used it. They drilled and tapped the rear screw hole of the lock-plate so that it sloped downward as it ran from the lock-plate toward the side-plate. The center of the hole, where it emerges on the left side of the stock, should be between 1/8 and ¼ inch below where it would be if drilled perpendicular to the lock-plate. To accomplish this calls for drilling between centers, as illustrated and briefly described on page 70. To locate the point of emergence on the left side of the stock, first draw on the wood a vertical line representing the end of the barrel, then to the rear of this a vertical line representing the centerline of the screw hole, as determined from the relationship on the right side of the barrel. Measure down along the lock-plate face to where the screw hole center will be, and mark its position with a punch. Mark its position on the left side, and then below that mark the point of emergence of the screw-hole center, perhaps 1/8, 3/16, or possibly for large barrels, even ¼ inch. Tapping the screw holes in the lock-plate must be done with care. For the forward screw, enlarge the hole in the stock to appropriate size to pass the screw. Then run in the tap from the left side of the stock, and tap the threads.

For the rear screw the same procedure should be used, if the shank of the tap is long enough. If the tap is not sufficiently long, then the plate will have to be clamped in a drill press at the appropriate angle, using the tap drill as the guide. Then with the tap in the tap holder open the chuck of the drill press to accommodate the upper end of the tap holder and guide its direction, as the threads are started by turning the tap holder by hand. Use tapping fluid with the tap, of course.

The lock screws now can be inserted in the stock holes and screwed into the lock-plate. Check that the bolster of the lock fits tightly against the side of the barrel, and that the plate is square with the top flat of the barrel. Everything being in order, cut off the screw ends flush with the outer surface of the lock-plate. Finish the installation by removing excess wood from the face of the lock-panel. The beveled edge of the lock-plate determines the finished surface, but for now leave an extra 1/16 inch of wood all around, to protect against dings and dents.

Now is the time to install the hammer on the plate, carefully removing any wood behind it that interferes with its movement. Then the mainspring is installed in the lock and the necessary inletting done in the stock. Use transfer color, and carefully remove no more wood than is necessary for the spring to operate freely. The lock region is the weakest part of the stock, and it is a long-established principle of gun building to leave as much wood there as possible.

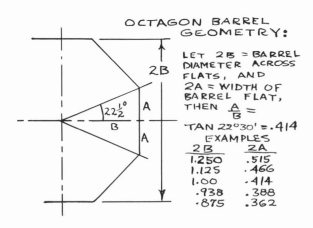

OCTAGON BARREL
GEOMETRY:

LET 2B = BARREL DIAMETER ACROSS FLATS, AND
2A = WIDTH OF BARREL FLAT, THEN $\frac{A}{B}$ =

TAN 22°30' = .414

EXAMPLES

2B	2A
1.250	.515
1.125	.466
1.00	.414
.938	.388
.875	.362

FROM THIS IT CAN BE SEEN THAT A DRUM ½ INCH IN DIAMETER WILL OVERHANG THE FLAT ON A BARREL LESS THAN 1¼ INCH ACROSS THE FLATS.

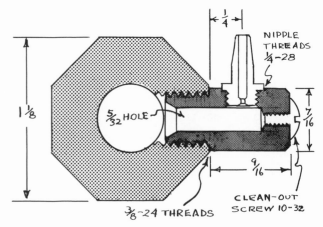

PERCUSSION DRUM 7/16 OD IN SIDE OF BARREL 1⅛ INCH ACROSS FLATS, .50 CALIBER.

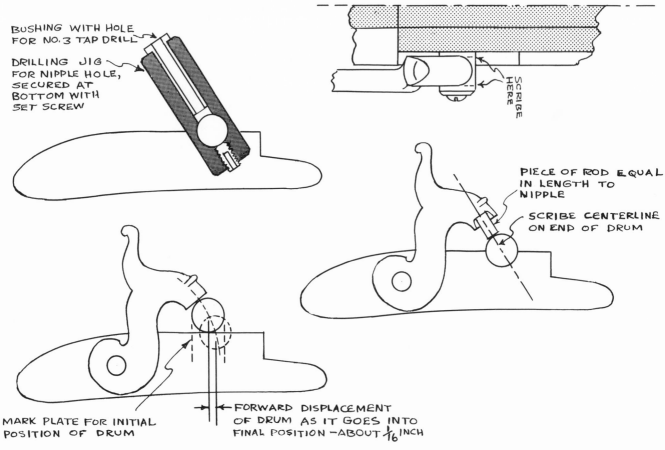

BUSHING WITH HOLE FOR NO. 3 TAP DRILL

DRILLING JIG FOR NIPPLE HOLE, SECURED AT BOTTOM WITH SET SCREW

SCRIBE HERE

PIECE OF ROD EQUAL IN LENGTH TO NIPPLE

SCRIBE CENTERLINE ON END OF DRUM

MARK PLATE FOR INITIAL POSITION OF DRUM

FORWARD DISPLACEMENT OF DRUM AS IT GOES INTO FINAL POSITION — ABOUT 1/16 INCH

Inletting the Percussion Lock

Before a percussion lock can be installed, the drum that holds the nipple must be installed in the barrel. Ready-made drums are available from dealers in muzzle-loading gun parts, or with the aid of a lathe they can be made. If a ready-made drum is to be used, get one without a hole drilled and tapped for a nipple, for it is much easier to drill the hole for the nipple in the correct location after the lock is installed, than to fiddle with a drum so that the hole lines up with the hammer.

Typical percussion drums are 7/16 or ½ inch outside diameter, and the external portion is between ½ and 5/8 inch long. The threaded portion that screws into the barrel can have threads of 5/16-18, 5/16-24, 3/8-16, or 3/8-24 size for either drum. The 3/8-24 thread is the strongest and is recommended for medium and large barrel sizes and calibers of .45 or more. Nipple threads normally are ¼ -28 size.

The drum should be installed in the center of the side flat of the barrel, and far enough forward that the threads do not interfere with the breech-plug. For a drum with a shank threaded 3/8 -24, the center of the hole should be just slightly more than 3/16 inch in front of the face of the breech-plug. Drill and tap the hole with the aid of the drill press, if possible. In drilling the hole, do it with the breech-plug removed, and proceed slowly and carefully. Be sure that the barrel is well clamped when drilling, for the drill may bind as it breaks through the bore. It can help to drill a small pilot hole first, about 1/8 inch diameter. In tapping the hole, avoid cutting full threads all the way through the side of the barrel. Make the threads with a starting tap and stop before the tap reaches full thread depth all the way through. Try the drum as you proceed. The object is a good snug fit. It may be necessary to countersink the hole slightly at the outer end, to allow for incomplete threading near the shoulder of the drum.

After the drum is screwed securely into the barrel, check the bore to see if the threaded shank penetrates into the bore. If so, score it from the breech end, remove, and file it with the help of a half-round file. Replace often to check progress. When it is filed flush with the bore, the inner end of the hole in the drum could be countersunk to aid the ignition process.

Some percussion locks have a semicircular cut in the bolster for the drum, and some do not, which is preferable. In the latter case, with the drum removed from the barrel, place it on top of the bolster and ease the hammer down on it. Move the drum so that the center of the hammer falls on the center of the drum. Scribe vertical lines to mark the position of the drum. Make a semicircular cut for the drum, which should be about 1/16 inch ahead of the scribed position to allow for displacement of rotation. Do the fitting carefully, for the lock-plate helps take the shock of the hammer as it strikes the nipple.

Next, replace the drum in the barrel and inlet the drum into the stock. Strip the lock of its internal parts and place it on the side of the stock so that the drum fits snugly into its recess in the bolster. As with a flintlock, move the nose of the lock until it lines up with the web between barrel channel and ramrod groove, and proceed to inlet it.

After inletting the lock, drill the drum for the nipple. Remove the clean-out screw that is part of most commercial drums. Let the hammer come down on the drum, and scribe the drum on either side of the hammer nose. The center of the nipple hole should lie halfway between the scribe marks. At this point it is perfectly reasonable to bend the shank of the hammer to one side or another if the nose of the hammer falls too close to the barrel or too far from it. Use the heat of a propane torch to help with the bending. Take a small piece of round stock the size of the shank of the nipple and place it on the drum, letting the hammer down to hold it in place. Scribe the top of the drum around this piece of metal, and while viewing the assembly from the side, scribe a centerline on the end of the drum.

Remove the drum and locate the hole for the nipple according to the scribed lines, but about 1/16 inch to the rear of the center suggested by the scribed lines. This will allow for a small bit of final adjustment, which can be accomplished by tightening the drum in the barrel. With a center punch, mark the position of the hole. Remove the drum from the barrel and drill the hole in the drum to accept the threaded base of the nipple. The nipple thread is size ¼ x 28, and the correct tap drill to use is the #3 drill 43(0.213 in.).ˊ The base of the nipple, where it fits against the outside of the drum, is flat, but the surface of the drum is cylindrical. The contact area can be filed flat after threading the hole, while the nipple is being fitted. However, for the neatest job, use a counterbore with pilot to make a seat for the nipple before drilling the tap hole. After drilling the tap hole, presumably done under the drill press, make use of the drill press to start the ¼ x 28 starting tap into the hole. It will not go in far enough to make full threads, so a bottoming tap is needed to complete the threads. The object is a firm snug fit for the nipple.

A handy drum drilling jig is available from Track of the Wolf, Inc. This consists of a cylinder of metal about ¾ inch in diameter and 1 ½ or 2 inches long, with a hole drilled transversely through it large enough to fit snugly over the drum. At one end of this cylinder is a set screw that locks it into position on the drum. At the other end of the drum is a hole into which fits a hardened bushing with a hole in it to take the #3 tap drill. After the hole is drilled, the bushing is removed and the tap is run into the drum through the larger hole in the cylinder.

Remove the nipple, install the drum in the barrel, and replace the nipple. With the hammer down on the nipple, turn the drum until the nipple is perfectly lined up with the center of the hammer nose. Replace the clean-out screw. If it will not screw in all the way, it probably is hitting the nipple, and it can be shortened as necessary.

Never let the hammer fall on the nipple from full cock without a cap on the nipple, for the fall will damage both the nipple and the hammer. Instead, buy some neoprene hose with an interior diameter suitable to fit snugly over the nipple. Cut a small section off, to fit over the nipple for trying the lock. The rest of the hose can be used to help clean out the rifle after shooting.

With the lock on half-cock, slip the hose over the nipple, and put the other end of the hose in a container of warm soapy water. Running the ramrod with a patch on the jag at the end up and down the barrel sucks water into the barrel through the nipple and forces it out again.

With the lock firmly imbedded in the stock, now is the time to bring the top and bottom profile lines of the wrist to their finished positions. An important objective is to end up with the tail of the lock centered on the side of the wrist or close to it.

TAP AND CLEARANCE DRILL SIZES

| SCREW THREAD OR TAP | | TAP DRILL | | | | CLEARANCE DRILL | | | |
| | Diameter | Drill | | Fractional | | Close Fit | | Fractional | |
Size	Inches	no.	Inches	Inch	Drills	No.	Inches	Inch	Drills
6-32	.138	36	.106	7/64	.109	25	.145	5/32	.156
6-40	.138	33	.113	7/64	.109	25	.149	5/32	.156
6-48	.138	31	.120	—		25	.149	5/32	.156
8-32	.164	29	.136	9/64	.141	19	.166	11/64	.172
8-40	.164	28	.140	9/64	.141	19	.166	11/64	.172
10-32	.190	21	.159	5/32	.156	9	.196	13/64	.203
12-24	.216	16	.177	11/64	.172	2	.221	7/32	.219
12-28	.216	14	.182	3/16	.188	2	.221	7/32	.219
¼-20	.250	7	.201	13/64	.203	F	.257	17/64	.266
¼-28	.250	3	.213	7/32	.219	F	.257	17/64	.266
5/16-18	.312	F	.257	1/4	.250	P	.323	21/64	.328
3/8-24	.375	Q	.332	21/64	.328	W	.386	25/64	.391

Notes:
It is preferable to use the numbered (wire gauge) drills as tap drills rather than drills sized to fractions of an inch, in most cases. The fractional inch drills are approximations to the needed sizes. The numbered or letter size clearance drills are for close fits. For freer fits, slightly larger drills can be used.

CHAPTER 11

SHAPING AND INLETTING THE BARREL TANG

Barrel tangs on old rifles are found to have a variety of shapes and sizes. The basic function of a barrel tang is to anchor the breech end of the barrel securely into the stock. But there are secondary and tertiary functions that a barrel tang can serve, and even a quaternary one. The secondary function, which is provided only by a long tang, is to reinforce the stock at the place where it is weakest, in the region of the lock and the wrist. A third function is to provide a place where peep sights can be installed. The fourth function would be decorative, as with the extra long tangs on some rifles of the southern Appalachians that reach clear to the butt-plate and are decorated with silver inlay.

Tradition favors the short tang. Practicality favors the long tang. The short tang was used on sporting arms of 17th and 18th century Europe. These European sporting arms were used infrequently and with care. The sporting rifles of central Europe had short barrels of generous diameter, and there was adequate wood at the lock and wrist to prevent breakage. The stock area around the tang, and on top of the wrist behind the tang, became a region for artistic decoration. Relief-carved design was common, if not almost mandatory and a decorative wrist inlay or escutcheon or thumb-piece was usual.

The longrifle of course evolved in early America from these European traditions. However, in the course of evolution the barrel became longer and much heavier, though the breech end of the barrel became smaller. And the wrist was made more slender. The result was a rifle that was structurally unsound as far as the strength of the stock in the region of the lock and wrist is concerned. As a consequence, many, many old rifles have been lost from broken stocks. Some of the survivors have old repairs to broken wrists.

Almost all American flintlock rifles of the 18th century were made with short tangs, and in Pennsylvania, Maryland, Virginia, and Ohio this trend continued during the 19th century. However, near the end of the 18th century, and into the 19th century, long tangs were used in the Appalachian mountain states, including western Virginia, and their use spread to the mid-western states during the percussion period. During the Golden Age of rifle making, in the post-Revolutionary years, tangs tended to be short and to have pointed finials. In the percussion period a simple rounded end was typical.

It is best to work out the length of the short tang with the help of a scale drawing made both on paper and on the left side of the stock. The length is related to the position of the tang screw. See p.47 for a sketch of the basic relationship. Aided by a side profile drawing of the trigger-guard drawn on paper, and the guard held against the edge of the stock, sketch in the trigger-plate and likely position of the trigger.

The tang screw should pierce the trigger-plate about ½ in. in front of the trigger, but of course the type of trigger used can affect what is possible to do. The end of the tang typically is ½ to ¾ in. to the rear of the tang screw center, and the tang screw center typically is about 1 in. from the end of the barrel.

The tang is first cut to the correct length, typically 1 ¾ to 2 in. and then is filed to shape. Be sure to file the edges at a slight angle, so that the tang is wider at the top than at the bottom. The taper angle is slight, being but a few degrees, but it is desirable to have in order to make a neat and tight mortise in the wood.

In general, the edges of almost all inlays and metal parts that fit into the wooden stock should have a slight inward bevel. For permanently installed pieces, such as inlays, it helps with the fitting. For parts that need to be removed from time to time, such as the lock, trigger-guard, trigger-plate, side-plate, and breech-plug tang, the beveled edge provides for easy removal. Also, it helps prevent problems that might arise under moist conditions, if the wood swelled slightly against metal parts with sides that were not slightly sloped.

Long tangs call for extra consideration. Generally they are held to the stock with two screws. The forward screw goes through the stock and threads into the trigger plate. The rear screw may be a wood screw, but usually is a machine screw that also goes through the wrist and threads into a long trigger plate. Thus it is necessary to deal with the trigger plate and tang together.

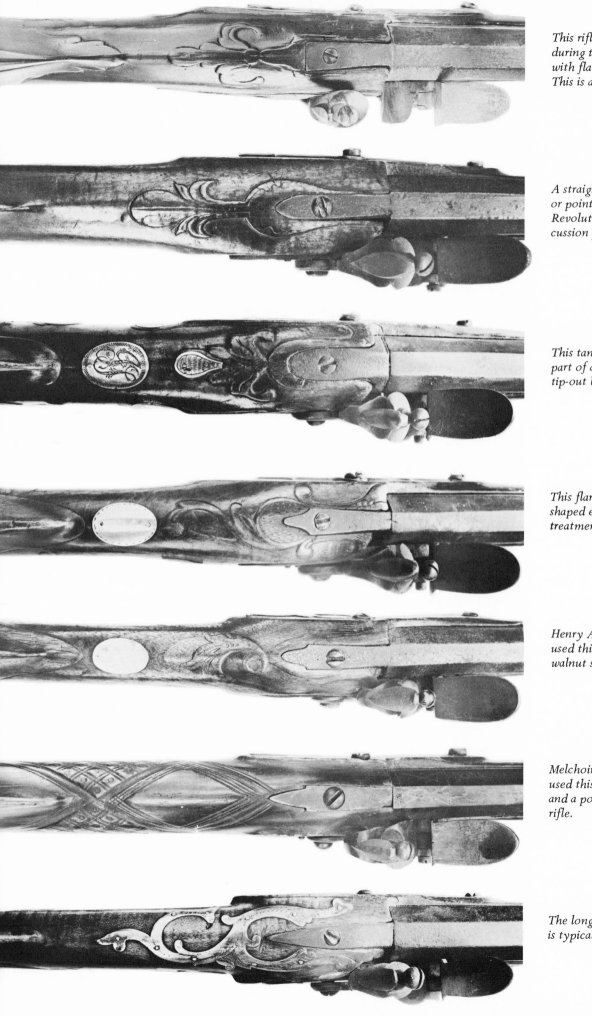

This rifle, made in York County, P
during the 1770's has a barrel tang
with flared sides and a squared end
This is a typical tang for the period

A straight sided tang with a rounde
or pointed end was used from the
Revolutionary years into the percussion period.

This tang, with its rounded end, is
part of a standing breech for a
tip-out barrel.

This flared tang with its attractively
shaped end is a typical Golden Age
treatment.

Henry Albright of Lancaster, Pa.,
used this slightly flared tang on a
walnut stocked rifle.

Melchoir Fordney of Lancaster, Pa.
used this tang, with square shoulde
and a pointed end, on a smoothbor
rifle.

The long pointed end on this tang
is typical of the years after 1820.

46

Long two-screw tang on a
North Carolina rifle by
Nathaniel Vogler.

Long two-screw tang
on a North Carolina rifle
by Henry Ledford.

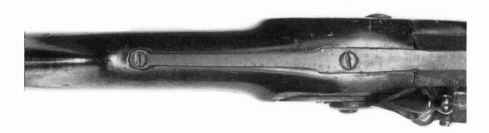

Full-length tang on a
North Carolina flintlock
rifle by John Gillespie.

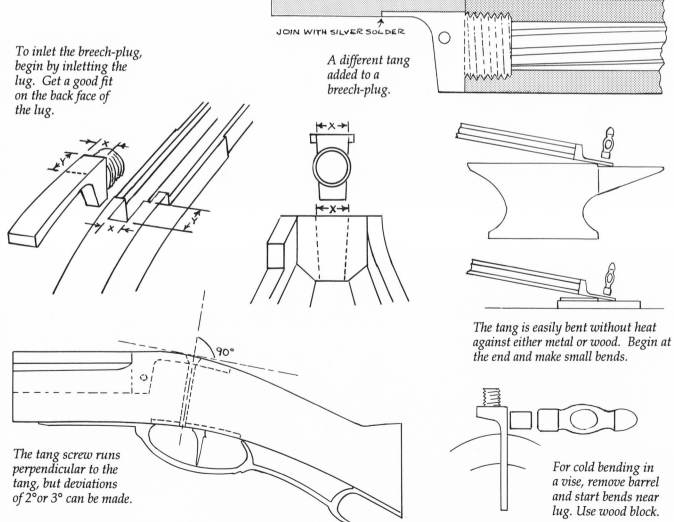

To inlet the breech-plug,
begin by inletting the
lug. Get a good fit
on the back face of
the lug.

JOIN WITH SILVER SOLDER

A different tang
added to a
breech-plug.

The tang is easily bent without heat
against either metal or wood. Begin at
the end and make small bends.

The tang screw runs
perpendicular to the
tang, but deviations
of 2° or 3° can be made.

90°

For cold bending in
a vise, remove barrel
and start bends near
lug. Use wood block.

The "pea-picker" rifle by Geo. Schreyer has a square-ended tang common in the late 18th century.

The breech plug tang will have to be bent to conform with the top profile of the stock, as viewed from the side. The amount of bending needed is not great, and it can be done with the metal in the cold state, i.e. at room temperature. Place a piece of metal about 1/8 inch thick on top of an anvil, a concrete floor, or even a sturdy workbench top. With the breech plug firmly screwed in place in the barrel, place the tang over the step created by the 1/8 inch thick piece of metal and pound on the underside of the tang. By moving the tang with respect to the step, a number of small bends can be made to effect a curve. The curve need not be perfect, because small imperfections can be removed by filing the top surface. It is best if the tang is bent so that the upper surface lies a little above the finish line of the stock, ideally about 1/32 inch, but if the tang is thick enough at the start, it can be 1/16 inch. However, the finished tang should in no case be less than 1/8 inch thick, and a thickness of 3/16 inch or more is best.

The tang also can be bent in a vise with the aid of an acetylene torch. And if the plug is removed from the barrel, the tang can be bent in its cold state while being held upright in a vise.

Inletting the tang into the wood must be done with care to avoid gaps in the wood-to-metal fit. First, remove the breech plug and place the barrel in the stock. Mark on top of the stock lines that are extensions of the edges of the top flat of the barrel. Measure how far back the lug of the breech plug will reach, and mark the position with a transverse line. At the rear end of the barrel channel mark the limits of the lug where it will be let into the wood. With a chisel, remove the wood from the region of the lug.

Replace the breech plug in the barrel, and start fitting the lug into the mortise cut for it. Transfer color will help with the final fitting. As the barrel moves down and back, the tang eventually makes contact with the top of the stock. Carefully scribe on each side of the tang, and cut out within these lines. Again use transfer color, and only cut where the metal contacts the wood. Make certain that the breech end of the barrel is fully up against the wood face. Put transfer color on the bottom flat of the barrel near the breech end, to indicate when the barrel is finally in place.

A final suggestion is to provide a little *breathing space* to the rear of a tang with a square end. The problem is that no matter how well the breech end face of a barrel is fitted against the wood at the end of the barrel channel, a small amount of movement of the barrel in a rearward direction is bound to occur as a result of the rifle, in use, being placed with its butt on the ground many times, and of being fired many times. Also, differential movement takes place as a result of moisture variations, and bending stresses on the wood. If the end of the tang starts out tight against the wood, it can result in chipping out the wood. The solution is to remove about 0.020 inch of metal from the end of the tang before the final finishing of the barrel and tang is done.

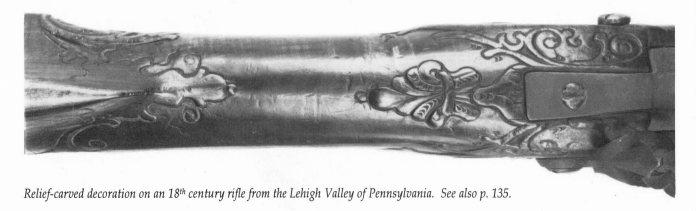

Relief-carved decoration on an 18th century rifle from the Lehigh Valley of Pennsylvania. See also p. 135.

CHAPTER 12

INSTALLING THE BUTT-PLATE

With the lock in place, the position of the trigger can be determined, as described in Chapter 15. With the trigger position marked, the exact trigger-reach distance and butt drop can be laid out, and the location of the butt-plate determined.

Butt-plates typically are purchased as rough sand castings, or as less rough investment castings, usually in brass or bronze, but also in iron. They usually have imperfections that need to be corrected before installation is started, or the piece may end up a little tilted or off-center. This involves file work on the inner surfaces that will contact the wood. Finishing the outer surfaces will be done later, as the stock is being brought to final shape.

The first part of the butt-plate to deal with is the cap, which is the extension that runs forward from the heel, along the top of the comb. There are two methods of inletting this part of the butt-plate. The first is the traditional method, used by many old time gunsmiths, in which the wood is left to fill the cavity under the cap. This holds the heel and cap securely in place and provides good support for the push rod of a patchbox release. The simpler method involves removing all the wood under the cap, leaving a flat surface to which the cap is easily fitted.

For either method, the first thing to do is to file smooth the front face of the extension, making sure that the surface is square with, and perpendicular to, a centerline scribed along the outside of the cap. A centerline also should be scribed on the inside of the butt-plate. A plane formed by the lower edges of the cap should be square with the inside centerline, and if it is not that way initially, one of the lower edges should be filed to make it square. A plastic drafting triangle with lines scribed on it with a knife point is the simple tool to use for this work. (p.50)

To inlet the butt-plate by the traditional method, the lower edge surfaces of the cap should slope inward. Some butt-plates come with this beveled edge already present, and it only needs to be cleaned up with a file. If the simpler method of installation is to be used, the lower edge surfaces need to be filed flat, to lie on the flat plane that will be cut in the stock.

The portion of the inner surface of the butt-plate that will lie in contact with the wood needs to be smoothed with a file. This is more or less a strip of the inner surface of about 3/16 to ¼ inch wide lying along either edge of the metal, plus the toe area. This portion of the metal will contact the wood near its outer edge. A straight-edge laid across the edges should be square with the centerline inside the cap, and if not, the edges should be filed until it is square. Next, file this contact strip along the outer edge of the plate so that it slopes inward, perhaps by an eyeball 10°. This makes it easier to inlet.

With the butt-plate prepared, and the trigger-reach and butt drop determined, place the butt-plate against the side of the stock. The top of the cap should line up with the comb line, but be about 1/16 inch below it. With a pencil, draw the outlines of the inner surfaces of the butt-plate on the stock. If the traditional installation method is to be used, draw a line 1/8 inch to the rear of the existing line. This new line determines where the initial cut is made at the butt end of the stock. The other line marks the finished position of the butt-plate. If you feel cautious, increase the distance between the two lines to 3/16 to even ¼ inch.

Next, draw a line parallel to, and about 1/8 inch above, the line marking the bottom edge of the cap. This line is the contact line between the wood and the outer edge of the extension. Mark this line on both sides of the butt.

Before doing any cutting, however, draw a center line along the top of the butt from the center of the top flat of the barrel to the butt end of the wood, and in line with the center of the barrel. Cast-off, which was mentioned in Chapter 2, enters the picture here. Most well-designed longrifles have butt-stocks that are cast-off to the right, when viewed from above. Typically this amounts to about ¼ inch. To introduce this amount of cast-off to the butt, make a mark ¼ inch to the right of the centerline near the butt end of the wood and at the position where the end of the butt-plate heel will lie. Make a second mark along the centerline at a distance to 5 ½ inches behind the breech end of the barrel or, as the

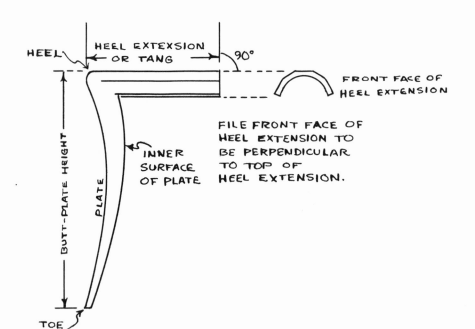

HEEL

HEEL EXTEXSION OR TANG

90°

BUTT-PLATE HEIGHT

PLATE

INNER SURFACE OF PLATE

TOE

FRONT FACE OF HEEL EXTENSION

FILE FRONT FACE OF HEEL EXTENSION TO BE PERPENDICULAR TO TOP OF HEEL EXTENSION.

LOWER SURFACES OF HEEL EXTENSION EDGES FILED FLAT FOR SIMPLE METHOD OF INLETTING.

LOWER SURFACES OF HEEL EXTENSION EDGES FILED TO SLOPE OF ABOUT 20° FOR TRADITIONAL INLETTING.

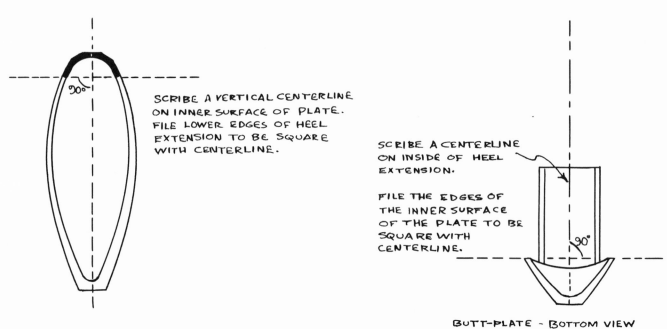

90°

SCRIBE A VERTICAL CENTERLINE ON INNER SURFACE OF PLATE. FILE LOWER EDGES OF HEEL EXTENSION TO BE SQUARE WITH CENTERLINE.

SCRIBE A CENTERLINE ON INSIDE OF HEEL EXTENSION.

FILE THE EDGES OF THE INNER SURFACE OF THE PLATE TO BE SQUARE WITH CENTERLINE.

90°

BUTT-PLATE - BOTTOM VIEW

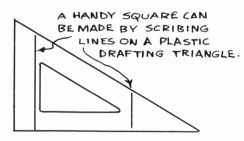

A HANDY SQUARE CAN BE MADE BY SCRIBING LINES ON A PLASTIC DRAFTING TRIANGLE.

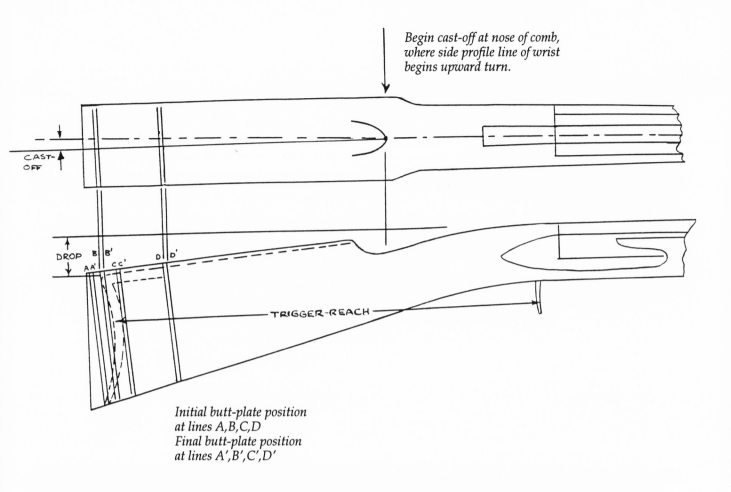

Begin cast-off at nose of comb, where side profile line of wrist begins upward turn.

CAST-OFF

DROP

B B'

A A' C C'

D D'

TRIGGER-REACH

Initial butt-plate position at lines A,B,C,D
Final butt-plate position at lines A',B',C',D'

drawing above suggests at the front end of the comb. Connect these two points and form the center-line for the cast-off butt. The wrist of the stock lies in line with the barrel, and the cast-off begins in the region where the front end of the comb terminates.

On the right side of the butt, draw lines representing the initial cut for the butt-plate and the finish line, i.e. to the toe, the heel, and to the points of tangency more or less halfway between toe and heel where the curve of the butt lies farthest forward. Then with a square lying on the cast-off centerline, transfer these lines to the top of the butt. The purpose is that the butt-plate has a bit of what also might be called cast-off, for it must lie in line with the cast-off centerline.

To inlet the butt-plate, begin by cutting the end of the stock blank to conform with the profile line already drawn. If a band-saw is available, tilt the table slightly and make the cut. If not, do it with hand tools and care. Then begin letting in the heel extension. Cut the grooves at the sides, almost to the limit lines drawn, and not to full depth. Then the dome of wood that fits under the extension is formed in the rough. From here on it is largely a matter of cut-and-try. Use transfer color, and proceed slowly.

The simple method makes use of the same basic lay-out lines, except that it is necessary to establish lines for making a cut parallel to, but about 1/8 inch to the rear of, the plane where the front face of the extension meets the wood. With a fine-toothed hand saw, or a jeweler's saw, make this cut. Then trim away the excess wood to form the plane where the lower side of the heel extension will lie. It is important that this plane is correctly oriented, because it determines whether or not the toe of the butt ends up correctly centered.

Now, centering the front of the heel extension on the cast-off centerline, gradually fit the butt-plate into its final position. Tap the heel of the butt-plate gently to make the transfer color show, because heavy pounding will distort it. Cut and try until the extension touches wood on its front face, underneath, and at its rear corners, and when the butt-plate edges are touching from the toe upward

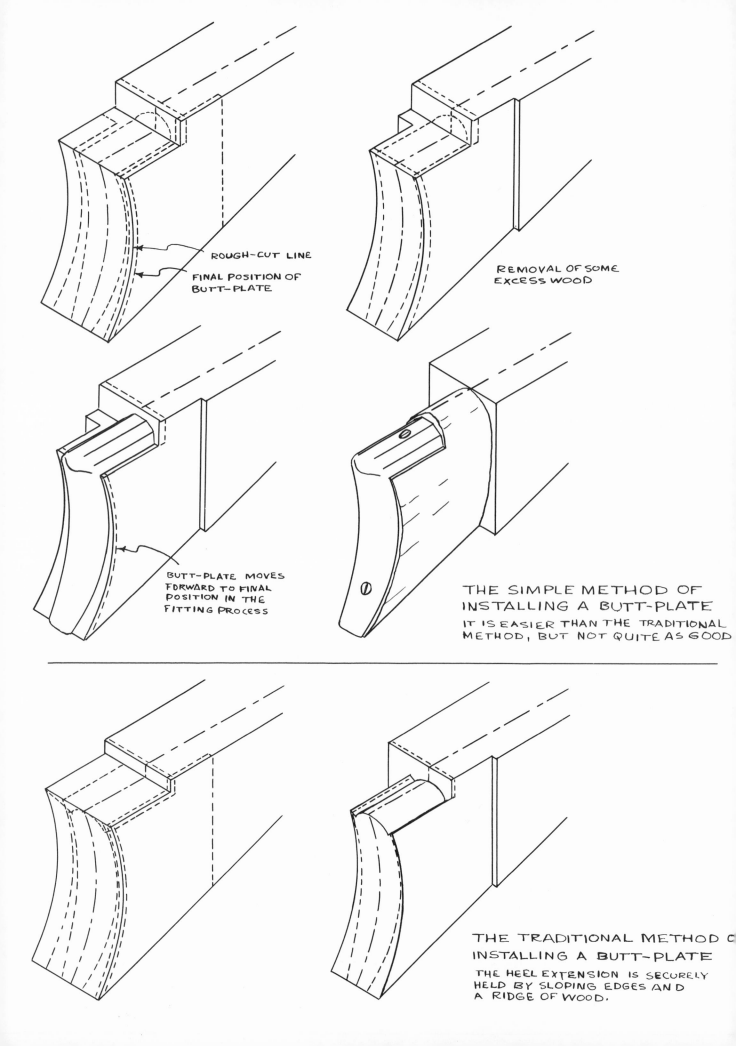

ROUGH-CUT LINE

FINAL POSITION OF
BUTT-PLATE

REMOVAL OF SOME
EXCESS WOOD

BUTT-PLATE MOVES
FORWARD TO FINAL
POSITION IN THE
FITTING PROCESS

THE SIMPLE METHOD OF
INSTALLING A BUTT-PLATE
IT IS EASIER THAN THE TRADITIONAL
METHOD, BUT NOT QUITE AS GOOD

THE TRADITIONAL METHOD C
INSTALLING A BUTT-PLATE
THE HEEL EXTENSION IS SECURELY
HELD BY SLOPING EDGES AND
A RIDGE OF WOOD.

for a distance of about 1 to 1 ½ inches. At this point you can continue inletting until it is close to perfect. But it can be very time consuming to close all of the gaps for the perfect fit. When a few gaps remain that are no wider than, say, 1/32 inch, it is possible to tap the edges of the plate into close contact.

If the final fitting is to be done by hammering, the butt-plate screws must be installed. Use # 8 or # 10 flat head screws, 1 inch long for the top screw, and ¾ or 5/8 inch long for the lower screw. These are temporary working screws that will be replaced later with somewhat longer screws. Mark the location of the upper hole on the top of the butt-plate extension, and drill it to receive the body of the screw. Place the butt-plate on the stock and with a sharp pencil, mark the location of the hole on the wood below it. Remove the plate again, and with a sharp punch, mark the drill location, placing it about 1/32 inch forward of the center of the circle. By installing the screw slightly forward of the center, the screw will tend to pull the extension forward for a good tight fit. The lower screw then is installed.

It may be necessary to modify the size of the screw heads, as the top screw head must be smaller in diameter than the width of the top flat of the extension. For these narrow butt-plates it would be best to use # 8 screws. With the aid of a file, the screw head can be modified if the screw is put in the chuck of a drill press or of an electric drill held in a vise. A finished screw should have a slightly domed head, and of course dome-head screws that resemble the old ones. It will be necessary to countersink the holes in the butt-plate to accept the heads of the screws. The compleat gunsmith later adjusts the fit of the screw head to the counter-sunk hole so that when the screw is turned in to a tight fit, the slot in the head is in line with the centerline of the comb or the vertical centerline of the butt-plate.

With the butt-plate firmly screwed in place, tap the edges of the plate into place against the wood with a small hammer. Modest force will serve better than the use of a heavy hand. With files, clean up the edges and the whole outer surface of the butt-plate, but final finishing will be done later. The edge flats of the butt-plates on fine old rifles often were relatively thin, typically about 1/16 inch wide.

The final comb line now is established as a flattened surface that conforms to the desired profile. Also, the profile of the lower edge of the butt-stock is brought to final shape. Be careful of the curve under the lock where the lower butt line enters that area. The lower edge of the butt must be kept perpendicular to the central plane of the butt.

Draw a centerline from the center of the toe to the center of the ramrod entry. This will not be one straight line, but rather two lines that meet at a slight angle in the region of the rear end of the trigger-guard at its widest point. The flat underside of the butt, where the rear extension of the trigger-guard is inletted, will be the width of the extension plus about 1/8 inch on either side. Estimate the position of the rear extension, and mark the dimensions on either side of the centerline.

This implies that the flat on the underside of the butt may be tapered, which will be the case if the toe of the butt-plate is relatively wide. This is an attractive feature that many fine old rifles had, particularly the 18th century pieces. Some butt-plates of the Golden Age period had butt-plates with somewhat narrow toes, and consequently the flat under the butt is more or less of uniform width.

Draw lines from the two marks already made to the corners of the toe of the butt-plate. From the rear end of the trigger-guard forward, the under flat does not taper, but is of uniform width, though adjustments may have to be made if the trigger-plate is wider than the rear extension of the trigger-guard, for there should be at least 3/32 inch of wood flat on either side of the trigger plate.

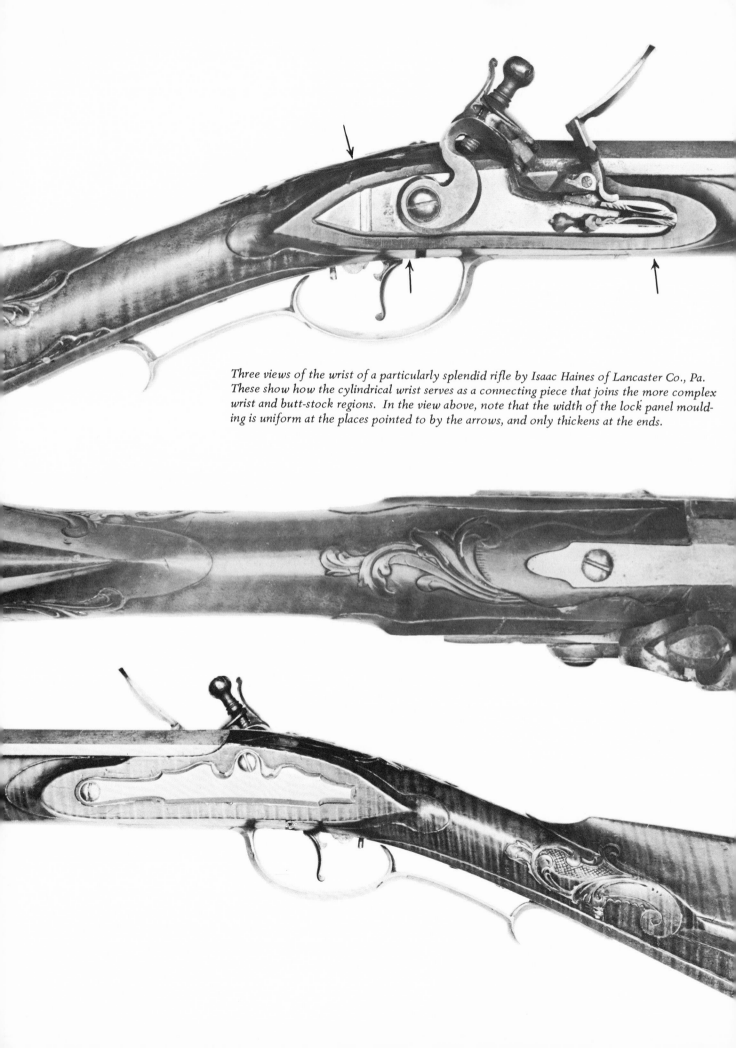

Three views of the wrist of a particularly splendid rifle by Isaac Haines of Lancaster Co., Pa. These show how the cylindrical wrist serves as a connecting piece that joins the more complex wrist and butt-stock regions. In the view above, note that the width of the lock panel moulding is uniform at the places pointed to by the arrows, and only thickens at the ends.

CHAPTER 13

PLANNING AND INITIAL SHAPING OF THE LOCK REGION AND WRIST

With the barrel tang, lock, and butt-plate installed, it is time to work on the lock and wrist region. Many important details and dimensions necessary for shaping the rest of the stock are established by dimensions in the region of the lock and wrist. The shaping of this region is not a simple matter, and for a good end result it must be planned with care and carefully done.

The lock panel is the flat wood surface surrounding the lock-plate. Its counter-part on the left side of the stock, usually of the same size and shape, is the side-plate panel. The wood behind these surfaces is essential in providing necessary strength to the stock in the region where breakage easily can take place. Beyond the outer edges of the lock and side-plate panels, where the wood slopes away from the panels, decorative mouldings sometimes are carved in relief, but on old rifles sometimes only a simple incised moulding line was carved instead.

It is possible and reasonable to finish a rifle without any carved mouldings or decoration in the lock and wrist region. Many old rifles were made this way, particularly in the late flintlock period and the percussion era. But from the artistic point of view, the "better" rifles have mouldings around the lock and side-plate panels, and around the barrel tang. To the rear of the tang, on top of the wrist, there is carved decoration. At the rear end of the lock and side-plate panels there are the traditional beaver-tail shaped lobes. Along the lower edges of the wrist the lower-butt moulding terminates near the trigger. And, at the front end of the lock-panel moulding, there may be a fore-stock moulding.

The challenge of building a longrifle, however, is to go the whole course, which in this case means relief-carved mouldings and decoration. The best way to get some feeling for how these mouldings, and the tang carving, were designed and made is to look at a lot of old rifles first hand. This being difficult for most people to do, the next best way is to get a book that shows a lot of good photos of them. A number of books have some useful illustrations to go by, but by far the most helpful book is RIFLES OF COLONIAL AMERICA by Geo. Shumway. In the present book we can show only an example or two.

But this decorative work is not part of the initial shaping of the wood in the lock and wrist region. Relief-carved features almost always stand less than 1/16 inch above the wood surrounding them, and the object now is to get the major amount of excess wood removed so that the surface is close to where the tops of relief features might be located.

Of primary importance here is drawing the shape of the lock-panel on the wood surface. When the lock was installed in the stock (Chapt. 10) the start of a lock-panel ¼ inch wide was begun at the breech end of the barrel. Draw the edge of the lock-panel at a uniform width of ¼ inch around the lock-plate, but with extra width at the front and rear ends, in the fashion shown by the Isaac Haines rifle illustrated here. The tail end of the lock-panel, of course, should be centered on the sides of what will be the wrist. Make a careful tracing of the lock-panel shape, and cut a stiff piece of paper to the same size. Then carefully transfer the shape to the left side of the stock to establish the shape of the side-plate panel.

It already has been mentioned, but is worth repeating, that the wood behind the lock-panel surfaces provides strength at the weakest part of the stock, and this is a very important reason for the lock-panel mouldings to exceed a minimal 1/8 inch width. This is the case for the Haines rifle shown on the opposing page. In contrast, most Germanic rifles of the 18th century, with short barrels that were large at the breech, and made for light service, typically have about 1/8 inch, or slightly more, of wood surrounding the edge of the lock. But for both American longrifles and their Germanic cousins, the side-plate panel repeats the shape of the lock-panel.

In addition to drawing the shape of the lock-panel on the flat wood on the right side of the stock, it also is helpful to draw representations of the front and rear finials for the lock moulding, including the beaver-tail finials to the rear if they are planned. The leading edge of the rounded moulding that lies in front of the lock-panel, and its left-side counterpart, may be between ½ to 2 inches from it. With the front end of the moulding determined, it then is possible to cut the fore-stock to the desired width, which is 1/8 inch plus an extra 1/32 inch.

Likewise, at the rear end of the lock panel is a finial shaped more or less like a beaver-tail, and the position of the end of this finial should be determined, with a little extra length to spare, so that the wrist that lies to the rear of it can be cut to the desired width without hesitation. Good thought should be given to designing the beaver-tail finial, for it ends up as a small yet prominent decorative detail. By looking with a critical eye at this finial in the photos of many old rifles, it will become apparent that a lot of them were poorly designed, being too small, or too large, or not shaped right, or not headed in the right direction. A thought for designing the beaver-tail is to extend the lines formed by the tail end of the lock moulding so that they cross each other, with the beaver-tail form centered between the lines.

As the illustrations of the Haines rifle so clearly show, the wrist is essentially overlain by tang carving, lock-panel mouldings, the comb-nose moulding, and the front end of the lower butt moulding. The initial shaping of the wrist should bring its surface to about 3/32 inch above the finished level, so that these various mouldings later can be left in relief as the wrist region is brought to its finished level.

The finished width of the wrist is essentially the same as the width of the fore-stock in front of the forward end of the moulding that surrounds the lock, i.e. the barrel width plus the thickness of the wood on either side of it, i.e. the barrel width plus 1/8 inch plus 1/8 inch.

Ideally, the height of the wrist should taper slightly from the barrel tang to the front end of the comb. If the wrist is much higher in the region of the tang than at the front end of the comb, it gives a "pinched wrist" appearance, which is detrimental to the appearance and perhaps to the strength of the wrist. If the wrist height increases to the rear it may affect the appearance adversely, but increases the strength. The old-time master gunsmith of Philadelphia, Jacob Kuntz, made some of his late-flint and early percussion rifles that way, but we do not recommend it.

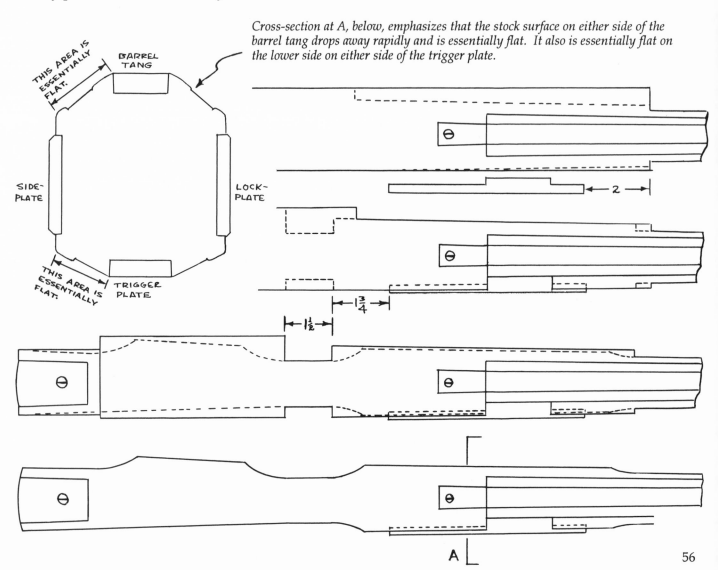

Cross-section at A, below, emphasizes that the stock surface on either side of the barrel tang drops away rapidly and is essentially flat. It also is essentially flat on the lower side on either side of the trigger plate.

CHAPTER 14

SHAPING THE BUTT-STOCK

In shaping the butt-stock, it is best to work on it as an integrated unit, rather than trying to work one side at a time. Work from side to side, gradually bringing it to final shape, and harmony with the lock and wrist region. If your rifle is to be styled closely after the work of some particular school or maker, then the shape of the butt may be pretty much pre-determined for you. But if your rifle is your own creation, then there will be the problem of determining exactly what you want to do before you plunge in. However, it probably is not possible for one who has never made a rifle before to pre-plan it all. The finished form of many of the contours must be determined by the eye as the finishing process goes on.

Drawings can help, however, and those suggested in Chapter 2, probably modified by now, can remain as a guide. The shaping of much of the right side of the butt is fairly well pre-determined by the limits of the butt-plate, the wrist, the flat under the butt, and the profile of the comb. The left side is more complex because of the cheek-piece. Both top-view and side-view drawings should be made for the butt. The exact position of the cheek-piece and the amount that it stands out from the body of the butt are particularly important to determine, and these should be worked out on paper.

It is well to think of the wrist and butt areas as a sequence of intersecting curved surfaces. The wrist is essentially a cylinder of round or oval cross-section, with an axis that has a curve to it. Think of this wrist cylinder as a shape that extends down into the butt, with the cheek-piece and the front end of the comb as masses of wood that extend forward over the wrist. See the cheek-piece surface as part of a cone. See the top surface of the comb as a separate curved surface, a portion of a cone. Visualize the intersection of the cheek-piece surface and the top-of-the-comb surface as a line of intersection, and when shaping the butt, actually make these separate surfaces meet along a line of intersection. The corner can be rounded off later. On the right side of the stock, near the front end of the comb, visualize the cylindrical wrist extending half way down the butt, and the right side of the comb meeting it along some line of intersection. To the rear of the cheek-piece visualize the wood surface as part of a cone with a point up in the region of the lock, and visualize the cheek-piece as a mass of wood glued on to this conical surface.

These are the major elements to consider in shaping the butt, and on a well made rifle they usually stand out clearly. Often relief mouldings and decorative carving purposely are used at the intersections of these surfaces, especially around the front end of the comb, and at either end of the cheek-piece. These mouldings and carving help emphasize the intersection of the surfaces, and in some situations can help to hide or minimize slightly awkward intersections, particularly on the left side of the stock where the front end of the comb, the front end of the cheek-piece, and the wrist all meet together.

Lines that mark the edges of the flat underside of the butt must be drawn on the wood before starting to shape the butt. It probably is best to draw the location of the finished edge, and then also to draw working lines about 1/16 inch outside the finished edge lines. The lower corners of the butt-plate, when it is filed to its finished size, mark the ends of the finished edge lines. Final finishing of the butt-plate edges and the adjacent wood will be done later, of course.

The right side of the butt is the easier side to bring to shape, so it is well to begin with it. It is helpful to draw some guidelines before proceeding. The wrist is delineated by two lines, one which marks the top profile line of the wrist extended under the front end of the comb. The top profile line of the wrist, from the barrel tang to the front end of the comb must be determined carefully, for it greatly affects the appearance of the rifle.

In shaping the right side of the butt, imagine lines that are elements of a cone running from the curved edge of the butt-plate to the wrist. With whatever tools serve best, shape the wood along these imaginary lines. Use a straight-edge to keep humps and swales from forming. For removing the wood, Sureform™ and wood rasps are helpful. For work on the comb and right side of the stock, and elsewhere too, a very sharp wood plane, with the blade held at an angle of about 45° to the grain direction can be used to advantage.

Essentially, the wood is taken off in a series of long narrow flats that converge in the appropriate regions of the wrist. However, because the wrist is in line with the axis of the barrel, as viewed from above, while the stock has cast-off, these converging lines, flats, or cone elements will tend to intersect the wrist at various places. In shaping the convergence zones, blend the two surfaces together by leaving extra wood in the initial shaping. It can be worked out in the final shaping. This region not only must look right, but it also must feel comfortable when the stock is held in the firing position.

The function of the cheek-piece is to position the cheek so that the eye is brought into alignment with the sights. Therefore, in shaping the cheek-piece it is a great advantage to have the front and rear sights on the rifle. So, at this stage, it is reasonable to make and install the finished sights on the barrel. A simpler alternative, however, is to take some pieces of sheet metal and make some approximations of sights to fasten on the barrel with tape. All that matters is that they are the correct height and shape.

The cheek-piece on an American longrifle has its origins in cheek-pieces on German jaeger rifles where they were very functional structures, necessary to rest the cheek so that the eye was positioned to see the sights. Jaeger rifles were held in a significantly different manner than longrifles, and their cheek-pieces tended to be low on the stock, and to project outward from the stock a considerable distance, anywhere from 3/8 inch to 1 inch.

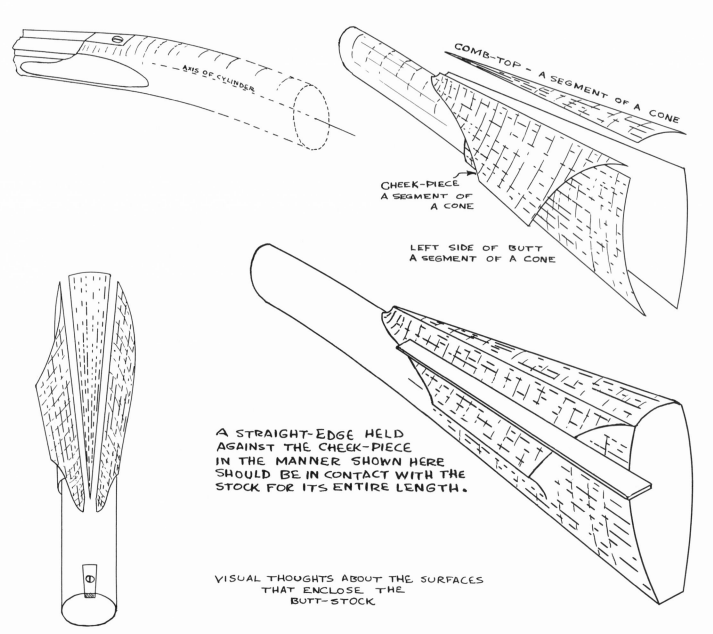

AXIS OF CYLINDER

COMB-TOP - A SEGMENT OF A CONE

CHEEK-PIECE
A SEGMENT OF
A CONE

LEFT SIDE OF BUTT
A SEGMENT OF A CONE

A STRAIGHT-EDGE HELD
AGAINST THE CHEEK-PIECE
IN THE MANNER SHOWN HERE
SHOULD BE IN CONTACT WITH THE
STOCK FOR ITS ENTIRE LENGTH.

VISUAL THOUGHTS ABOUT THE SURFACES
THAT ENCLOSE THE
BUTT-STOCK

In contrast, cheek-pieces on longrifles are modest structures that catch our eye because of their basic shape, and because usually they are accompanied by artistic stock decorations to the front, the rear, below, and also on their projecting lower edge. Longrifle cheek-pieces of the Golden Age rarely project more than ¼ inch above the surrounding stock. Old rifles of the 1780s and earlier, with wider butts, may have cheek-pieces that project as much as ½ inch above the surrounding stock at the rear end. The rear end of the cheek-piece usually stands farther from the stock than the front end.

The effectiveness of a longrifle cheek-piece owes less to its height than to the cast-off and drop of the butt-stock. But it also depends upon the physical nature of the shooter. If at all possible, a rifle-builder should study existing rifles similar in design to the one under construction to get ideas about cheek-piece dimensions. But with a good stock profile design to start with, good cheek-piece dimensions evolve as the butt-stock is brought to shape by gradual cutting and trying.

Before laying out the cheek-piece, it is advisable to plan and draw on the squared butt a lower butt moulding. This feature is strictly decorative, and a desirable one to have. Most old rifles that were carved in relief had lower butt mouldings in relief. Rifles with incised decoration usually had an incised line as a lower moulding. Often the moulding tapers in width from the butt end toward the front. With the moulding drawn in place, it is easier to judge the positioning of the cheek-piece. Typically, the moulding of uniform width is a raised bead 3/32 to 5/32 inch wide and with relief or 1/32 to 1/16 inch. The tapered moulding may be as much as 5/16 inch wide at the butt, and taper to 1/8 inch.

In laying out the cheek-piece, pay particular attention to the direction of the lower edge in relation to the upper and lower profile lines of the butt. The cheek-piece edge never should lie parallel to either the upper or lower profile line, but instead should have a direction lying between the two, so that all three linear elements converge toward the wrist. On longrifles of the Golden Age, most cheek-piece edges point toward the tail end of the side-plate panel. On German jaeger rifles, however, and on early longrifles with related butt-stock architecture, the cheek-piece edge often points lower, toward the upper portion of the trigger.

As a general rule, it can be stated that parallel lines are to be avoided like the plague in designing a longrifle. The longrifle as a work of art is a product of hand crafting, and was brought to its end by the machine age. Parallel lines are the product of the rectilinear machine. In the field of art, parallel lines generally have less appeal than non-parallel lines. The longrifle is a machine made for function and appreciation by human beings. It is a beautiful, visible, product of handcrafting that stands in opposition to the products of the factory. The significant lines on the longrifle butt are not parallel, and parallel lines should be avoided there if at all possible.

The comb needs some special attention too, for it is not just a rounded ridge that connects the two sides of the stock. The front end of the comb comes almost to a point, and at the most is about 1/8 inch wide. From the nose of the comb back for 1 to 1 ½ inches, the sides drop steeply into the wrist, although the sides usually flare out as they approach the wrist. Mr. Buchele's full-sized drawing of an old rifle by Frederick Sell, which is included with this volume, show cross-sections of typical shape.

The top of the comb should be treated as a separate curved stock surface, basically a segment of a cone. This curved surface meets the two sides of the stock along definite lines of intersection. These lines of intersection may be eliminated by rounding as the final shaping of the stock is done, but they are very helpful to retain as the main shaping is done. Also, it is possible to add architectural interest to the butt by rounding off this edge of intersection only slightly, so that one can see the intersection of the two surfaces.

At the rear end of the comb is the cap of the butt-plate, and this essentially determines the way the top of the comb is to be shaped. The comb top is rounded to conform to the curve of the metal, first using a rasp or plane, then finishing with sandpaper backed by a substantial piece of cardboard. It is preferable to work from the wood toward the metal in this process. The metal butt-cap is included in the finish sanding to make a neat joint. The four oblique flats of the butt-plate cap may end up slightly rounded where their edges meet. With a file give these flats slightly convex surfaces and their edges can be made to meet again.

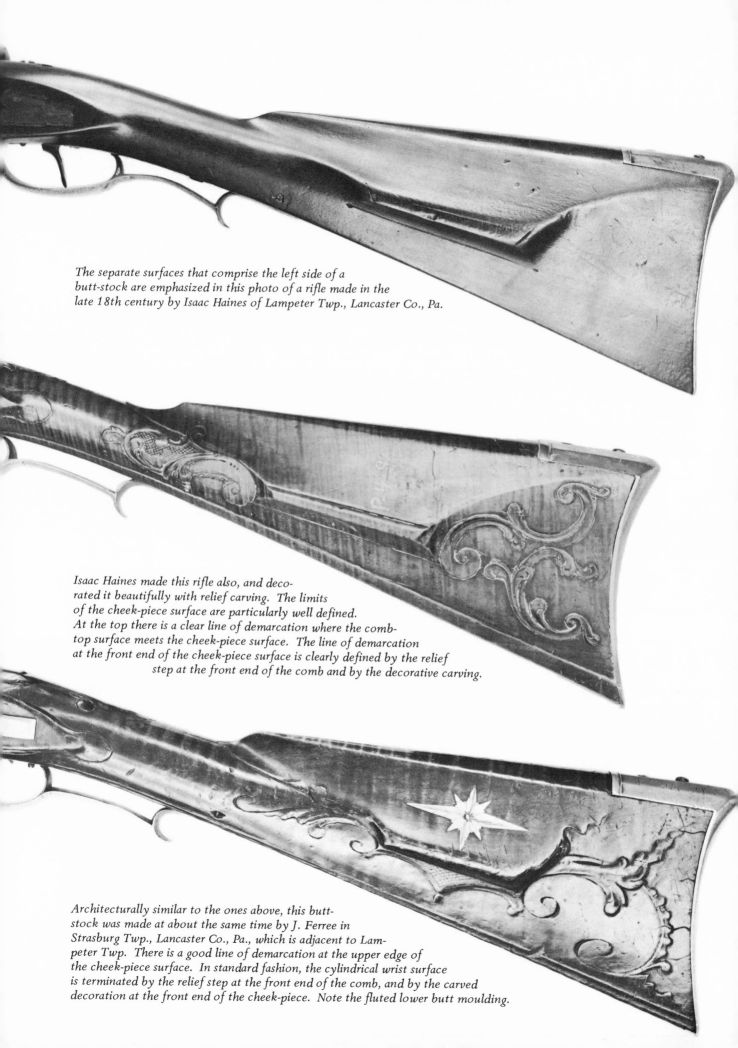

The separate surfaces that comprise the left side of a
butt-stock are emphasized in this photo of a rifle made in the
late 18th century by Isaac Haines of Lampeter Twp., Lancaster Co., Pa.

Isaac Haines made this rifle also, and decorated it beautifully with relief carving. The limits
of the cheek-piece surface are particularly well defined.
At the top there is a clear line of demarcation where the comb-
top surface meets the cheek-piece surface. The line of demarcation
at the front end of the cheek-piece surface is clearly defined by the relief
step at the front end of the comb and by the decorative carving.

Architecturally similar to the ones above, this butt-
stock was made at about the same time by J. Ferree in
Strasburg Twp., Lancaster Co., Pa., which is adjacent to Lampeter Twp. There is a good line of demarcation at the upper edge of
the cheek-piece surface. In standard fashion, the cylindrical wrist surface
is terminated by the relief step at the front end of the comb, and by the carved
decoration at the front end of the cheek-piece. Note the fluted lower butt moulding.

Right-side view of the carved rifle by Isaac Haines showing clearly the line of intersection where the top surface of the comb meets the side of the comb.

A partially completed butt-stock with a well-defined cheek-piece surface. Note how the rear edge of the cheek-piece surface is a curve that terminates at the corner of the butt-plate.

Silhouette photo of the partially shaped butt-stock illustrated above, as viewed from the bottom. A straight-edged card, with a cut-out for the cheek-piece, was held on the side of the stock. At the right end where the wood meets the butt-plate, the card is about 1/8 inch above the wood, showing that about 1/8 inch of wood should be removed in the region behind the cheek-piece. Likewise, at the left end of the card there is a gap of about 1/16 inch, showing that the side of the wrist should be cut back by that amount.

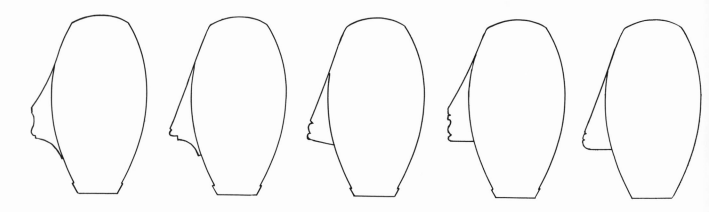

Cheek-piece Profiles-
The lower edge may be a horizontal plane, or a sloping plane. The concave surface, ending in a relief step offers the best opportunity to integrate the cheek-piece into relief-carved designs.

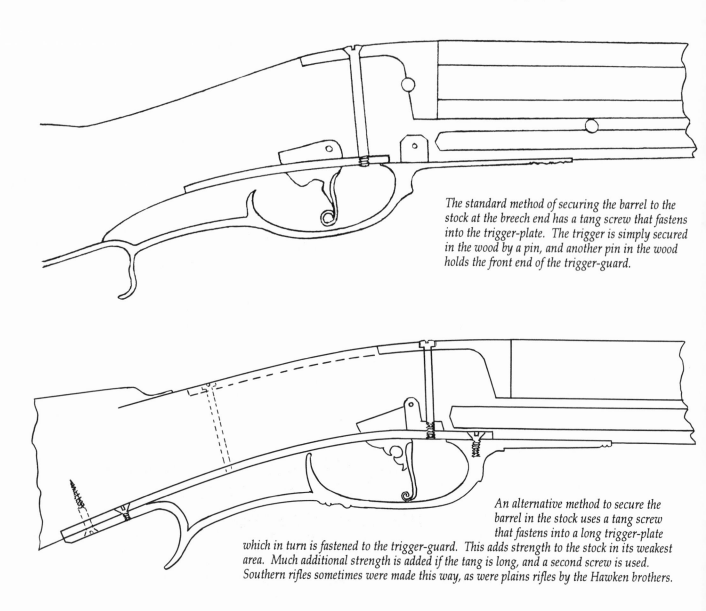

The standard method of securing the barrel to the stock at the breech end has a tang screw that fastens into the trigger-plate. The trigger is simply secured in the wood by a pin, and another pin in the wood holds the front end of the trigger-guard.

An alternative method to secure the barrel in the stock uses a tang screw that fastens into a long trigger-plate which in turn is fastened to the trigger-guard. This adds strength to the stock in its weakest area. Much additional strength is added if the tang is long, and a second screw is used. Southern rifles sometimes were made this way, as were plains rifles by the Hawken brothers.

62

Chapter 15

TRIGGERS

In the old days rifles were made with simple single triggers as well as with double set triggers. The simple trigger, if carefully made, will work well for all but the most exacting target work, and in retrospect it seems a bit silly that so many old rifles were equipped with double set triggers in view of the low and poorly made open sights they had. It was, of course, a fad. The tradition for double set triggers on fine rifles came from old Germany, Switzerland, and Austria where a great deal of precision offhand target shooting was done. The tradition, in fact, went back to the days of crossbow shooting when such refinements as double set triggers, peep sights, and even miniature plumb bobs attached to the rear sights were used. But the American frontiersman squeezing off on a deer from rest behind a log or rock, or taking a snap shot at the fleeting white tail, had little need for the set trigger mechanism, yet his rifle may have had one. In the pre-Revolutionary and Revolutionary periods, double set triggers rarely were used, but as time passed and the rifle became more of a sporting arm, the set trigger mechanism became popular.

Likewise, today the set trigger mechanism probably is put on many more rifles than it needs to be. For precision target shooting the general inadequacy of open sights is far more important than the difference between a well made single trigger and a set trigger mechanism. The choice is yours to make.

SINGLE TRIGGERS

In its simplest form the single trigger is merely a piece of metal set in a slot in the underside of the stock and held in place in the wood by an iron pin that goes transversely through the stock from the lock mortise to the side-plate panel. A trigger plate usually is present with a slot for the blade of the trigger, and a threaded hole at the front to receive the tang screw. Thus the trigger plate serves a dual purpose: by means of the tang screw it anchors the breech end of the barrel in the stock, and it restrains the sideward motion of the trigger blade. The plate is let into the underside of the stock with its surface flush with the wood surface, and it is held in place by the tang screw near the front end. It is best to secure the rear end of the plate to the stock with a flat-head wood screw, but on many old rifles there was neither a screw nor other fastening there.

There are advantages and disadvantages to the simple method of pinning the trigger through the stock. The major advantage is simplicity. A secondary advantage is that it requires the least possible removal of wood in the weakest region of the stock. A disadvantage is the difficulty of removing the trigger if adjustments are needed, though this really is minor. A more important disadvantage is that if the pivot pin is to be located close to the sear bar location, as it should be, there is little or no wood to support the pin because the cavity cut for the sear bar must extend at least 3/32 inch forward of the sear bar.

A better form of trigger assembly, in wide use today, is the kind that has a metal lug attached to the upper or inside surface of the trigger plate, into which the trigger is pinned. It is possible to buy castings made for this purpose. But it is simple to make one by fastening a lug to a 1/8 inch thick trigger plate by means of silver solder. The main advantage of this assembly is that it is possible to locate the trigger pin exactly where desired with respect to the sear bar. In addition, it provides better support for the trigger, and makes it easier to remove.

Carrying the trigger plate assembly one step further yields an improvement in the rifle. This involves using a trigger plate long enough to span the distance between the two ends of the trigger-guard. The plate is fastened to the guard with two screws from the inside, one of which is hidden, and the other can be a brass machine screw filed flush with the tail of the guard and hence almost invisible. The guard and plate thus form a rigid unit, held firmly in place at the front end by the tang screw. At the rear end it can be held in place by the traditional lug and a pin in the wood, or by a wood screw. Best of all, however, is to use it with a long barrel tang, and to secure the rear end of the long trigger plate by means of a long screw that starts at the rear end of the long tang and passes completely

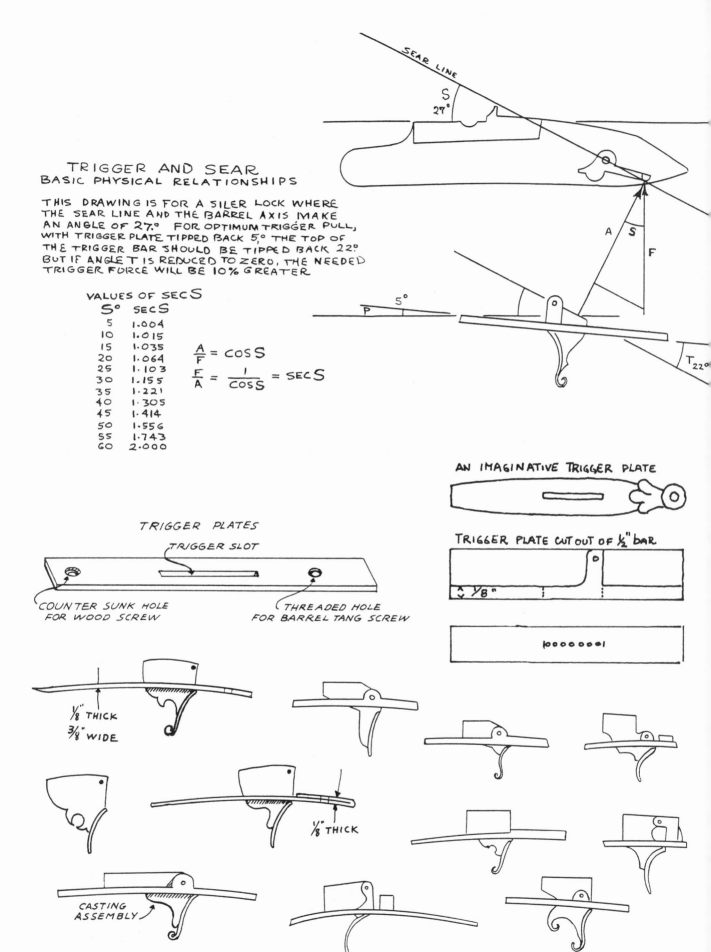

TRIGGER AND SEAR
BASIC PHYSICAL RELATIONSHIPS

THIS DRAWING IS FOR A SILER LOCK WHERE
THE SEAR LINE AND THE BARREL AXIS MAKE
AN ANGLE OF 27.° FOR OPTIMUM TRIGGER PULL,
WITH TRIGGER PLATE TIPPED BACK 5° THE TOP OF
THE TRIGGER BAR SHOULD BE TIPPED BACK 22°
BUT IF ANGLE T IS REDUCED TO ZERO, THE NEEDED
TRIGGER FORCE WILL BE 10% GREATER

SEAR LINE

S 27°

A S F

5° P

T₂₂°

VALUES OF SEC S

S°	SEC S
5	1.004
10	1.015
15	1.035
20	1.064
25	1.103
30	1.155
35	1.221
40	1.305
45	1.414
50	1.556
55	1.743
60	2.000

$$\frac{A}{F} = \cos S$$

$$\frac{F}{A} = \frac{1}{\cos S} = \sec S$$

AN IMAGINATIVE TRIGGER PLATE

TRIGGER PLATE CUT OUT OF ½" BAR

⅛"

TRIGGER PLATES

TRIGGER SLOT

COUNTER SUNK HOLE
FOR WOOD SCREW

THREADED HOLE
FOR BARREL TANG SCREW

⅛" THICK
⅜" WIDE

⅛" THICK

CASTING
ASSEMBLY

through the stock. This greatly strengthens the stock at its weakest point, the wrist. Hawken rifles and other well-made arms of the percussion era were made this way. The system can be used for both simple triggers and double-set triggers, and for both flintlock and percussion systems. Another advantage of this system is that it eliminates the lug at the front end of the trigger-guard, and as a consequence the ramrod hole can be deepened by at least ½ inch, and possibly more. For practical shooting this is a decided advantage, and makes it possible to use a ramrod longer than the bore. But this system is not traditional for eastern longrifles, and if that is a concern, pass it by.

LEVERAGE AND THE TRIGGER

A prime requirement of a good rifle is a trigger mechanism that fires the lock easily and smoothly. The *trigger pull force* is the amount of force applied to the trigger that is needed to fire the lock. A simple trigger is merely a simple lever. By altering the distance from the pivot pin to the sear bar, the needed trigger pull force can be altered by a factor of two or even three within the reasonable limits allowable in a typical gun stock. If the pivot-pin-to-sear-bar distance is ¼ inch, the needed trigger pull force will be only one-half that needed if the distance is ½ inch. A distance of ¼ inch is about as small as one should use, and it can be 5/16 or 3/8 inch. As the diagram at the left shows, for optimum mechanical advantage, the force applied by the trigger bar to the sear arm should be exerted perpendicular to the sear line that runs from the bottom of the sear arm through the axis of the sear screw. This shows that it is best to have the top of the trigger bar in line with the pivot pin and sloping to the rear at the same angle as the sear line. However, if the tip of the trigger bar is horizontal it will add only about 10% to the trigger force, which may be of no practical consequence.

OFFSETTING THE TRIGGER

Triggers usually are installed to lie along the centerline of the stock, but some fine old rifles had them offset. Certain advantages can be achieved by offsetting the trigger toward the lock. The amount of offset may amount to about 1/16 inch with a 3/8 inch wide trigger plate, and 1/8 inch for ½ inch wide plate. One advantage is that the finger may have better access to the trigger, but this is affected by the size of the hand and the circumference of the stock wrist. Another advantage is that the trigger will contact the sear bar closer to the lock-plate, which is better mechanically. The third advantage is that the hole in the stock for the sear is less deep.

MAKING THE TRIGGER PLATE

The trigger plate assembly consists of a trigger plate and an attached lug projecting upward from it to receive the trigger-pin. The plate can be made from flat rectangular steel, or brass, 1/8 inch thick and 3/8 to ½ inch wide. The length of the plate is determined by the particular geometry of the rifle. Traditionally, the front end of the plate reaches to the front end of the trigger-guard bow, so that the front end of the plate lies under the front end of the bow.

The plate can extend about 1 ¼ inches to the rear of the trigger for good appearance, with the rear portion tapering somewhat. As an alternative, the plate can extend rearward to stop underneath the rear end of the trigger-guard bow. The plate does not have to be a simple rectangle. The sides can be curved, the tail end can come to a point, and the surface can be engraved for decorative purposes.

To make the trigger plate, begin with a rectangular piece of metal of the desired width, thickness, and length. Cold rolled steel 1/8 x ½ in. in cross section is easy to get and suitable. Make the slot first, which is easily done by bending the plate in a curve where the slot is to be, then, with a hacksaw, cut a slot in the curved metal long enough to take the saw blade. Straighten the metal and finish the slot.

Next, prepare a piece of metal that will be the lug to hold the trigger pin, but do not make the slot for the trigger blade. A piece ½ inch wide, ½ inch high, and 5/8 in. long would be suitable. Fasten the lug to the plate with silver solder. Then put the saw blade through the slot in the plate and cut the slot in the lug. Cut away the front part of the lug so that the side profile is similar to that shown at the bottom of p. 62.

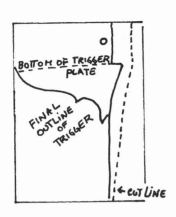

BOTTOM OF TRIGGER PLATE

FINAL OUTLINE OF TRIGGER

← CUT LINE

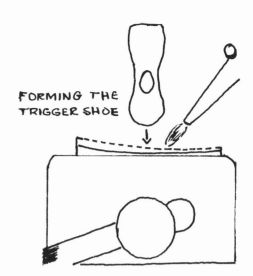

FORMING THE TRIGGER SHOE

MAKING THE TRIGGER

The 18ᵗʰ century flintlock rifle traditionally had a single trigger with a front edge or shoe that was relatively wide. The shoe is the part of the trigger that the finger presses against, and on early rifles it often was ¼ to as much as 3/8 inch wide. However, for good shooting an excessively wide shoe can be detrimental, and about ¼ inch is reasonable, while 3/8 inch is too much. On these early rifles the end of the shoe sometimes ended with a scroll or curve. The exposed part of the trigger blade, behind the shoe, often had a decorative profile.

To make a trigger, begin with a piece of steel 1/8 in. thick, and scribe the pattern of the trigger on it, including the position of the pivot pin. For final adjusting, leave about 1/8 in. of metal above the calculated finish line at the top of the blade. If a decorative scroll is planned for the lower end of the shoe, calculate its length straightened out, and draw it on the pattern as a straight piece. The curl will be produced later, by bending. At the front edge of the shoe, as designed, scribe a second line parallel to the finish line, but about 1/8 or 5/32 in. away from it, which is the line for cutting the front edge of the trigger. The top end of the trigger shoe can have a function in stopping the forward movement of the trigger, or it can be arrested by other means, but in any case, the top end of the trigger shoe needs to be long enough to reach the trigger plate. With hacksaw and files, cut the front edge of the trigger to shape.

Place the partially cut out trigger in a vise so that the finished edge of the shoe is at the top of the vise, and tighten it very well. With the help of heat from a torch, peen out the trigger shoe to the desired width, plus a little extra width for final shaping of the edges. Then saw out the remainder of the trigger shape. The peened area should be filed so that its thickness (front to back) is about 1/8 to 3/32 inch in the finger region, then tapering to about 1/16 inch thick at the bottom. Then the face of the shoe is filed to the planned curve, and the tail is filed and thinned further. The square corners on the front edge are removed to yield a cross section that is flat on the back surface, and curved on the front surface. The tail end should be thinned to about 1/32 inch at the very end. The trigger blade now is carefully thinned from 1/8 inch to slightly more than 1/16 inch, and carefully fitted into the trigger slot. Be sure to make a fit that leaves little or no side-play for the blade.

As may be noted in the diagram at the top of p. 64, the sear line slopes downward from the trigger pin, but the exact angle for minimum trigger force is determined by the geometry of the parts. Variations in the slop of the sear line typically are of the order of a few degrees and affect the trigger force by only a few percentage points.

As the trigger swings forward, its motion may be stopped by the top end of the trigger shoe making contact with the trigger plate, or by the leading edge of the blade, above the shoe, as it comes into contact with the slot in the plate. If the rear portion of the plate lying above the plate extends beyond the end of the slot, then it may meet the top of the plate and stop the forward motion.

SIMPLE DOUBLE-SET TRIGGERS

A double-set trigger mechanism is a mechanical relay that serves to set off a flintlock or percussion lock action as a result of a very slight force being exerted on the trigger. When well made and correctly adjusted, it can serve its intended function very nicely. For shooters involved in precision target shooting it is a necessity. For those involved with hunting, and informal or semi-formal offhand target shooting, it may be a help. For beginners and others not sure of themselves, it can be a psychological help. But for typical longrifle usage – hunting, informal target shooting, etc., - it is an unnecessary complication.

Various double-set trigger mechanisms can be purchased from parts suppliers today, and it is not unreasonable to make use of one. But if one is to be used, the challenge is to make it, and here a commercial product might be a useful guide for your own efforts.

The simple double-set trigger mechanism, as shown by the illustrations, activates the lock when the front end of the rear trigger flies rapidly upward and strikes the sear arm or bar. A stiff main-spring to the rear of the rear trigger provides the power. The forward trigger serves as a latch, to hold the rear trigger in its cocked position against the force of the spring. A light pull on the forward trigger releases the rear trigger, which flies upward and strikes the sear bar, which in turn releases the tumbler of the lock so that the hammer can fall forward. Between the two triggers is an adjusting screw that determines the amount of overlap in the latch and therefore the amount of force needed for release.

For either kind of double-set trigger mechanism, it is advisable to make a drawing and a pattern to try out in relation to the trigger-guard and other features of the stock. Trigger-guards are made with large bows for double-set triggers, and smaller bows for simple single triggers. But even with the larger bow, there is not a lot of room in many of them for two triggers and adequate finger room. The rear trigger moves backward a significant distance as it is being cocked, and there must be adequate room for it within the bow.

The trigger plate is made from a piece of mild steel bar stock 3/16 inch thick and ½ inch wide. The length should be 3 ½ inches minimum, and about 7 inches if it is to extend backward to the end of the trigger-guard. Two slots are first cut in the plate, each almost 1/8 inch wide, with a separation between of 3/16 to ¼ inch. The slots are made by first drilling with a 3/32 inch drill, cutting out with a jeweler's saw, and finishing with files. These slots lie in line, centered on the centerline of the plate.

The triggers are made from 1/8 inch thick flat stock. The trigger shoes are peened out just as for the simple trigger. The curve of the rear trigger is a bit more difficult to make, but it can be done by peening the upper part of the curve and leaving the lower part straight, to be bent after peening. Some 18th century German rifles had rear triggers that sloped backward at an angle of about 45°, and very slender, round forward triggers, appearing as a slender stiff wire. A very slender forward trigger can be suitable for a target rifle, but for a longrifle that will be carried afield, and used for hunting, the forward trigger needs to be amply strong, though it still can be slender.

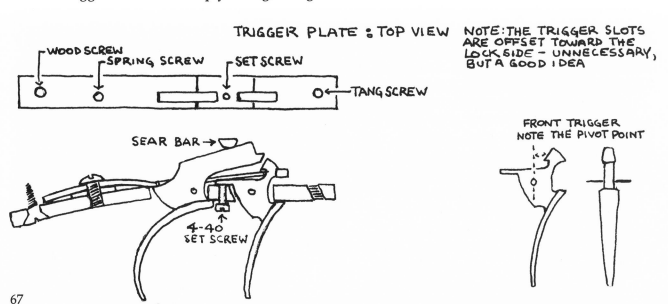

TRIGGER PLATE : TOP VIEW

NOTE: THE TRIGGER SLOTS ARE OFFSET TOWARD THE LOCK SIDE – UNNECESSARY, BUT A GOOD IDEA

WOOD SCREW
SPRING SCREW
SET SCREW
TANG SCREW

SEAR BAR →

4-40 SET SCREW

FRONT TRIGGER NOTE THE PIVOT POINT

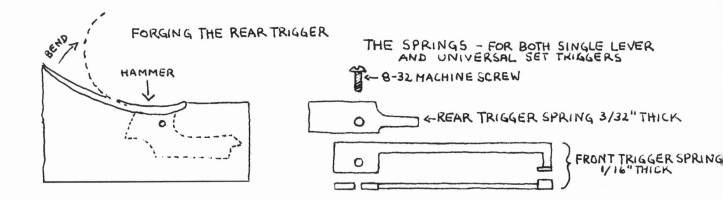

FORGING THE REAR TRIGGER

BEND

HAMMER

THE SPRINGS – FOR BOTH SINGLE LEVER AND UNIVERSAL SET TRIGGERS

←8-32 MACHINE SCREW

←REAR TRIGGER SPRING 3/32" THICK

} FRONT TRIGGER SPRING 1/16" THICK

In order that the trigger mechanism work properly, it is important that the pivot pin holes be correctly located. The pivot pin hole in the rear trigger should be located as far forward as possible from the shelf, or edge of the plate, upon which the mainspring rests, in order to provide an adequate lever arm to the rear of the pin, so that the spring's effect can be adequate. The pivot point of the forward trigger must be placed to the rear of the edge of the latch or hook, and also well to the rear of the trigger stop, which is the upper end of the shoe. This gives a stable balance of forces when the mechanism is set. If the pivot point lies ahead of a line connecting the trigger stop with the edge of the latch, the acting forces provide an unstable situation which the weak trigger spring is not adequate to resist.

The triggers are individually fit into their slots, pinned in place, and then the hooks on both triggers are roughly filed to shape, leaving adequate overlap. The final fitting of the engagement is done only after the trigger plate is bent to conform to the stock, and inletted. Adequate metal should be left on the top of the bar of the rear trigger for final fitting. For now, leave the trigger shoes extra long and straight.

After the triggers are installed in the plate, the assembly is let into the stock, (see the following chapter) which calls for some bending of the plate. Then the two springs are prepared. Annealed spring stock is available from many suppliers. The mainspring is made from 3/32 inch thick stock, and the front trigger spring from stock 1/16 inch thick. The front spring is long and thin for most of its length, to pass by both triggers. File the spring notch in the front trigger, but wait until after the mainspring is fastened into place with a 8-32 screw to locate the hole in the rear end of the front spring. The springs are filed smooth and polished. Then they are heated to a cherry red color, and quenched, by plunging them vertically into oil. When cool, polish each spring to remove the surface coloration. Then temper each spring in the flame of a propane torch, starting at one end and heating with care until a robin's egg blue color appears: chase this color up the spring, and then let it cool. It is now ready for use. Such is the process of hardening and tempering springs.

To finish the assembly, a set screw hole is drilled, and tapped for 4/40 thread, in the plate between the two triggers, and a screw installed. The trigger plate is held in position at the front end by the tang screw. If the plate is short, it can be held in position at the rear end with a wood screw. If the plate and tang are long, a screw can pass vertically through the wrist to connect the two pieces of metal.

UNIVERSAL DOUBLE-SET TRIGGERS

Universal double-set triggers are basically the same as simple double-sets, with the exception of an added lever attached to the front trigger. This, together with a different kind of action to the rear trigger, allows the lock to be fired even if the trigger mechanism is not set, which is a decided advantage for the uncertainties of hunting situations. It also makes it possible to release the hammer from half and full cock by holding back on the front trigger. However, it is necessary to use locks with flies in their tumblers for universal double-set triggers.

With simple double-set triggers, the front trigger releases the rear, or set trigger, to fly up, hit the sear off the full cock notch, and then to hold the sear up as the tumbler rotates. Therefore the rear trigger must be cocked again before the hammer can be returned to half or full cock. In contrast, the universal triggers allow the lock to be fired set or unset, so the mainspring and set trigger engagement must be adjusted in such a way that when the set trigger is at rest, no spring pressure pushes its trigger bar against the sear. When release from its set position, the trigger bar flies upward, hits the sear a sharp rap to release it from the full cock notch, and then falls back to its rest position.

The plate is made in the same manner as for the simple double-sets, except that the slots should be 3/16 inch wide. They may be prepared with the aid of a 1/8 inch drill. The triggers should be made from stock that is ¼ inch thick. Because of the thick metal, little peening of the shoe surface will be necessary, but it would be well to do some anyway for the rear trigger, which is comfortable with a good wide shoe. The front trigger shoe can be filed to whatever thinness is desired.

The rear trigger pattern is laid out on the flat stock, and the pivot pin center is punched and drilled. The trigger shoe is forged and roughly filed to shape. As the trigger is fitted into the slot in the plate, the trigger stop, which is the top of the shoe, is carefully cut and filed to restrain the trigger from moving forward. An extra 1/8 inch of material is left on top of the rear trigger bar.

The front trigger is rounded out and installed in its slot in the same way. A decision has to be made as to which side of each trigger is to be cut away to allow passage of the other trigger. The illustration shows the lever of the front trigger on the left side, which probably is best in as much as it allows the set trigger lever to be closest to the lock plate. The front trigger is most easily made by a sequence of cuts as shown in the illustration. In the first step the lever is scribed for half-thickness and sawed but with the jeweler's saw or hacksaw, keeping safely away from the scribed finish line. In the second step the bottom of the hook is cut out, again to half thickness. In the third step a needle file is used to reduce the angle of the hook face, to clean up and sharpen the bottom of the hook, and to smooth the surface cut by the saw.

The rear trigger is much easier to cut out. Be careful to cut away the proper side. The next step is to fit the trigger together in the trigger plate. Using the trigger pins, mount the triggers on the side of the plate, to see how they will operate with each other. Eyeball measurements will indicate the position of the notch on the set trigger lever, as well as what material has to be trimmed from the ends of both triggers. The fitting is a slow process of "cut and try."

When the triggers are almost at final fit, it is best to inlet the trigger plate. As with the simple double sets, the springs then are prepared and installed. The operation of the mainspring here is somewhat complex, as it must allow much greater free motion of the set trigger than with the simple double-sets. When the set trigger is at rest, there is very little, or no spring pressure on the trigger. This is accomplished by carefully filing the shelf, but leave this final adjustment until the trigger mechanism is installed in the stock.

Last, but not least, the adjusting screw is installed. This should be a 4-40 screw. The position of the screw should be located carefully, so that it bears only on the bottom of the front trigger lever.

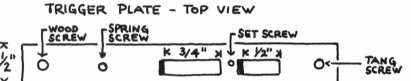

TRIGGER PLATE - TOP VIEW

IT'S A GOOD IDEA TO OFFSET THE TRIGGER SLOTS TOWARD THE TRIGGER FINGER SIDE. HERE, THE SLOTS ARE ⅛" FROM THE RIGHT SIDE, LEAVING 3/16" ON THE LEFT FOR THE FRONT TRIGGER SPRING.

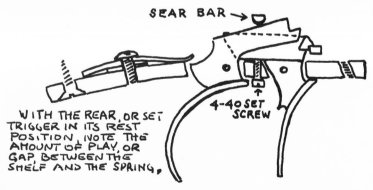

WITH THE REAR, OR SET TRIGGER IN ITS REST POSITION, NOTE THE AMOUNT OF PLAY, OR GAP, BETWEEN THE SHELF AND THE SPRING.

CUTTING OUT THE FRONT TRIGGER

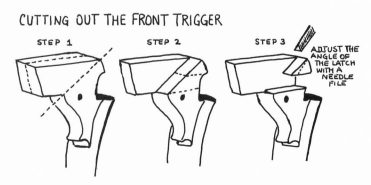

SINGLE-SET TRIGGERS

Single-set triggers also were made and used in the old days. They were not used in great abundance on longrifles, but there were some very fine rifles made in the late 18th and early 19th centuries that had them, including pieces by the gunsmiths Joel Feree and Isaac Haines. The single-set trigger is cocked by pushing the single trigger in a forward direction, and this must be done before setting the hammer on half cock or full cock. The lever-operated mechanism illustrated here works as smoothly as a double-set trigger assembly, and there is no trigger over-travel. There is an adjustment for the trigger-pull force.

SINGLE SET TRIGGER FOR RIFLE OR PISTOL

MAIN SPRING   CATCH

LIGHT SPRING   SET

SMOOTH AS A DOUBLE SET — NO TRIGGER OVERTRAVEL

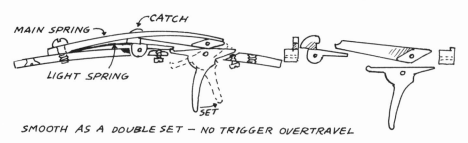

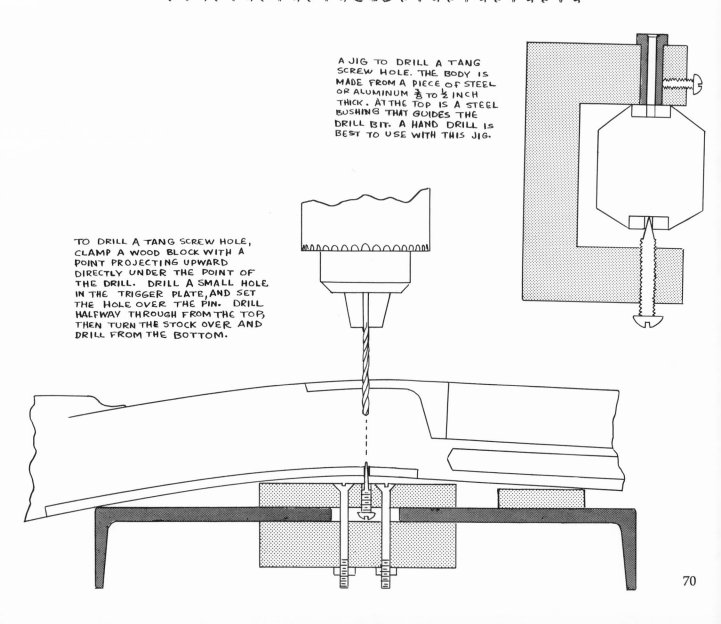

A JIG TO DRILL A TANG SCREW HOLE. THE BODY IS MADE FROM A PIECE OF STEEL OR ALUMINUM ⅜ TO ½ INCH THICK. AT THE TOP IS A STEEL BUSHING THAT GUIDES THE DRILL BIT. A HAND DRILL IS BEST TO USE WITH THIS JIG.

TO DRILL A TANG SCREW HOLE, CLAMP A WOOD BLOCK WITH A POINT PROJECTING UPWARD DIRECTLY UNDER THE POINT OF THE DRILL. DRILL A SMALL HOLE IN THE TRIGGER PLATE, AND SET THE HOLE OVER THE PIN. DRILL HALFWAY THROUGH FROM THE TOP, THEN TURN THE STOCK OVER AND DRILL FROM THE BOTTOM.

CHAPTER 16

INLETTING THE TRIGGER AND TRIGGER-GUARD

Installation of the trigger and trigger-guard calls for some thought and careful planning. The location of the sear arm of the lock determines the fore-and-aft position of the trigger and its trigger plate. The position of the trigger determines the position of the trigger-guard within certain limits. It is customary and almost necessary to install the trigger plate and trigger first, and then to install the guard. For a simple single trigger the position of the guard might lie as much as ¼ inch forward or backward from some intermediate optimum location. For double-set or universal-set triggers there is less room for fore-and-aft adjustment, 1/8 inch or at the most 3/16 inch.

INLETTING THE TRIGGER AND DRILLING THE TANG SCREW HOLE

To inlet the trigger plate, first remove the trigger or trigger mechanism. Remove the lock from the stock. Then bend the plate to conform to the underside of the stock. Slight imperfections in the bending can be corrected by filing the plate flush with the surface of the wood. If the trigger plate has a lug at the front end, this is first inletted, so that the plate can lie on the surface of the stock. With a sharply pointed knife, mark the plate location on the stock, and then carefully remove wood to let the plate settle into place, with just enough projecting that the entire plate can be filed flush with the wood surface, but wait until later to do the filing.

Installing the tang screw is next, and the remarks that follow are based upon using a screw of 8-32 thread size, with a head diameter of 5/16 inch. But of course the general procedure would apply for other screw sizes. The main problem is to drill a hole of small diameter completely through the wrist and have it come out exactly where desired on the other side.

The first operation is to make a recess in the tang for the head of the screw. This screw presumably has a square shoulder where the head meets the shank. The best and most professional way to make the recess is to use a counterbore of 5/16 inch diameter with a 1/8 inch pilot. This can be procured from a machinery supply company at moderate cost and is well worth having. It has a second use on the rifle in making recessed seats in the side-plate for the lock screws. The counterbore should enter the tang at the same angle as that of the hole that the tang screw will follow. Therefore it is best to clamp the stock under the drill press with the help of the centering pin described below and illustrated on the opposite page. With the stock clamped in position, first drill a 1/8 inch hole through the tang to accept the pilot, and then make the recess with the counterbore. It is possible to get along without a counterbore by simply using a 5/16 inch drill. This leaves a conical bottom to the hole, and the screw head must be shaped to fit it, which can be done by spinning the screw in a drill press, drill, or lathe, and using a file to shape the lower part of the head.

In drilling the hole through the wrist it is best to drill halfway through from either side, starting with a drill somewhat smaller than the finished hole will be. It is possible to line up the drill for this work by eyeball, preferably with the help of a second person's eyeball. But there are better ways of doing it. It is recommended that a drill press be used for the hole. The drill bit in a drill press tends to go straight up and down, though it may be deflected slightly under some conditions. The problem arises in determining the exact direction that the drill should go through the wood. This is solved by firmly clamping to the table of the drill press a small sharply pointed piece of metal that is directly in line with the drill axis. The location of the hole in the trigger-plate is punched and then drilled with a 3/32 inch drill. The stock is clamped in a position such that the hole in the trigger plate is impaled on the small locating pin, and the hole in the tang is directly under the drill point. Drill a little more than halfway through from the top, and then repeat the process from the other direction. The holes should meet, but even with this procedure the meeting may not be exact. In any case, enlarge the hole from the top, using a # 29 drill, and run it clear through the hole in the trigger plate. Remove the trigger plate and enlarge the hole in the tang and the stock to the body size for an 8-32 screws, which is a # 19 drill. Replace the trigger plate in the stock and run an 8-32 tap down the hole to make threads in the trigger plate. To finish up, enlarge the hole in the wood only, with a # 18 or # 17 drill, so that there is ample clearance in the wood for the tang screw. In drilling a long hole through a piece of wood there always is some compression of the wood fibers, which in time spring back to diminish the hole size slightly. Damp conditions could further diminish the hole size, making a very tight hole for the tang screw.

A drilling jig also can be made that does not require the use of a drill press, as Cliff Noll has pointed out. Using 3/8 inch thick aluminum, he made a device somewhat like a C-clamp, which is clamped to the wrist of the rifle. At the upper end of the clamp is a hole in which fits a steel bushing with a hole for the drill bit. At the lower end is a pointed piece of metal exactly in line with the hole in the bushing. This metal point fits in a small hole drilled in the trigger plate where it is intended that the tang screw will emerge.

The head of the screw may be finished flush with the top of the tang, or be slightly rounded. And the finished screw, when firmly tightened into place, should have its slot parallel with the axis of the barrel. However, these finishing touches are better left until later, for the tang screw will be run in and out many times before the rifle is finished.

Next, the trigger or trigger mechanism is inletted. If a simple pinned trigger is to be used, mark its position through the slot in the plate, and cut out a thin mortise. A narrow chisel ground down to 1/16 inch width is desirable to have, or one can be made from an old knife blade of about 3/32 inch thickness. The mortise actually needs to be somewhat wider than the trigger in order that the wood never contacts the trigger. With the trigger inletted, carefully mark the location of the pin hole in the lock mortise or cavity, and with the trigger firmly held in place, drill through the wood, through the trigger blade, and on through the wood behind the trigger. On old rifles the pinhole traditionally runs completely through the stock, so that the pin always can be removed with the help of a punch. The direction of the pin hole can be adjusted so that it either emerges behind the side-plate, or in the middle of the narrow wood moulding just below the edge of the side-plate. With an elaborately designed side-plate, having piercings, and not intended for removal, the pinhole should emerge below the plate. A third alternative is to use a short pin that does not pass all the way through the stock, but such a pin needs to have a small rectangular T-shaped head on it, and a recess cut in the wood so that the head of the pin can be grasped with pliers for removal.

If a simple trigger pinned to a lug on the trigger-plate is used, the process is about the same, but without the pin hole problem. With set triggers, inlet each trigger separately, then the springs, and use transfer color to help locate any wood that might bind the action. With a simple trigger, now is the time to trim the end to the correct length, or to curl the long tail into a volute, after holding the trigger-guard at the side to determine the correct length. The trigger shoe should well fill the distance from bow to trigger plate, with about 3/32 inch clearance at the bottom.

ADJUSTING THE SIMPLE TRIGGER

Some careful filing of the trigger blade, where it comes into contact with the sear arm, must now be done. The idea is to file as little as possible off the bar while allowing the tumbler to come safely to half cock and firmly to full cock. Do this with the help of transfer color applied to the under side of the sear arm, and file only in the region of the transfer mark. Repeat the process until the trigger assembly fits tightly in its mortise and the tang screw can be taken up tightly. The lower end of the trigger should be allowed a small amount of free travel, typically 1/8 to 3/32 inch at whichever of the three tumbler positions is most restrictive of its movement. In other words, the position of the sear arm is not necessarily at exactly the same position with the tumbler full forward, on half cock, or on full cock, and at one of these positions it may be closest to the lower edge of the lock-plate.

A few words of warning are in order here concerning flintlocks. If the hammer of a flintlock should fall without striking the frizzen on the way down, its abrupt stopping at the end of the fall might fracture it. The frizzen slows the hammer in its fall and prevents damage. At this stage of work, fitting the trigger, the mechanism may need to be tried repeatedly. It is advisable to make a small piece of wood in the shape of a flint with a blunt leading edge, and install it in the hammer jaws.

With the trigger in place, the lock should function well, and safely. There should be no tendency whatsoever for the gun to go off half-cocked, and the hammer should be held firmly by the sear in the full cock position.

If the hammer does not hold well in the full cock position, and the trigger is not the problem, then it will be necessary to inspect the lock in detail, and possibly to stone the leading edge of the sear and the edge of the tumbler notch; see Chapter 36.

ADJUSTING DOUBLE-SET TRIGGERS

No realistic adjustment of any trigger is possible until the trigger plate is held firmly in the stock. The double-set trigger plate is held in the stock both by the tang screw at the front and by a screw at the rear end of the plate. Adjusting the double-set trigger mechanism is done by filing the rear trigger bar until the bar is low enough to allow the sear to fall into its notches, and high enough to fire the lock when it is released.

Adjusting the universal-set trigger mechanism is more time consuming. First the rear trigger is removed, and the front trigger adjusted to the sear exactly the same way as the single trigger. The rear trigger then is re-installed, and the trigger bar filed down, very carefully, until the lock fires. It then should work both set and un-set. Some filing of the shelf on which the mainspring bears also may be necessary. If the mechanism is not working perfectly, it is possible that the front trigger is actually setting off the mechanism rather than the rear trigger. Work with the action carefully, "feeling" what is happening. Remove the triggers and file down the front trigger blade until it lies slightly below the rear trigger bar, and until you are certain that when you release the mechanism, the rear trigger is firing the lock. Of course the front trigger now will have a greater travel before it fires the lock with the rear trigger un-set, but with careful filing this movement can be kept to a minimum.

INLETTING THE TRIGGER-GUARD

For any relationship between trigger and trigger-guard, practical use requires that there be ample room for the trigger finger to function. Deer hunting season in many states takes place in late fall or early winter. The muzzle-loading hunting season for deer in Pennsylvania takes place in December. Cold weather or not, the use of a double-set or universal-set trigger on a hunting rifle calls for the bare hand. With a single trigger, however, it may be practical at times to hunt with a gloved hand. This calls for a trigger-guard bow of ample size, and a trigger located far enough back within the bow that a gloved finger can enter with ease.

Without a doubt, the shape of the trigger-guard, and its location relative to the architecture of the butt-stock, affect the overall aesthetics of the rifle design. However, the location of the guard bow relative to the triggers is primary, and what happens to the rest of the guard must follow the primary function. The length of the grip rail connecting the bow with the spur at the rear end may vary from one guard design to another. Fortunately, many well-designed trigger-guards have good relationships of bow, grip-rail, and spur, and produce a good looking result when used with a well-designed butt-stock. The perfectionist gun stocker may choose to alter a cast guard to meet his special needs. With the help of silver solder, parts of guards can be altered as desired, and pieces from two or more guards can be combined. The shortening of a grip-rail can be done by means of a neatly filed dovetail joint secured with silver solder. A much-altered guard can be taken to a brass foundry and used as a pattern for a new casting.

If the rifle being built is styled after some particular school, or maker, then the placement of the trigger-guard also becomes a factor in the overall design of the rifle. The front post of the guard bow may have a particular relationship to the location of the hammer of the lock. The rear spur of the guard can help determine the point where the comb meets the wrist. The rear end of the bow may help determine how far behind the tail of the lock the tapering lock panel terminates, and how far beyond that the beaver-tail finial extends.

The finishing of a rough cast brass trigger-guard should begin at the front and rear extensions. Work first on the underside, squaring it up and making sure that it is not twisted or bent. The fastening lugs will need to be trued up. Leave them full length for now. The edges of the front and rear extensions should be filed straight. Then, as with all inlays, the edges should be filed to have a small bevel of a few degrees as an aid to inletting. Proceed to the other inner surfaces of the guard, first removing the parting lines left from the mould, then doing the preliminary finishing with fine files of appropriate shape. Further progress can be made with finer and finer abrasive paper wrapped around blocks of wood of suitable shape. Always support the abrasive paper with blocks, for without support the paper will tend to remove the sharp edges where various planes meet. The same is true of buffing wheels, which should not be used at all.

Next, file flat the edges of the bow, grip-rail, and spur, curving them as the casting dictates. A trigger-guard is difficult to hold in a vise for effective filing and polishing, and must be protected from the vise jaws with some kind of padding. It may be worthwhile to prepare two wooden jigs to hold the piece for this work, and there are one or more commercial jigs for this purpose available today.

Now file the outer surfaces of the guard, taking care to make the moulding on the back of the bow sharp and clear, and the lines straight where various flats meet. There is more to filing a rough guard than merely cleaning the roughness off the brass. The edges of the rear spur, grip-rail, and bow need to be filed to a thin line. The thin edge of the bow continues forward until it broadens into a flat region, with one edge line curving upward toward the stock and the other curving forward to meet the spur. The guard is not really thin, but this thin edge helps give it a thin appearance, and this helps the finished rifle have beautiful flowing lines from the side view, part of the art of the longrifle.

Having filed the outer surfaces of the guard, and having created the thin edges, the guard can be finished with progressively finer abrasive paper. However, the outer surfaces of the front and rear extensions should not be finished until after the guard is inletted.

With the position of the trigger-guard relative to the triggers determined, the position of the lugs is marked on the centerline of the stock. Mortises for both lugs are made in the stock, the front one being done first. Then the front extension of the guard is inlet to a depth of about 3/32 inch. The finished edges of the front extension typically are 1/16 to 3/32 inch thick, and it is good to inlet the extension slightly below the wood level so that the finished wood level ends up in the right place.

After the front extension is inletted, it is a convenience to pin it in place before working on the rear extension. The pin enters through the lock mortise and emerges on the left side of the stock either behind the side-plate or in the middle of the wood moulding just below the plate. Then the rear extension is inlet and pinned in place. The extensions of many trigger-guards have chamfered or beveled edges. The edge lines should end up at the surface of the finished wood. This calls for filing the upper surfaces of the extensions to the proper level, and adjusting the wood level slightly, if necessary.

On many rifles of pre-Revolutionary and Revolutionary War vintage the rear extension of the trigger-guard was secured with a wood screw rather than a pin. If a pin is used, it should be located well up into the stock for strength.

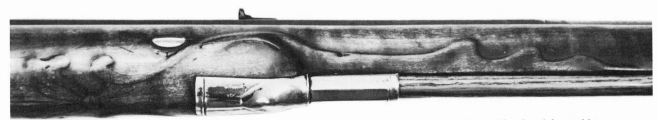

A brass barrel wedge with a head formed by bending down a tab was used on this rifle by the early York Co. PA gunsmith, George Schreyer.

CHAPTER 17

BARREL LOOPS

The fore-stock is held to the rifle barrel by means of little tabs of metal fixed to the underside of the barrel. In the old days these were called barrel loops and it is a valid term today. Round metal pins, or rectangular metal keys, pass transversely through the stock and the barrel loops to keep the wood and metal firmly together. In building a full-stocked rifle it matters not at all whether pins or keys are used, as far as strength and function are concerned, but there are some other factors to consider.

If you are recreating a rifle of the Golden Age, the late flintlock period, or of the percussion era, keys may be in order. If you are recreating the work of a particular school or of a particular maker, then keys may be necessary. On the other hand, pins almost invariably were used during the pre-Revolutionary and Revolutionary War periods. And pins continued in use on many American rifles throughout the 19th century. The pin is a thoroughly adequate stock fastening device. It is inconspicuous, and it is considerably easier to install than the key.

The key has a decided advantage for guns and rifles designed to be taken apart repeatedly. Half-stock rifles and shotguns often had tip-out barrels that were readily removed by simply pulling out a few keys. The key also is a stronger holding device than a pin. It has no particular advantage on a rifle or gun with a full stock and a barrel well fastened at the tang. But on a half-stock arm the only things holding the front end of the piece together are the two keys that pass through the stock in front of the lock. Here pins of adequate size can serve, but keys can serve better. In addition, the generous use of metal inlays on American rifles during the Golden Age and the late flint period encouraged the use of keys. The most appropriate inlays for a fore-stock are decorative escutcheons to surround the slots where barrel keys go.

The most traditional method of fastening barrel loops to the underside of the barrel is by means of dovetail slots similar to those used for sights. This is a simple and very sturdy method. Its only disadvantage is that the transverse cuts on the underside of a long barrel could affect the rigidity of the barrel, particularly if the slots are cut very deep or the barrel wall is thin. A number of other methods can be used for fastening barrel loops, and most all of these can be found on old gun barrels. Anything that does the job in a neat and strong manner can be used, for the loops are merely functional pieces that remain out of sight.

Dovetail slots for barrel loops should be no more than 1/16 inch deep. They can be cut easily with a milling machine and a dovetail cutter, but for those without access to such equipment, the job can be just as easily done by hand. The slot typically is ½ inch in length, and 1/16 inch deep. Paint the barrel with machinist's blue or with a black marker pen where the loop is to go, and carefully scribe the dimensions of the loop on the bottom and contiguous flats of the barrel. With a three-cornered file, cut a series of small transverse notches along the bottom flat within the scribed boundaries. Then take a jeweler's saw or hacksaw and make a series of parallel cuts almost down to the scribed lines on the oblique flats marking the depth of 1/16 inch. Then carefully file away all of the metal between the slots.

To make the 60° dovetail cuts at either end of the slot, it is necessary to have a triangular file of small size with the teeth completely ground away on one of the flats. A 5, 5 ½ , or 6 inch file is particularly good, but in addition it is handy to have a fine-toothed triangular needle file similarly ground. Using the side of a grinding wheel, or a flat carborundum stone, grind away the teeth until no trace of them remains, leaving a flat surface with good sharp corners. If a grinding wheel is used, proceed very slowly, alternately grinding for a second or two, and dipping the file in water to keep it cool, so that the hardness of the metal is not lost. With the smooth side of the file laying on the bottom of the slot in the barrel, the dovetail cuts can be made. The two dovetail corners need not be exactly parallel, for it is an advantage in fitting the loop to have a slightly tapered slot.

Barrel loops can be purchased ready-made in various forms, ranging from machined strips of T-shaped cross section to individual pieces made by investment casting. These can serve very well, but the beginner can easily make them and thereby gain one more degree of independence. With hacksaw

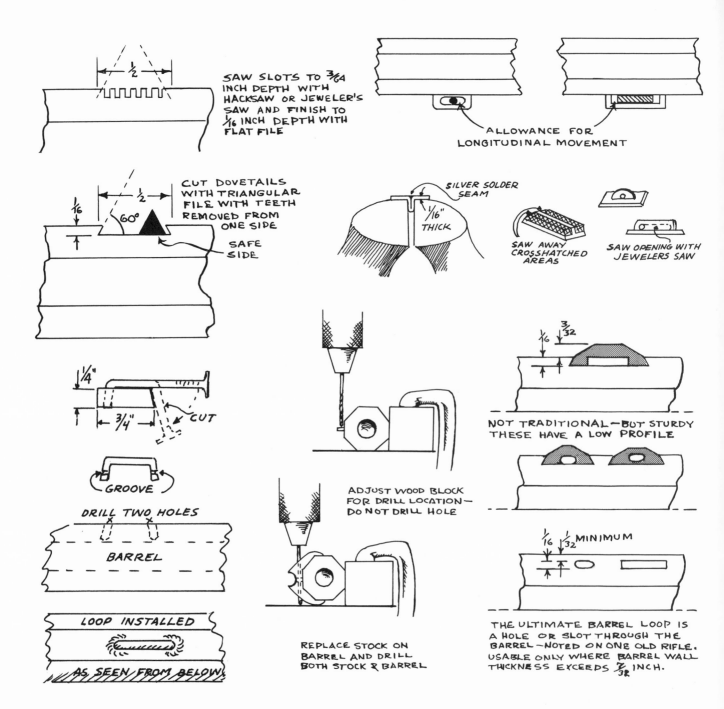

SAW SLOTS TO 3/64 INCH DEPTH WITH HACKSAW OR JEWELER'S SAW AND FINISH TO 1/16 INCH DEPTH WITH FLAT FILE

ALLOWANCE FOR LONGITUDINAL MOVEMENT

CUT DOVETAILS WITH TRIANGULAR FILE WITH TEETH REMOVED FROM ONE SIDE

SAFE SIDE

SILVER SOLDER SEAM

1/16" THICK

SAW AWAY CROSSHATCHED AREAS

SAW OPENING WITH JEWELERS SAW

CUT

GROOVE

DRILL TWO HOLES

BARREL

LOOP INSTALLED

AS SEEN FROM BELOW

ADJUST WOOD BLOCK FOR DRILL LOCATION— DO NOT DRILL HOLE

REPLACE STOCK ON BARREL AND DRILL BOTH STOCK & BARREL

NOT TRADITIONAL—BUT STURDY THESE HAVE A LOW PROFILE

MINIMUM

THE ULTIMATE BARREL LOOP IS A HOLE OR SLOT THROUGH THE BARREL—NOTED ON ONE OLD RIFLE. USABLE ONLY WHERE BARREL WALL THICKNESS EXCEEDS 7/32 INCH.

and file they can be made from a piece of steel ¼ inch thick. Another method is to use 1/16 inch metal and join the two pieces with silver solder. Also, sheet metal 3/64 to 1/16 inch thick can be used. It is bent with the help of a vise and the seam fastened with silver solder. The tongue can be 1/16 to 1/8 inch thick, and should stand above the surface of the barrel about 3/16 inch. Loops generally were made out of iron in the old days, but occasionally brass was used.

The base of the barrel loop is made a little longer than the base of the slot in the barrel. The loop then is prepared for installation by filing the 60° dovetail angles at either end of the base. This is done by mounting the tongue in the vise with the base of the loop parallel with the upper surface of the vise and slightly above it. With the smooth side of the triangular file against the top surface of the vise, the 60° cuts on the ends of the loop base are readily made.

Now, by filing the barrel slot, fit the base of the loop into the barrel so that the tongue is centered on the barrel flat. Punch the ends of the barrel dovetail so that the loop is held firmly in place. File the top surface of the base so that it is flush with the barrel. Clean up the tongue so that it is smooth, and file the sides to a slight taper, wider at the base than at the top.

Some old gunsmiths of Bedford County, Pennsylvania, and the nearby Potomac Valley of Maryland and Virginia, used a blind pin and hook to fasten the stock to the barrel. This was done in the late flint and percussion periods, when straight or parallel-sided barrels were being used. Hooks more or less like loops with the rear leg cut off were fastened under the barrel. Transverse pins were put through the fore-stock and the ends of these pins were hidden with silver inlays. To put the barrel in place, it was set in the channel a little ahead of the final position and then it was slid back so that the hooks engaged the pins. To use this method the tang must be short, and have little or no curvature.

The number and location of barrel loops takes some thought. Generally, longrifles had three or four loops. Barrels 40 to 42 inches long used either 3 or 4 loops, but 4 are preferable for strength. Longer barrels had 4 loops. If you are recreating the work of some particular maker the decision about the number of loops would follow from what he used. Another consideration is to be certain that the loops and the ramrod pipes do not interfere with each other.

Generally, the rear loop is positioned equidistant between the front of the lock moulding and the ramrod entry. Some makers, like George Schreyer of Hanover, Pennsylvania, placed their rear loops much nearer the ramrod entry. The front loop goes as close to the muzzle as you can get it, within reason, but behind the muzzle cap. Typically it will be about ¾ inch behind the muzzle cap, but if escutcheon inlays are planned then more space will be needed. The middle loop, or loops, are equally spaced between the front and rear loops.

Before installing all of the loops, consider that it is easiest to install only one loop at a time, inletting it into the stock before putting the second one in place. To inlet a loop, coat the loop with inletting black and, making sure that the breech end of the barrel is tight against the wood, set the barrel in the channel so that the position of the loop is marked in the bottom of the barrel channel. The wooden web below the barrel should be 1/8 to 3/16 inch thick, so the barrel loop will go all the way through the wood and emerge in the ramrod groove. Thus to inlet the loop, drill a series of holes and finish up the mortise with small chisels.

Barrel loop pins need not be more than 1/16 inch in diameter. The best material to use for them is 1/16 inch drill rod, which is of uniform diameter and truly round. An alternative is the ever-present nail, which may not be uniformly round, but which has been used on many a rifle anyway. At this state it is best to make temporary pins, longer than the width of the stock they will traverse, and for convenience, a ¼ inch long piece of the pin at one end is bent to a 90° angle, to provide for the many removals that will be made with it before the rifle is complete.

In drilling the pin holes it is best to make use of a drill press. Have the stock with the barrel in it securely clamped in position. Drill very slowly, clearing the flutes of the drill repeatedly as you proceed downward. This should minimize any tendency of the slender drill to wander from the desired path.

The top flat of the barrel is the guide that determines the vertical placement of the drill hole. With the barrel removed from the stock, and held in the drill press vise by itself, adjust and firmly clamp the vise to the drill press table so that the drill will go where desired. The top flat of the barrel should be against the non-moveable side of the vise. At the same time, mark the forward-and-aft position of the barrel in relation to the fixed side of the vise, and the drill should be poised above the desired position. The vertical position of the hole can lie right next to the barrel, or be as much as 1/32 inch below it. There is little or no extra space to work with here if the wood web is between 1/8 and 3/16 inch thick.

Replace the barrel in the stock and clamp barrel and stock in the vise. The hole should go almost exactly where it was planned. If you wish, drill just far enough that the drill marks the barrel loop (assuming that the loop is a blade without a hole in it). Then remove the barrel from the stock and examine the position of the hole. If all is well, replace the barrel in the stock, locate the stock under the drill accurately, and continue the hole on through the stock. The newly drilled hole in the barrel loop will help to keep the drill from wandering as it passes through the lower portion of the stock.

An alternative method is to locate the pins or keys on a line halfway between the bottom of the barrel and the upper edge of the ramrod hole. Lines representing the bottom of the barrel and the upper edge of the ramrod hole are drawn on the two sides of the stock, and also a line midway between. Then on both sides of the stock the location of the barrel loops are marked. If pins are to be used, the centers of the loops are where they will be located. If keys are intended, marks 1/8 inch on either side of the center provide the location for the loops and the slots in the fore-stock.

Making slots for keys is more involved, but it can be done. It involves drilling a hole near either end of the slot, and then removing the wood between the holes. The problem of drill wandering can be of some concern here. For a pin hole, if the drill wanders 1/32 inch, or even 1/16 inch, it will not be noticeable and may not be easily detectable. But in drilling holes at either end of a key slot, if the drill wanders 1/32 inch upward at one end and 1/32 inch downward at the other end, the slot will end up tilted with respect to the axis of the barrel.

One method of dealing with this potential problem is to proceed as with a single pin hole, drilling one hole all the way through. Drill the second hole only half way through. Then turn the stock over and drill the second hole, starting in the correct location as determined by a carefully scribed line.

The alternative method is to drill two holes only half way through from one side. Then by careful use of scribe and square, transfer the desired hole locations to the other side of the stock. Then drill the holes halfway through from the other side of the stock. If all went well, the holes will meet, more or less. Remove the barrel from the stock, and with jeweler's saw and needle files, join the holes in the barrel loop, thus creating a true loop.

To join the holes in the stock, it is necessary to make two tools out of an old hacksaw blade, which is conveniently about 1/16 inch thick. The first tool is a small saw, pointed at one end and about 3/16 inch wide for the main part of the blade. The teeth point backward. It is tapped into the wood and then pulled out, cutting as it is removed. The other tool is basically a small chisel that is used to clean up the slot. The final finishing of the slots can be done with a parallel-sided needle file.

A problem that must be recognized and allowed for when installing either pins or keys is that of differential longitudinal movement between barrel and fore-stock. Under varying conditions of temperature and moisture, the 42-inch long fore-stock will expand and shrink. In addition to this lengthening and shortening, there probably will occur a small permanent gradual shortening of the wood as it seasons further. The fore-stocks of old rifles sometimes are found to be pulled apart and separated by as much as 1/8 inch from failure to allow for this movement. Allowance is readily made for either pins or keys by having barrel loops with slots in them that are longer than the width of the pins or keys that go in them.

With the barrel in the stock, and temporary pins or keys in their holes, mark where the excess material should be trimmed off the barrel loops where they extend into the barrel channel. Remove the barrel and trim them almost to size. Then replace the barrel, and with the help of carborundum paper wrapped around a steel rod or the wood piece used to sand the ramrod channel, take the barrel loops down so that they are flush with the ramrod groove.

In this chapter only a few of the many ways of making and affixing barrel loops have been mentioned. In the old days a lot of other ways of doing the job were invented and used. For example, loops often were fastened to thin-walled fowling piece barrels with soft solder. Today, modern technology may provide still other possibilities. It is a place where today's rifle builder can be a little bit creative if the desire is there.

Another idea to consider is that of making barrel loops that do not show through at the bottom of the ramrod channel. Well-swamped barrels may leave a web 3/16 to ¼ inch thick for most of the fore-stock. A carefully made set of loops need not project more than about 1/8 inch below the barrel. Thus the loop does not have to project into the ramrod channel. Offset barrel loops are another possibility, set near one edge of the lower barrel flat instead of in the center. The wood is thicker there and they can easily remain concealed.

SLOTTED
WEDGE

BENDING
THE HEADS

COLD FORGING
HEADED WEDGES

CHAPTER 18

BARREL LOOP KEYS

Barrel loop keys cannot be made in finished form until the fore-stock is completely shaped. At this stage in building a rifle, only temporary keys are needed. But the subject of finished keys is treated here because it follows as a logical continuation of the subject from the preceding chapter.

Typical keys are made of steel or iron, but brass can serve also. Some very fine old rifles had brass keys. A key usually is about 1/16 inch thick, and ¼ to 5/16 inch wide. The thickness is uniform, but the sides taper slightly. Initially, the temporary keys should be about 1 to 1 ½ inches longer than the calculated finished length, for convenience in removing and replacing as the rifle is built. As the fore-stock takes shape, the temporary keys can be shortened for convenience. Keys are not interchangeable, and each must be fitted to its particular slot. Keys should be numbered to avoid confusion.

Keys always have a head on one end, and traditionally enter the stock from the left side. The simplest way to make a head for a key is to bend down the outer end and then file it to the desired shape. Some very fine old rifles had this kind of key, including many made by George Schreyer. Heads of brass, silver, German silver, or steel can be fastened on steel keys with silver solder. But if this method is used, the end of the key should be filed to the appropriate slope angle of the fore-stock before soldering.

Heads can be put on steel keys by peening the end with a hammer. The piece is firmly clamped in a vise with about 1/8 inch protruding. The application of heat from a propane torch or oxy-acetylene torch helps the process along. With careful peening, the head will upset or mushroom to a suitable size. The head will have to be bent to an angle corresponding with the slope of the fore-stock. A bending fixture to hold in the vise can help make neat bends.

Heads can be peened on brass keys. The usual practice for shaping brass is to hammer it cold, for a limited time, stopping to anneal it before it cracks by work-hardening. In forming the head on a brass key, it is suitable to keep the head hot with a torch while peening it to shape.

Old North Carolina rifles frequently have large silver heads on the keys. These heads can be as much as 1 inch long and 5/16 inch wide, and frequently have a domed surface, and are engraved. On the right side of the stock there usually are matching silver escutcheons inlaid in the wood.

If escutcheons are planned, do not trim the ends of the keys to the stock surface until the escutcheons are inletted, as considered in Chapter 27. With the stock finished and the keys trimmed, a lengthwise slot can be cut in the key so that it can be pinned, to prevent loss. Drill two or more holes of 3/32 inch size and join them with the jeweler's saw and needle files. The slot need only be long enough to clear the barrel loop when withdrawn. Start the pin hole with an awl in the bottom side flat of the barrel channel. Cut steel carpet tacks make good pins to secure slotted keys in the stock. The point is, or can easily be, curved. Tap it almost into place, then pull it and cut off the head and then drive it back into place until it is flush with the barrel channel.

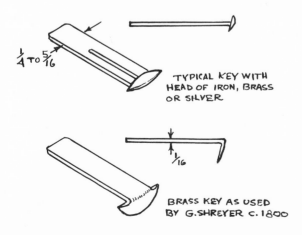

TYPICAL KEY WITH HEAD OF IRON, BRASS OR SILVER

¼ TO 5/16

1/16

BRASS KEY AS USED BY G. SHREYER c. 1800

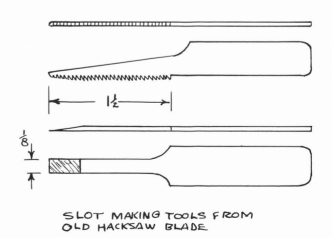

1½

1/8

SLOT MAKING TOOLS FROM OLD HACKSAW BLADE

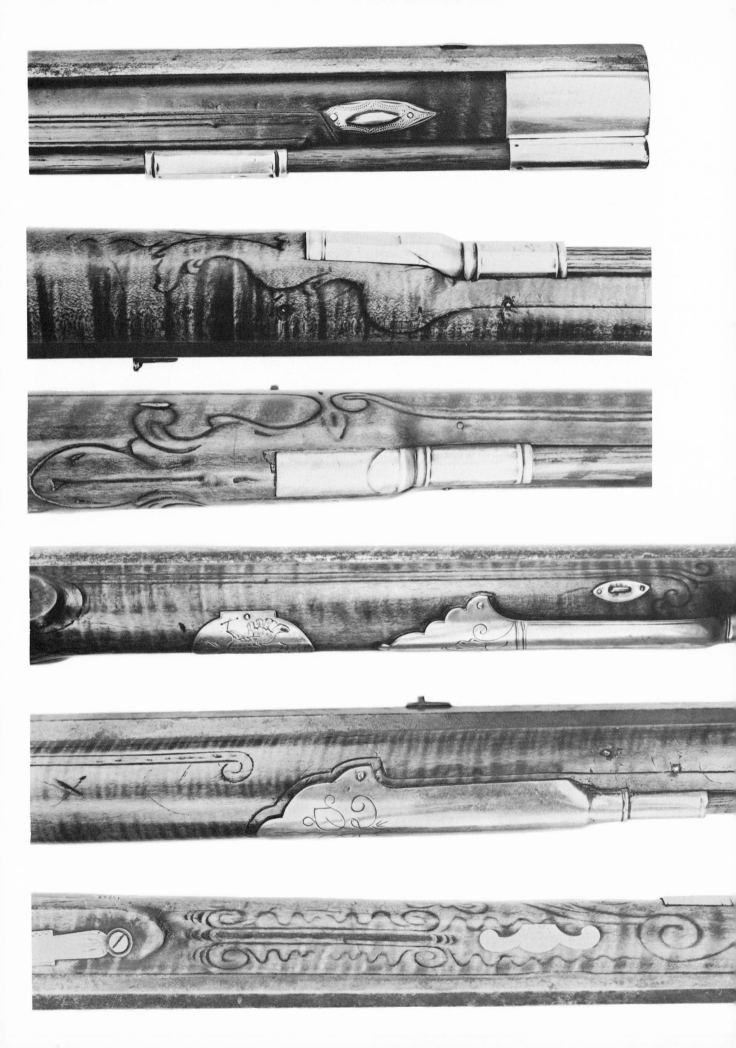

CHAPTER 19

MAKING AND INSTALLING RAMROD PIPES

With the fore-stock not yet shaped, the forward ramrod pipes can be installed. The rear ramrod pipe is a more complicated project than the other pipes, so it is well to leave it until after the shaping is completed. A fundamental decision is how many pipes to have in front of the rear pipe. For a typical rifle, with a barrel of about 42 inches in length, it will suffice to have two pipes out front. An additional pipe may be put on the stock, and some old rifles had them, particularly those with barrels 45 or more inches in length, but shooting experience suggests that the fewer pipes the better, for in returning the ramrod to the stock it can at times catch on the pipes.

The length of the ramrod pipes varies, with some pistol pipes being but ½ inch long, and some rifle pipes being 2 ½ to 3 inches long. Generally, early rifles had shorter pipes, in the range between 1 and 1 ½ inches, while the later makers used them longer. Some typical pipe lengths used by well known makers of the past are: Jacob Dickert 1 5/16; Isaac Haines 1 ½; Jacob Graef 1 ½; George Schreyer 1 7/8; John Armstrong 1 13/16; John Noll 2 1/16; Melchior Fordney 2 5/16; inches. These are merely rough guidelines and of course even the makers cited varied their pipe lengths a bit.

It is possible to buy both brass castings of ramrod pipes and pre-formed sheet metal pipes. Pipes of cast brass were used on English-Pattern trade rifles and on some American rifles of the 18th century. There is, of course, nothing wrong in using manufactured pipes if they can be found of suitable shape and size. But the beginning rifle maker will benefit from the experience of making them.

For sheet brass pipes, it is desirable to use stock that is 0.040 inches thick. Brass thinner than this is easily dinged out of shape, and brass much thicker may appear heavy. Pipes should have an inside diameter slightly larger than the finished diameter of the ramrod to be used, but the holes should not be so large that collectively they provide no friction to keep the rod in place when the muzzle of the rifle is pointed downward. If the pipe hole diameter is equal to the nominal ramrod diameter, the needed clearance is provided in sanding and finishing the ramrod. The pipes are formed around a mandrel, which can be a drill bit shank.

To make a pipe, cut a rectangle of sheet brass about 1/8 inch longer than the length intended for the pipe, and of suitable width as determined by wrapping a piece of paper around the mandrel. Carefully mark the paper pattern for the location of the bends that will be made to form the tabs. If you can detect a grain direction in the sheet brass, let it run parallel to the length of the pipe. Anneal the brass by heating to a good red color and quickly dunking in water. Use the paper pattern to mark the position of the bends on the brass. Then bend the tabs to a 90° angle, and then bend the sheet brass around the mandrel and clamp in a vise for a good tight fit. If the fit is not quite right, unbend the brass and adjust one of the 90° bends. The tabs that secured old ramrod pipes into the stock usually were not fastened together, but joining them with silver solder is an option.

The rear ramrod pipe is more complicated to make. It can be made all from one piece of brass, or it can be formed from two pieces. In the old days both methods were used. In either case there is a curved nose to make that involves more than simple bending. It involves some swaging of the metal to form a surface convex on the outside. It is possible to do this with the help of a cavity cut in a hard

21/64" DRILL

90°

SILVER SOLDER

WHEN SILVER SOLDER MELTS, SQUEEZE LIPS "X" TOGETHER WITH OTHER PLIARS wood block, which the metal is pounded into after the cylindrical part of the pipe is formed and the tabs fastened with solder. A more satisfactory method, however, is to make a metal mandrel.

To make a wooden forming device, start with two blocks of hardwood 1 ½ x 3 x 6 inches. Fasten these together with two ¼ x 3 ½ inch carriage bolts, putting the holes 1 ½ inch from one end, and ¾ inch from the sides. Make recesses for the heads so that they will be flush with the surface of the lower block. Relieve the holes in the upper block by drilling it out to 17/64 inch after putting through the initial hole of ¼ inch diameter. Then drill a hole lengthwise through the pair of blocks while they are clamped together. For a pipe to be used for a 3/8 inch ramrod, made around a mandrel of 3/8 inch diameter, and using brass 0.040 inch thick, the hole should be 0.375 + .04 + .04 = 0.455 inches, and for this use a drill of 29/64 inch size. To ensure that the axis of the hole will lie along the joining plane of the blocks, separate the blocks first, mark a centerline along the inside surface of each block, make a small groove along the centerline of each block, then clamp the blocks together. Use a small drill at first, and drill from each end. Gradually enlarge the hole to 29/64 inch size. Remove the upper block and mark the center of the semicircular groove. Then with a fine-toothed saw, cut a slot to take the tab or fin of the ramrod pipe. The entire cylindrical part of the pipe should fit snugly within the slotted hole thus made. The exposed semicircular groove is then cut away to provide a recess into which the exposed metal is hammered to form the tang of the pipe. This recess should be cut no lower than 1/8 inch below the bottom of the drilled groove. The distance from the bottom of the cavity to the bottom of the drilled hole is a measure of the amount of wood that there will be below the ramrod hole, and 1/8 inch is about the maximum it should be. A wood thickness slightly less than 1/8 inch is suitable, and on some old rifles it is as little as 1/16 inch.

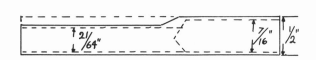

A REAR RAMROD PIPE CAN BE MADE FROM A BRASS ROD ½ INCH IN DIAMETER OR LARGER, BY DRILLING AND TURNING THE RAMROD TUBE OFF CENTER, THEN FILING TO SHAPE.

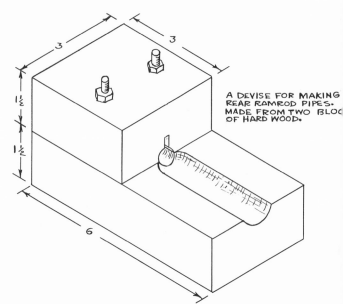

A DEVISE FOR MAKING REAR RAMROD PIPES. MADE FROM TWO BLOC OF HARD WOOD.

Another effective way to make the rear pipe is with the help of a metal mandrel, such as the one used by Jim Chambers and Earl Lanning, which is illustrated here. The larger part of this tool is a rod 7/8 inch in diameter and 3 ½ inches long, with the front end rounded to make the surface against which the tang of the ramrod pipe is formed. A smaller rod, 3/8 inch in diameter is fastened into the front of the larger rod, either by means of threads, or with silver solder after the rod is inserted in a 3/8 inch hole. The smaller rod should extend out of the larger one about 3 inches. The hole for the smaller rod must be offset from the center of the larger rod so that an edge of the small rod lies between 1/16 and 1/8 inch from the edge of the larger rod.

To use this mandrel, make a paper pattern for the pipe, including the tang, and then cut out a corresponding piece of sheet brass. This brass can be 0.040 inches thick, but it is better to use brass 1/16 inch thick as the extra material is needed in shaping the tang. The forward pipes, with a 3/8 inch diameter hole and walls 0.040 inch thick, have a net outside diameter of about 0.455 inches. It is desir-

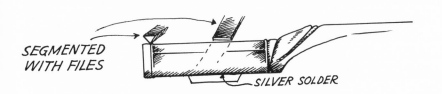

SEGMENTED WITH FILES

SILVER SOLDER

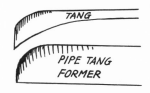

TANG

PIPE TANG FORMER

SILVER SOLDER

MANDREL FOR MAKING REAR RAMROD PIPE

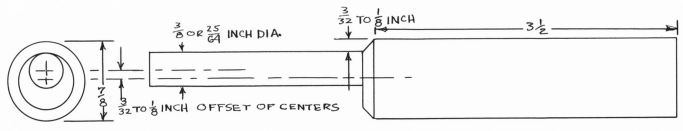

$\frac{3}{8}$ OR $\frac{25}{64}$ INCH DIA.

$\frac{3}{32}$ TO $\frac{1}{8}$ INCH

$3\frac{1}{2}$

$\frac{7}{8}$

$\frac{3}{32}$ TO $\frac{1}{8}$ INCH OFFSET OF CENTERS

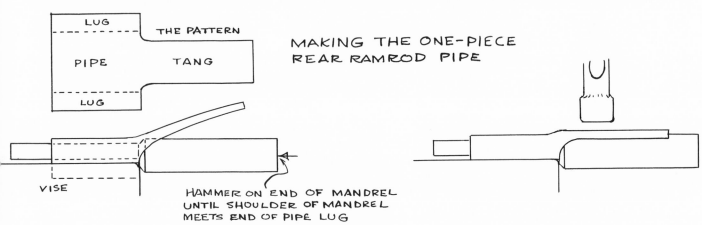

LUG

THE PATTERN

PIPE   TANG

LUG

VISE

HAMMER ON END OF MANDREL UNTIL SHOULDER OF MANDREL MEETS END OF PIPE LUG

MAKING THE ONE-PIECE REAR RAMROD PIPE

MAKING A TWO-PIECE PIPE WITH THE HELP OF THE MANDREL.

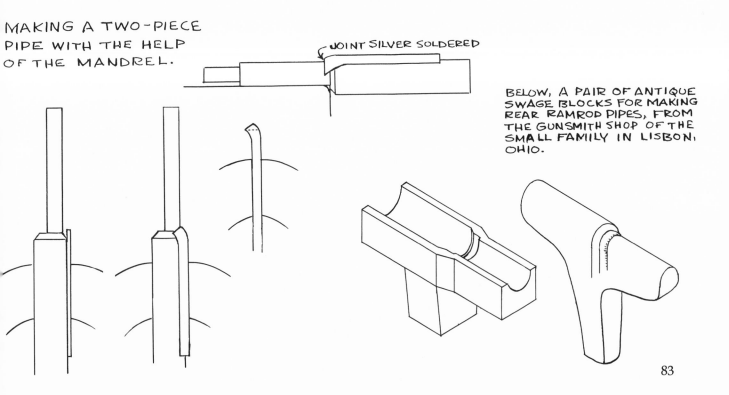

JOINT SILVER SOLDERED

BELOW, A PAIR OF ANTIQUE SWAGE BLOCKS FOR MAKING REAR RAMROD PIPES, FROM THE GUNSMITH SHOP OF THE SMALL FAMILY IN LISBON, OHIO.

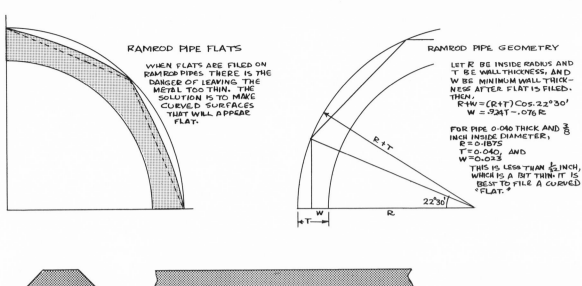

RAMROD PIPE FLATS

WHEN FLATS ARE FILED ON RAMROD PIPES THERE IS THE DANGER OF LEAVING THE METAL TOO THIN. THE SOLUTION IS TO MAKE CURVED SURFACES THAT WILL APPEAR FLAT.

RAMROD PIPE GEOMETRY

LET R BE INSIDE RADIUS AND T BE WALL THICKNESS, AND W BE MINIMUM WALL THICKNESS AFTER FLAT IS FILED. THEN,

$$R+W = (R+T) \cos 22°30'$$
$$W = .924T - .076R$$

FOR PIPE 0.040 THICK AND $\frac{3}{8}$ INCH INSIDE DIAMETER,
R = 0.1875
T = 0.040, AND
W = 0.023

THIS IS LESS THAN $\frac{1}{32}$ INCH, WHICH IS A BIT THIN. IT IS BEST TO FILE A CURVED "FLAT."

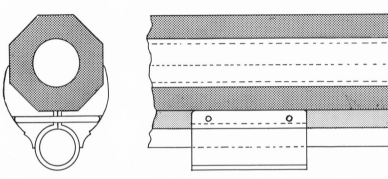

AN ALTERNATIVE FASTENING METHOD USES SCREWS AND A METAL PLATE LET INTO THE BOTTOM OF THE BARREL CHANNEL. THIS IS NEITHER CONVENTIONAL NOR AUTHENTIC, BUT IS STRONG AND DOES NOT CALL FOR PIN HOLES THROUGH THE FORE-STOCK

Typical rear ramrod pipes on American longrifles have the large square-ended tangs exhibited by the two examples shown here. Eighteenth century German rifles often were made with such rear pipes, and their widespread use in America is a direct carry-over from this German heritage. The pipe above is typical. The one below is unusual in having engraved designs on the tang and in having pairs of parallel engraved lines where the facets of the pipe meet.

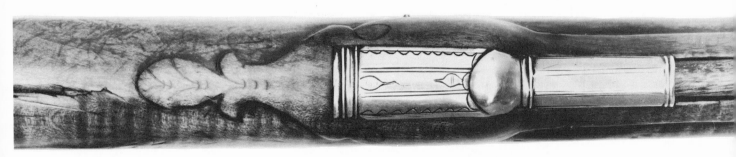

able for the outside diameter of the rear pipe to be of the same size, so it is best to use a smaller mandrel for the tube of this pipe. This would be 0.455 − 0.125 = 0.330 = about 11/64 inch, which would be the mandrel size. The hole can be drilled out to 3/8 inch size later. Form the pipe around the small mandrel, and fasten the joint with silver solder. Then clamp the pipe tightly in the vise with the tang sticking out and the end of the lug flush with the end of the vise. The mandrel then is hammered in until the shoulder of the large rod reaches the rear end of the cylindrical pipe and lug. This forces the tang upward. It then is hammered and peened down around the larger rod.

Some rear ramrod pipes are made with a bit of extra relief, or dome, on the nose of the tang. It is possible to form this by placing the nose of the tang on a large chunk of lead and hammering on the inside against a suitably shaped piece of metal, such as a piece of rod with a rounded end. However, by making the tang from brass of 1/16 inch thickness, this dome usually can be produced by filing.

A two-piece pipe also can be made with the help of this mandrel. In this case the cylindrical part of the pipe can be made from the same stock used for the other pipes, and the tang from 0.062 inch stock. The tang piece, after being annealed, is beat into shape around the mandrel. After filing the front end of the tang to suitable shape, apply flux separately to the joint surface of each part, and then a small amount of silver solder. Using the mandrel as a guide to hold the two parts in proper position; apply sufficient heat to join the pieces.

The ends of all of the pipes now should be squared up and carefully trimmed to exactly the same length. The sides of the fastening lugs should be smoothed, and the thickness of the lug for the rear pipe should be made equal to that of the other two.

The exteriors of the ramrod pipes now are filed to shape. The traditional exterior has flat surfaces filed on it to appear octagonal in shape. About half of the pipe is beneath the surface of the wood, so only 5 of the 8 flats need to be filed. The flats of the pipe do not extend to the ends of the pipes, but terminate somewhat short of the ends, leaving cylindrical ends with one or more beads or rings filed in them.

With the pipes completed, it is time to install them. The final position of the rear pipe must be first established. It is possible to move it back somewhat if the position of the entry hole seems too far forward. The front end of the front pipe is best located between 3 ½ and 5 ½ inches back from the muzzle. These measurements bear no relationship to the length of the barrel. A distance of 4 inches is good, and provides ample space for gripping and pulling out the ramrod, which is one of the important reasons for leaving ample space. But in keeping the front pipe back from the muzzle it also adds to the appearance of the rifle. The middle pipe is located halfway between the other two. But in any case, the location of the two forward pipes must not conflict with the barrel loops.

To install a ramrod pipe after its position is determined, mark the position of the fastening lug and cut this opening clear through the thin web. Put the pipe in place and make a vertical cut at each end of the pipe. Then with the help of transfer color, settle the pipe into place. The lug will be too long and can be shortened almost to final length. After the pipe is firmly pinned in place, the end of the lug can be carefully fitted to lie snugly against the barrel.

The rear ramrod pipe is a more difficult task to inlet. It is very helpful to start the inletting by taking one of the forward pipes and inletting it in the rear pipe position. Then after the tang of the rear pipe is filed to shape, the entire pipe can be let into place with a minimum of difficulty. Re-draw the centerline on the bottom of the stock as an aid in centering the tang. Then lay the pipe in place and start the cutting. With the help of transfer color, remove wood only where the contacts are made. Gradually settle the tang into place. Some final filing and shaping of the tang may be necessary. And while the inletting is being done, some extra wood will have to be trimmed away from the stock in the surrounding region.

The pipes are pinned in place, preferably with pins made from drill rod 1/16 or 5/64 inch in diameter. The smooth and sloping sides of the fore-stock may give difficulty in getting the hole started, so it may be necessary to make a start for it with a sharply pointed tool. One pin is adequate to hold each of the forward pipes in place, though two pins will hold them even more securely. But in any case, the rear pipe should be fastened with two pins, to prevent any possibility of the tang working loose. After the pipes are pinned in place it is well to wrap some fine abrasive paper around a suitable rod and run it through the pipes to remove any roughness or unevenness that may remain. At this stage it is well to leave the pins a little long, to aid in their removal during the finishing of the rifle. After the final finishing and staining is done, the pins can be cut off so that the ends lie a little below the surface of the wood, and the holes filled with brown wax. And it is well to have each pipe marked both for position on the stock and for the forward direction of the pipe.

The tapered rear ramrod pipe tang was common on English guns of the 18th century as well as those of France. In Germany it usually was used on smoothbore guns and sometimes on rifles. In early America tapered tangs often were used on rifles of New England, as in the example shown here, and fairly often on rifles from the pre-Revolutionary period. The tapered ramrod pipe tang saw much use on early American smoothbore guns and related smooth rifles.

Muzzle end of an iron-mounted flintlock longrifle of southern origin. The barrel is signed "SB". Below is a view of the butt-stock.

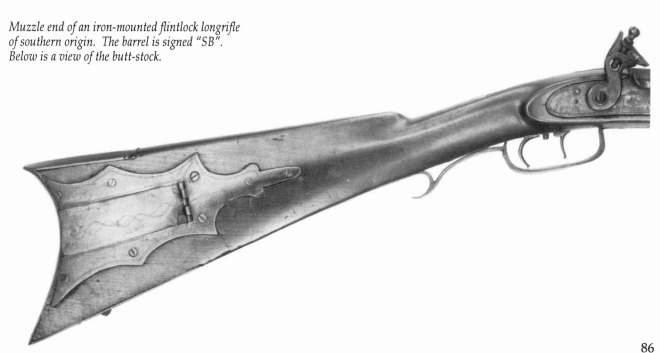

CHAPTER 20

FORE-STOCK AND MUZZLE-CAP

The fore-stock, as last seen, had the barrel inletted and the ramrod groove made. The side walls of wood on either side of the barrel were cut to a thickness of 1/8 inch along the lower fore-stock. Now is the time to reduce the side walls of the remainder of the fore-stock to a thickness of 1/8 inch, with the understanding that in the final shaping this thickness may be reduced even further, to as little as 3/32 or even 1/16 inch for very slender rifles. Keep the sides perpendicular to the top flat of the barrel.

In finishing off the front end of a rifle, the profile of the barrel can be a determining factor. A slender barrel of uniform diameter, or a barrel that tapers uniformly from breech to muzzle calls for a slender stock termination at the front end. On these rifles there is a general trend of the linear elements to produce a slenderizing effect clear to the muzzle. But the front end treatment for a rifle with a tapered-and-flared barrel, particularly one with a somewhat exaggerated flare at the muzzle, calls for additional consideration. German flintlock rifles sometimes had muzzle-caps made of horn. The front end of a horn cap used with a well flared barrel muzzle often was made with a thickened zone, or swelling, near its front end. Likewise, when using a brass cap at the end of a well flared barrel, it is appropriate to make the side-wall thickness of the muzzle-cap, plus the wood behind it, slightly greater than the side-wall thickness of the stock in the region where the barrel has it minimum diameter.

Thus, in making a very slender rifle using a straight-sided barrel of 13/16, 7/8 or 15/16 inch diameter across the flats, or a uniformly tapered barrel that ends up with a similar muzzle diameter, the side-wall thickness near the muzzle and at the muzzle should be between 3/32 and 1/16 inch. For a well swamped barrel, say 1 1/8 inch at the breech, 7/8 in. at the minimum diameter, and 1 inch at the muzzle, the side wall thickness would taper to about 3/32 or even 1/16 inch in the region of minimum barrel diameter, then increase slightly to 3/32 or even 1/8 inch at the muzzle. In either case, if a muzzle-cap is to be made, the fore-stock should be well completed first, with some final shaping near the muzzle to be done after the cap is installed.

The cross sections of old rifle upper fore-stocks can be roughly classified as having either V-shaped, or U-shaped profiles. For example, rifles from the Lehigh Valley of Pennsylvania, and Maryland, have V-shaped profiles, while rifles from Lancaster and York Counties in Pennsylvania have U-shaped profiles. The V-shaped profile has surfaces that are essentially flat on either side of the ramrod groove, with the upper third of the side being curved, to meet the barrel.

The fore-stock moulding is a feature that many old rifles had. It serves no functional purpose, and is strictly decorative. Those in a hurry to finish a rifle can leave it out. But a fore-stock moulding adds interest and beauty to a rifle stock, and it belongs on any rifle that has decorative carving, moulded lock and side-plate panels, and a lower butt moulding. On modestly decorated rifles, particularly those decorated with incised carving, the fore-stock moulding often is merely one, or perhaps two incised lines running the full length of the fore-stock, from the muzzle-cap to the rear ramrod pipe. On fully decorated rifles, with relief carving, the fore-stock moulding usually is a relief-carved feature. Often it consists of a simple flute that runs along either side of the ramrod groove, and which is separated from the curved sides of the fore-stock by a relief step. And that treatment can be further elaborated. In any case, the making of a good fore-stock moulding depends upon being able to cut the long lines that are necessary, and to have them be perfectly straight. And if more than one line is to be cut, they must be perfectly parallel to each other. To do this is not difficult if the ramrod groove is used as a guide for special tools that run in the groove and cut lines along the stock or shape the flutes.

To start the shaping of the fore-stock it is helpful to draw some guidelines. One of these is drawn along each side of the fore-stock about one-third of the way down from the top. This is the "break point," about where the maximum width of the wood is located. Draw another line on either side half-way down. These lines are only guidelines for some preliminary cutting, so their exact location is

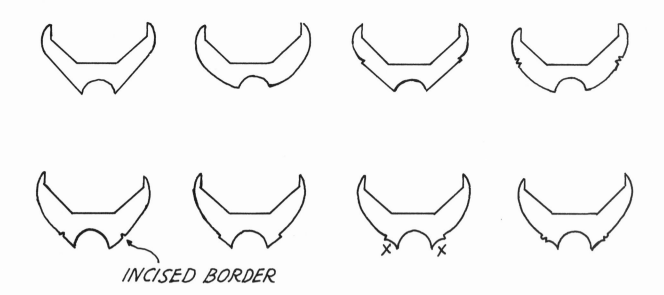

INCISED BORDER

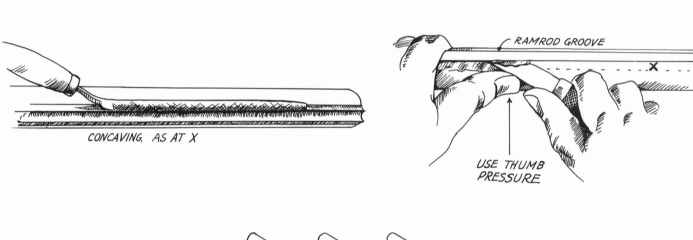

CONCAVING, AS AT X

RAMROD GROOVE

USE THUMB PRESSURE

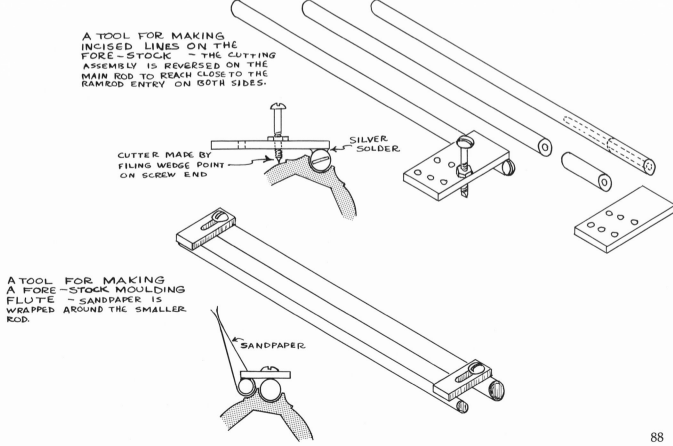

A TOOL FOR MAKING INCISED LINES ON THE FORE-STOCK — THE CUTTING ASSEMBLY IS REVERSED ON THE MAIN ROD TO REACH CLOSE TO THE RAMROD ENTRY ON BOTH SIDES.

CUTTER MADE BY FILING WEDGE POINT ON SCREW END

SILVER SOLDER

A TOOL FOR MAKING A FORE-STOCK MOULDING FLUTE — SANDPAPER IS WRAPPED AROUND THE SMALLER ROD.

SANDPAPER

not critical. However, they can be drawn or scribed accurately if the barrel is removed from the stock, and a marking gauge used that rides on the top flat of the wood. Also, draw lines on the underside of the stock about 1/16 inch from the edges of the ramrod groove.

On the lower fore-stock, between the lock region and the ramrod entry, a break point line needs to be scribed, which again is about one-third of the way down, but because the stock has a greater vertical thickness here, this line will lie below that on the upper fore-stock. Also, draw a centerline underneath the stock from the front of the trigger-guard to the ramrod entry. Now it is time to start shaping the wood.

With the barrel replaced in the stock, remove wood on the upper fore-stock between the line half-way down and the line marked near the ramrod groove. Some preliminary rounding of the upper part of both the lower and upper fore-stock can next be done, and also some preliminary rounding of the lower part of the lower fore-stock. Then there are two ways to proceed. One is to continue shaping the fore-stock to nearly its finished shape, and then make and install the muzzle-cap. The other way is to prepare the muzzle-cap to a pre-determined shape and install it, then finish out the wood to conform to the shape of the muzzle-cap.

FORE-STOCK MOULDINGS

The purpose of the fore-stock moulding is to provide something of visual interest that leads the eye lengthwise along the stock. A fore-stock that has nothing more to offer than a simple rounded surface between the side of the barrel and the ramrod groove is visually uninteresting in most cases. The fore-stock moulding on American rifles traditionally is confined to the lower third or, in some special situations, to the lower half of the side of the stock. It ranges from a single incised line to a complex series of flutes, raised beads, incised lines, and relief steps. On some rifles made in the old days in the Potomac Valley, complex mouldings were made that were interrupted where barrel key escutcheons were located. Decorative terminations were made for the moulding on either side of the escutcheons. The rifles and smoothbore guns of central Europe during the flintlock period usually carried an upper fore-stock moulding consisting of a simple relief bead running from lock to muzzle at the upper edge of the fore-stock, where it meets the barrel. American rifles almost never had such mouldings.

Fore-stock moulding lines and linear features lie close to the ramrod groove, and run parallel to it. The only problem in making them is to ensure that they run straight and in the right direction. They can be laid out with the help of a long straight-edge, dividers, and other drafting tools, and then cut in by following closely the lay-out lines, using chisels, knives, and files. An alternative method of making the moulding is to devise special tools that are guided by a rod that slides in the ramrod channel. These tools help do some tasks with nearly perfect results, and are well worth the small effort of making them.

One of the most common forms of moulding is a flute or shallow, round-bottomed groove that lies on either side of the ramrod groove. The edge of this flute is a relief step that separates it from the curved side of the stock. This alone makes a very effective moulding, but of course the scene can be further complicated with the addition of lines, a bead, or other simple linear features.

To make a fluted moulding with a relief step with tools at hand, first mark the location on the top edge of the concavity, where the step will be. Then make a vertical cut along the line. Mark a guideline further up on the side of the stock, and remove wood from the guideline to the cut. Use a very sharp knife for the cutting, or a good sharp wood chisel 1 inch wide. With either tool cut across the grain, toward the vertical cut. After the rough cutting is done, smooth the surface with a flat file. If the cutting teeth on one edge of this file are ground off there will be no tendency for the edge of the file to remove wood beyond the vertical cut. A 4-inch file is ideal for this work, though larger ones will do. The concavity of the moulding, or flute, is created by sliding a round file along the surface of the panel, carefully guiding it with the fingers. The flute should be no more than about 1/16 inch deep, and it terminates at the ramrod entry. Finishing work on the flute is done with the help of sandpaper wrapped around a rod 7 or 8 inches long and about 3/16 inch diameter.

A better way of making the vertical cut and the flute is with the help of two simple tools that slide

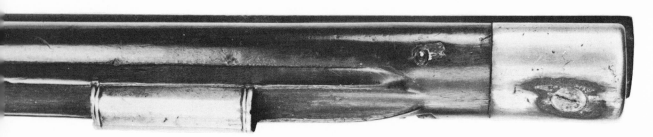

Screw-fastened one-piece muzzle-cap on late 18th century Berks Co., Pa., rifle.

Note rounded front end on muzzle-cap made in one piece, 3rd qtr. 18th century, Berks Co., Pa.

A decorative termination for front end of the fore-stock moulding, J. Dickert, maker.

Chevron decoration on muzzle-cap with ramrod groove, J. Schreit, maker.

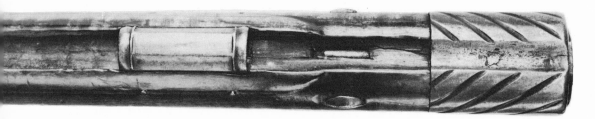

Chevron decoration on muzzle-cap with ramrod groove, J. Dickert, maker.

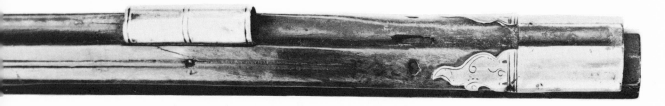

Lehigh Valley rifle by Herman Rupp has two parallel incised lines as a fore-stock moulding. The muzzle-cap has a deep groove for the ramrod. Note that the ramrod pipe is held with only one pin. Three of the six illustrations here show ramrod pipes held with one pin, and three show two pins.

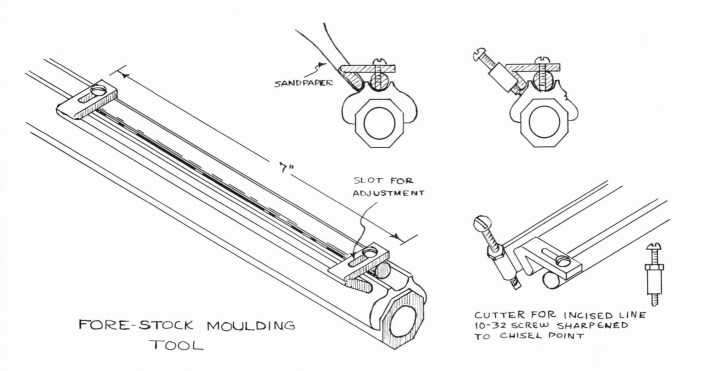

SANDPAPER

SLOT FOR
ADJUSTMENT

FORE-STOCK MOULDING
TOOL

CUTTER FOR INCISED LINE
10-32 SCREW SHARPENED
TO CHISEL POINT

in the ramrod groove. Take a piece of metal rod of suitable diameter to fit snugly in the ramrod groove, presumably a 3/8 inch rod for a 3/8 inch groove, and cut off a piece about 8 inches long. Using a lathe, center-drill one end, and then with a # 29 drill, make a hole about 1 ¼ inch deep in one end. With an 8-32 tap, run threads down this hole. Cut a piece of rod ½ inch long off the threaded end. Round off the sharp edges at both ends of both the long rod and the short piece. Then make a cutter bar from a piece of steel about 1/8 x ½ x 7/8 inch, and bend it to more or less conform with the curve of the lower part of the fore-stock. With the help of silver solder, fasten one end tangent to the short piece of rod. Use an 8-32 screw to fasten the short rod to the long rod. Mark the cutter bar for the location of the cutter, and drill and tap for an 8-32 screw. Make a cutter from an 8-32 screw by simply filing a wedge-like end on it with a round or half-round file. Secure the cutter in the cutter bar with the help of a lock nut. This tool will help cut a very even and precise line on both sides of the ramrod groove. The cutting assembly must be reversed to reach close to the ramrod entry on both sides. Additional threaded holes can be made in the cutter bar for cutting lines at other distances from the ramrod groove.

A tool to aid in cutting the flute that runs beside the ramrod groove can be made easily also. Start with a piece of rod about 7 inches long and of suitable size to fit snugly in the ramrod groove. Take a second rod of 3/16, or at the most ¼ inch, diameter and of the same length. Take two pieces of steel about 1/8 x ½ x 1 inch, and cut a lengthwise slot in each large enough to take an 8-32 screw. At the extreme ends of the smaller diameter rod fasten these slotted pieces of metal so that one of the flat sides is tangent to the rod. Then drill and tap screw holes in the larger rod so that the two pieces can be fastened to it. The distance between the two rods is adjustable. By wrapping a piece of sandpaper around the smaller rod, the tool will easily cut a very neat flute.

Before the muzzle-cap can be installed it is necessary to terminate at the front end the fluted moulding, which also forms the sides of the ramrod groove. This typically ends about ½ inch back of the muzzle-cap. The relief step at the edge of each flute can be curved around at the front end, and the high wood between the ramrod groove and the flutes reduced in level to that of the relief step.

MAKING AND INSTALLING THE MUZZLE-CAP

The muzzle-cap traditionally is made of brass, to go along with the other brass furniture. On old iron-mounted rifles the caps often were made of iron, and such rifles made today would utilize steel. On German-style rifles horn frequently was used, and on rare occasion it was used in America on half-stock rifles of the late flintlock period and percussion era. The length of muzzle-caps on old rifles varied considerably, from pieces as short as 1 inch to pieces as long as 2 ½ inches. In the pre-Revolutionary and Revolutionary period caps tended to be short. Rifles of the late flintlock and percussion periods frequently had the longer caps. In some schools of gunsmithing, such as at Bedford County, Pennsylvania, and Emmitsburg, Maryland, long caps almost always were used. Gunsmiths of Lancaster and York, Pennsylvania used caps of about 1 ¼ to 1 ½ inch length. It is only reasonable that rifles styled to a particular school should have muzzle-caps of appropriate length.

The muzzle-cap is a functional piece of furniture that binds together the two sides of the fore-stock at its fragile front end. It is permanently fastened to the wood, and on most old American rifles it is in no way fastened to the barrel. However, on some pre-Revolutionary American rifles the muzzle-cap is fastened to the barrel by means of a screw that passes directly through the lower side of the cap and into a threaded piece of metal that is fastened under the barrel by means of a dovetail slot. This fastening by means of a screw is a direct carry-over from the traditional German way of dealing with the muzzle-cap, which almost invariably made use of a screw. The screw fastening for the muzzle-cap is a particularly sound method of fastening the front end of a rifle together. But it does have a drawback. The problem is that it removes any possibility for differential movement between the front end of the stock and the barrel. Most German rifle barrels are relatively short, typically 24 to 30 inches in length, and the usual wood for stocks was straight-grained walnut. Apparently the differential movement was not a great problem. But the long barrel of an American rifle in combination with a long, wavy-grained maple fore-stock, creates a potential problem. This can be solved by making a short slot in the underside of the muzzle-cap instead of a simple screw hole, and by adjusting the length of the fastening screw so that it comes up tight in its threaded hole while leaving the muzzle-cap free to move longitudinally if necessary.

The muzzle-cap is somewhat of a problem to make. Usually it is made from a piece of sheet brass bent to the shape of the fore-stock, and having a plate fastened within the front end by silver solder. In the old days these caps often were made out of one piece of sheet metal by swaging the front end into shape. However, this called for making matching blocks of iron or steel in the shape of the finished sides of the cap. These were clamped together with the sheet brass between, and a small amount of brass protruding at one end. This then was hammered to form the front end. This was a very useful tool for making many caps of the same particular size, but impractical for making one or two.

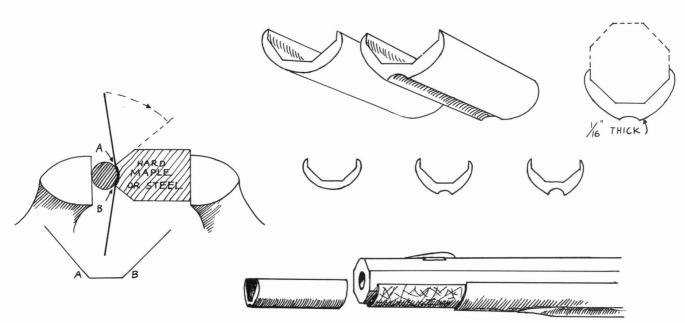

Sheet brass between 0.030 and 0.040 inches thick is used to make the cap. The small front end plate is made from brass between 1/16 and 1/8 inches thick. But begin the process by making a pattern of paper, and also one of thin sheet aluminum if some is available.

The finished front end of the cap should lie 1/16 and 3/32 inch back from the finished front end of the barrel. Accordingly, the front end of the wood first should be cut back to allow for this set-back. Try for a good square cut.

Depending upon relationships at the front end of the stock, the cross-section of the cap either is one continuous curve, or has two curved sides with a depression where the ramrod groove continues across it. In either case, the first thing is to prepare a mortise in the wood for the cap. Mark the sides of the wood where the rear end of the cap will meet the wood. Also, draw the pattern of the cap on the front face of the wood. Then proceed, very carefully, to cut away the wood where the cap will go. To make a neat cut where the rear end of the cap will join the wood, clamp a straight-edged strip of sheet brass or aluminum around the stock and barrel, and use it as a guide for cutting in the line with a sharp knife. Cut away wood to the depth necessary for the cap.

With paper and/or sheet aluminum, work out the exact size of the cap. Then work with the brass to make it conform with the shape of the wood. It is advisable to anneal the brass before doing this bending. If the cap will have a groove or depression at the position of the ramrod, make this first. This is best done with the help of a small block of hardwood with a groove of suitable size cut in it, and the adjacent sides shaped similar to those of the stock. With the brass placed on the block, clamp a rod on top to force the brass into the groove, and bend the sides down. Remove the brass from the bending block and clamp in place on the stock, then continue the bending. Strive for a good tight fit. Leave a little extra metal where the cap meets the side of the barrel, so that a good tight fit can be made.

Next, prepare the face plate for the cap. Make a cut-out for the barrel that is considerably under-size, and too small to fit on the barrel. The face-plate fits inside of the sheet brass sides, and should be carefully filed to a good fit. Slide the cap forward to test the fit. It is possible to fasten the two pieces of brass together with soft solder, and this can be done while the cap is clamped in place around the stock, if the barrel is removed. Alternatively, the cap can be riveted in place to the wood before the face plate is soldered in place. This assures a perfect fit for the cap. However, soft solder has its weakness. For a stronger joint, use silver solder. But the high heat required makes it necessary to remove the brass from the wood, and then the problem arises of holding the brass in exactly the right shape while the heat is being applied. It may be helpful to cut out a piece of metal with the same outside shape as the face plate, place it at the rear end of the cap, and hold the assembly together with wires and clamps.

On most old rifles the cap was held in place with a small copper or brass rivet along the ramrod groove. The wood is thin and fragile here. It is not unreasonable to use two additional rivets where the wood is thicker. On the inner side of the wood the head of the rivets will have to lie flush with the surface of the wood, so the wood will have to be countersunk accordingly. The hole or holes drilled in the cap to take the rivets should have a small countersink at its outside edge. To rivet the rivets in place, replace the barrel in the stock and peen the ends of the rivets, which are backed up by the barrel. A small amount of epoxy glue also could be used to help hold the cap in place.

With the riveting completed, the wood and the muzzle-cap should be finished up with files and abrasive paper, always moving the file so that it cuts wood before brass. Finish with fine abrasive paper. With the cap in place, further finishing of the front end of the fore-stock moulding may be necessary.

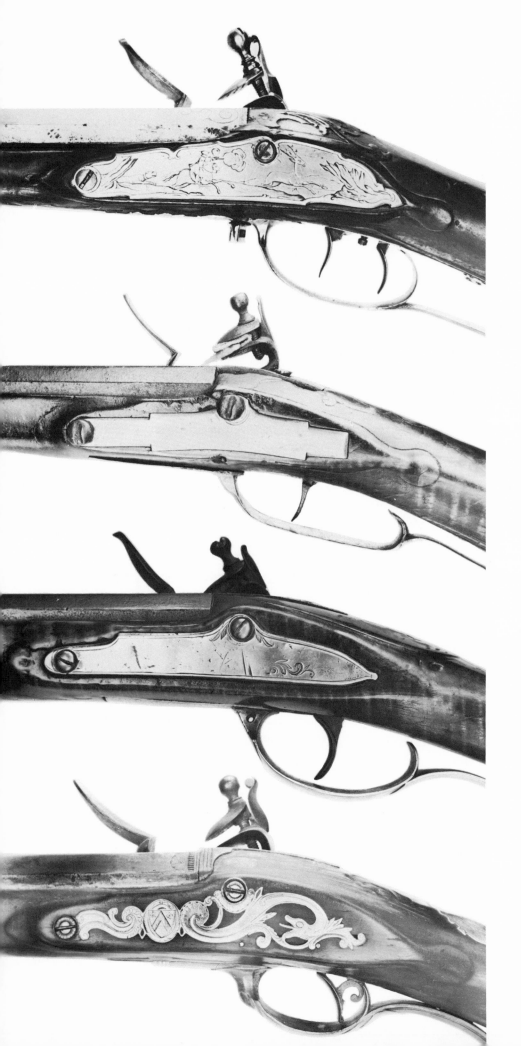

Continental European gunsmiths took full advantage of the side-plate for artistic decoration, often making it as large as the lock-plate, and of similar shape. This example is by Caspar Zelner of Wien, c. 1725.

In contrast to the decorative European side-plate, early American side-plates often were a combination of rectangular shapes that did not relate artistically to the curves of the side-plate panel. This example, which is very typical, is from a rifle by Jacob Dickert of Lancaster, Pennsylvania.

This side-plate, more or less in the shape of a lock-plate, has a graceful outline and fits well in the side-plate panel. This example is on a rifle by H. Deming who may have worked in the South.

Elaborate European baroque side-plates were the inspiration for this elegant piece used by Thomas Earle of Leicester Massachusetts, on a rifle in the 1780's or 1790's. Though essentially of baroque design, the scroll ends on either side of the oval crest have shell-like rococo designs engraved on them.

94

CHAPTER 21

SIDE-PLATE

The side-plate is basically a piece of metal on the left side of the stock, opposite the lock, through which pass the two screws that hold the lock in place. In its simplest form the side-plate is not a single piece of metal, but two metal washers that protect the wood from the heads of the screws. In its most attractive form it is a beautiful metal inlay, decoratively shaped and elegantly engraved. The side-plate was a particularly important place for artistic expression on the finer European arms, both wheellock and flintlock, of the 17th and early 18th centuries.

Following in the European tradition, a few early American gunsmiths took full advantage of the side-plate as a place for artistic expression. Others took partial advantage of it. But alas, most American gunsmiths used a simple side-plate design that has little to offer artistically, and it certainly can be considered as the standard American side-plate. There were some regional differences in the details of the design of the side-plate, as for example, the arrowhead-shaped feature at the tail of side-plates from the Lehigh Valley of eastern Pennsylvania.

Today's rifle builder has the choice of using the simple side-plate design appropriate for the styling of the rifle, being made, or of designing a more artistic piece. One certainly will not be wrong to opt for the simpler solution. On the other hand, it is good food for the mind to look critically at old side-plate designs of the simple type and see how easy it is to improve upon them.

The traditional side-plate is a bar of brass about 1/8 inch thick through which pass the two screw holes. It is inlet about 1/16 inch deep, with the remainder of the brass projecting above the wood level. To avoid sharp corners, the edges of the side-plate have substantial bevels. These side-plates were usual on rifles of the late 18th century and up to the time of the War of 1812. In the late flintlock period and percussion era, side-plates often were made of sheet metal about 1/16 inch thick, and they were mounted with the surface flush with the wood. However, thin flush-mounted plates were used in pre-Revolutionary years also, and thick plates of standard design were used in the later periods.

The flush-mounted side-plates of thin sheet metal usually are rather long in the tail, and require a small screw to assure that the tail stays in place. Usually they were decorated with engraving. In contrast, the thick plates of the earlier years often were finished without any engraving. Plates intermediate between these two types also were used. The outer surface of such plates stands about 1/32 inch above the level of the wood, and the metal has a small beveled edge.

If a thick plate is to be used, a minor professional touch can be added by counter-boring recesses for the screw heads. The 5/16 inch counter-bore can be used to advantage here, by cutting to a depth of about 1/16 inch. The screw heads are finished to be slightly domed or rounded.

Many different types of side-plates are available today from commercial sources, in sand-cast yellow brass, investment-cast yellow bronze, investment-cast steel, and investment-cast German silver. And if one of these can be found of correct size and agreeable shape, there is nothing wrong in making use of it, of course. However, for the beginning rifle maker there is more to be gained in making one.

To design a side-plate, first make a rubbing of the edges of the side-plate panel on a piece of paper, and cut it out. Then transfer the pattern to other pieces of paper and draw away. For side-plates of more elaborate shape, either thick or thin, books also can be a help to start one off. For starters, reproduce the outline of the lock-plate, which of course is similar in shape to the side-plate panel. In any case, the shape of the side-plate should have a good artistic relationship to the shape of the wood panel. Various designs can be tried out in place on the wood if they are cut out of heavy paper, or better, out of thin sheet aluminum or brass.

With the side-plate pattern worked out, transfer the design to the metal from which the finished plate will be cut. Mark the screw hole locations, and drill the rear screw hole. If counter-boring is planned, drill for the 1/8 inch pilot, counter-bore, and then drill for the body of the screw. Then fasten the over-size piece of metal to the stock with the one screw. Locate the position of the second screw

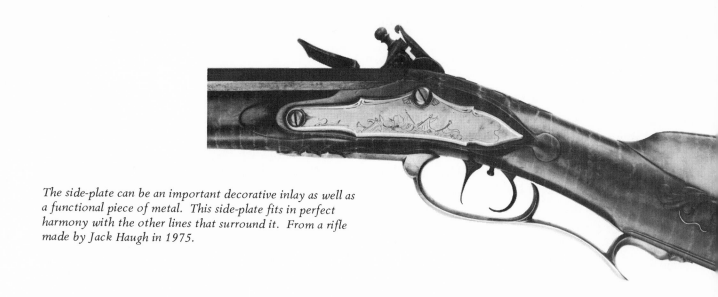

The side-plate can be an important decorative inlay as well as a functional piece of metal. This side-plate fits in perfect harmony with the other lines that surround it. From a rifle made by Jack Haugh in 1975.

hole by means of a drill bit passed through the hole in the lock-plate and through the stock. Remove the side-plate metal from the stock, drill for the pilot hole, counter-bore, and drill for the screw body. Then mark the pattern of the side-plate on the metal and cut to shape. When filing the edge to finished shape, be sure to put a very small slope on the edges to help ensure a tight fit when inletting. With final form achieved, screw the plate in place on the wood and make a vertical cut about 1/32 inch deep around the edge of the plate, using a very sharp knife. The vertical cut really should be made to slope slightly inward. Use appropriate knives or chisels to remove the wood between the vertical cuts, and gradually let the plate into place, aided by transfer color.

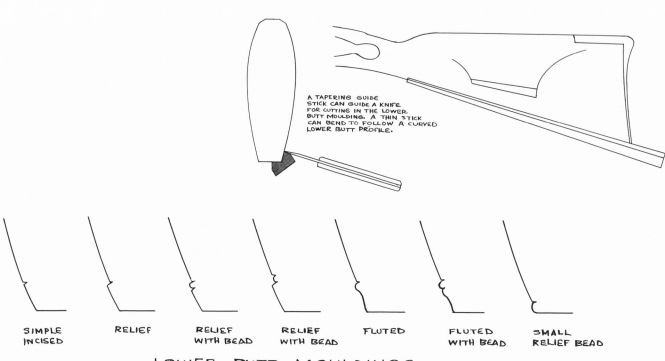

A TAPERING GUIDE
STICK CAN GUIDE A KNIFE
FOR CUTTING IN THE LOWER
BUTT MOULDING. A THIN STICK
CAN BEND TO FOLLOW A CURVED
LOWER BUTT PROFILE.

| SIMPLE INCISED | RELIEF | RELIEF WITH BEAD | RELIEF WITH BEAD | FLUTED | FLUTED WITH BEAD | SMALL RELIEF BEAD |

LOWER BUTT MOULDINGS

CHAPTER 22

LOWER BUTT MOULDING

The lower butt moulding is an important, but not major, decorative feature that a rifle ought to have. Rifles devoid of carving, and those styled to the late flintlock or percussion periods, often did not have this moulding, but most decorated rifles of the 18th century and the Golden Age did have it. At this stage in making the rifle it is best to establish the position of the moulding, and to make it. On the right side of the stock, the upper edge of the moulding helps determine the position of the patch-box, which lies between it and the extension of the butt-plate. On the left side of the stock the edge of the moulding forms one of the boundaries within which the decorative carving must lie.

The lower butt moulding may consist of a narrow relief bead of uniform width that runs from the butt-plate to about where the end of the trigger-guard bow is located. This bead may have a width of between 1/16 inch and 1/8 inch. The second type of moulding is one that tapers as it goes forward. It may be as much as 5/16 inch wide at the butt-plate, and taper to about 1/8 inch width at its forward end. This tapered moulding may be a simple relief bead, or it may be more elaborate in profile. In its simplest form, the moulding may consist of nothing more than an incised line. In planning the moulding, the toe-plate must be reckoned with, for its edge forms part of the moulding. The relief moulding generally has a relief of between 1/32 and 1/16 inch. Often relief moulding is tied in with re-lief carving at its forward end.

For a lower butt moulding to look good, it must be laid out and cut with precision. This can be done with a line carefully laid out by straightedge and cut freehand with a veining tool or knife. However, some simple tools can be made that will do the job to perfection, which makes freehand virtuosity unnecessary.

To make the cut for a bead of uniform width, take a block of hardwood about 1 x 1 ½ x 2 inches, and cut one side so that it can slide along the underside of the butt and have a lip that overhangs the side of the stock about 3/8 inch. The inner surface of this lip should be at approximately the same angle as the side of the stock, with respect to the bottom plane of the stock. It will help to make the surface of the outer edge of the block parallel with the inside edge of the lip. For a 1/8 inch wide bead, measure upward from the inside corner of the block about 1/8 inch, and drill a hole with a # 29 drill. Tap the hole for 8-32 threads. Make a cutter by filing the end of an 8-32 screw to a knife edge. Place a lock-nut on the screw, and then run the screw into the block so that the cutter projects a suitable distance. In using this tool for the first time, make a very light initial cut, hardly more than a surface scratch.

A tool such as this is of no use for cutting the edge of a tapering moulding. A tapering guide stick can be made, however, that will ensure a good initial cut. This stick is made out of a piece of fine-grained hardwood, such as maple or some forms of poplar. Make it 4 or 5 inches longer than the length of the moulding. Start with a piece about 16 inches long, and large enough to hold in a vise or with the aid of clamps. With router, table saw, radial arm saw, or by hand if necessary, cut a step into one corner of the wood piece about ½ inch on each side. Then cut one of the inside surfaces so that the 90° inner angle is increased to about the angle formed between the lower edge of the stock and the flat underside of the stock. This angle will vary from rifle to rifle, but will be about 110° +/- 10°. After smoothing the two inner surfaces of the stick, use a pair of sharp-pointed dividers to mark the limits of the sides that will taper. With the stick being 4 or 5 inches longer than the length of the intended moulding, the excess length on either end will allow for some final adjustment of moulding width before the cut is made. Now cut the two sides of the stick down to the limits of the lines marked on the inside, being sure that the plane of the cutting is perpendicular to the adjacent inner surfaces, so that a knife guided by the stick will yield a perpendicular cut. Lastly, cut a back surface on the stick perpendicular to the center plane of the stick, but not quite perpendicular to the side of the stick. This stick is flexible enough to work with butt-stocks having curved lower profiles.

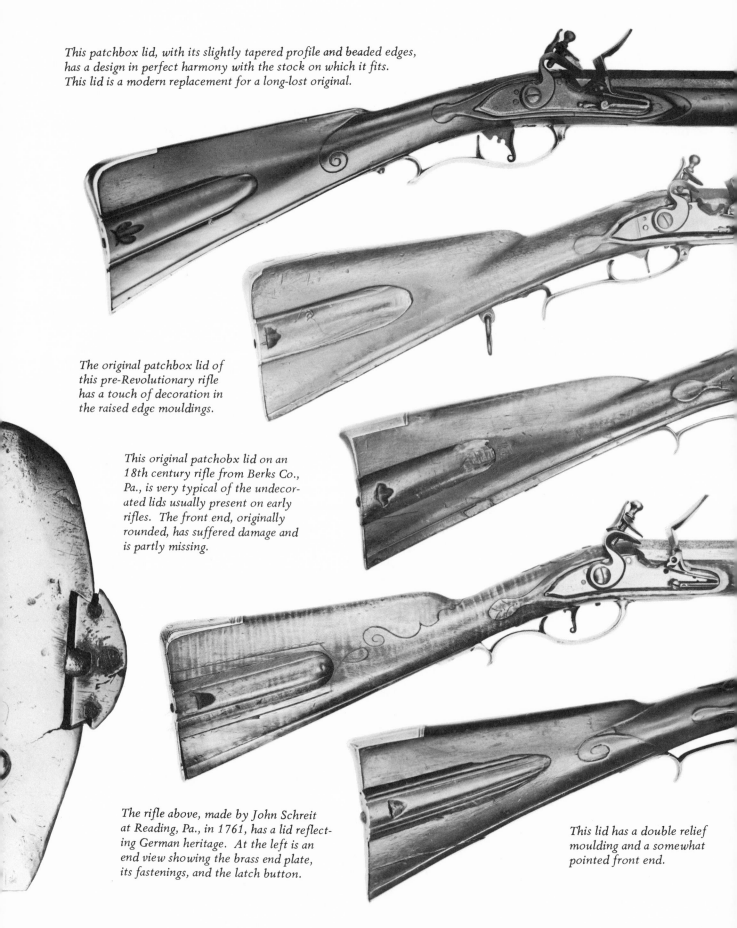

This patchbox lid, with its slightly tapered profile and beaded edges, has a design in perfect harmony with the stock on which it fits. This lid is a modern replacement for a long-lost original.

The original patchbox lid of this pre-Revolutionary rifle has a touch of decoration in the raised edge mouldings.

This original patchobx lid on an 18th century rifle from Berks Co., Pa., is very typical of the undecorated lids usually present on early rifles. The front end, originally rounded, has suffered damage and is partly missing.

The rifle above, made by John Schreit at Reading, Pa., in 1761, has a lid reflecting German heritage. At the left is an end view showing the brass end plate, its fastenings, and the latch button.

This lid has a double relief moulding and a somewhat pointed front end.

CHAPTER 23

SLIDING WOOD PATCHBOX LID AND CAVITY

A longrifle just doesn't seem to be a longrifle without a patchbox. But many rifles were made without them. Before plunging ahead with a patchbox, it is well to take a critical look at them in general and to note their functions. The patchbox tradition came from old continental Europe, where patchboxes with sliding wooden lids traditionally were put on wheellock rifles, presumably to hold cloth patches. German and Austrian flintlock rifles from the first quarter of the 18th century were equipped with patchboxes having sliding wooden lids, and the tradition was carried on into the 19th century.

The patchbox tradition came to early America along with the rest of the German rifle making traditions. American rifles of the pre-Revolutionary period often had sliding wooden patchbox lids. But American gunsmiths also began to use, and apparently started the significant use of metal patchboxes during the 1770s. Usually these were made of cast brass, though iron was put to use also. Brass patchboxes could be made much more attractive than wooden ones, and apparently they became popular to the extent that a rifle was hardly a rifle without one. In the post-Revolutionary decades, as the rifle developed and evolved, the sliding wood patchbox fell out of use, and the metal patchbox became of increasing importance as an outlet for decoration. In the southern Appalachian Mountains, iron-mounted rifles were made with simple iron patchboxes, or sometimes were simply equipped with a hole in the butt-stock to hold tallow for lubricating the patch.

Today's occasional shooter generally does not use his patchbox for any functional purpose, it being handier to get patches and balls out of the hunting bag. If so, why have one? The answer is that relatively plain rifles, without any decorative carving or inlays, can get along without a patchbox. But if a rifle is to be decorated, it simply has to have a patchbox. At this point it would be reasonable to ask why not just install a large and decorative brass inlay of patchbox size and forego the difficulties of making a four-piece patchbox with complicated hinge and release mechanism. Heretical though this thought is, it is worth pondering.

On the early American rifle the time period of the sliding wood patchbox was the 18th century. It fell into disuse in the 1790s and was rarely used after 1800, though there are exceptions, of course. The design of a wooden patchbox lid may seem easy, but it really must be worked out with great care, for it lies in a prominent position on the right side of the stock. With a paper pattern decided upon, it would not be wasted effort to take a piece of soft pine and carve out a try-piece that represents the part of the lid that will lie above the surface of the stock.

A typical wooden lid is about 5 to 6 inches long and about 1 ½ inches wide at the butt-plate. The sides should taper in keeping with the lines of the butt, though in most cases it is not practical to have both the upper and lower edges follow the radiating lines determined by the convergence of the upper and lower profile lines of the butt. It seems to work out best to have the lower edge of the lid lie almost along one of the radial lines. The front end of the lid is either rounded or pointed. Surviving old original patchbox lids are scarce. Almost all of them are rather simple in exterior design, with a simple rounded exterior and a cut-out near the rear to assist in removal. A beaded or simply moulded edge is appropriate, but elaborate relief carving is not suitable. And care must be taken in choosing the wood for the lid, when the stock is made of curly maple. The problem is that if well curled wood is used for the lid it may clash with the curl of the wood on either side of it, either because the direction of the curl lines is not in line with the curl lines of the stock, or because the curl lines of the lid stand out more than those of the stock. The solution is to choose a piece of wood with relatively little curl, and then to be certain that the curl direction is correct.

With the pattern for the lid established, its outline is drawn on the stock. Then the cutting begins. First, flatten the stock within the outline, including the edge of the butt-plate. This surface must be absolutely flat, with no dips or irregularities. Use a straight-edge both lengthwise and transversely on the area, and finish the wood surface with sandpapers on a block, progressing to a 400 grit finish. If the finished area is larger than the intended lid size, round the stock back to the outline.

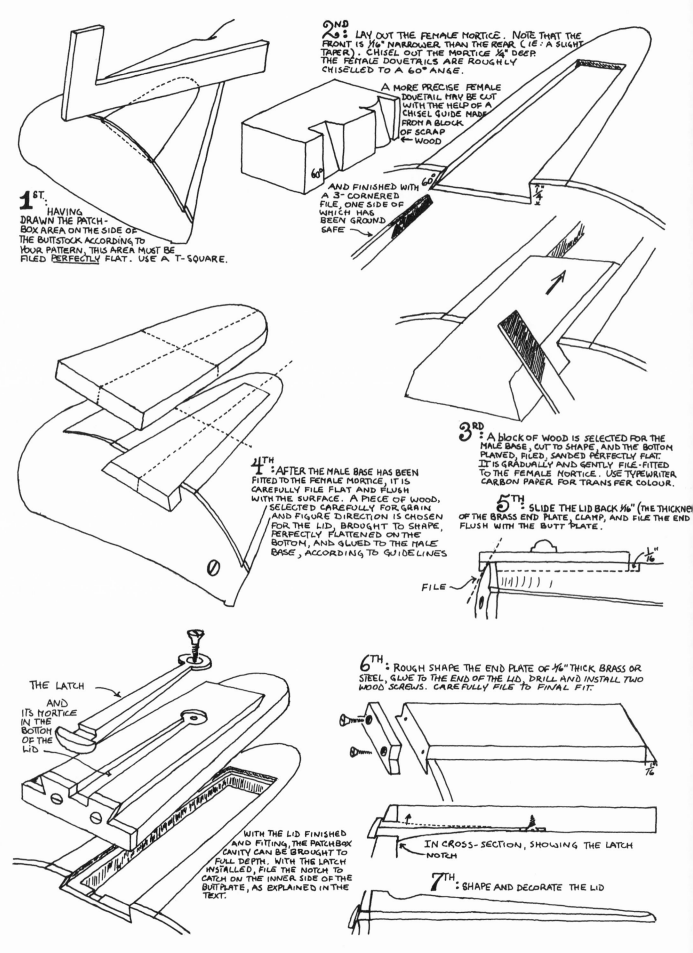

2ND: LAY OUT THE FEMALE MORTICE. NOTE THAT THE FRONT IS 1/16" NARROWER THAN THE REAR (IE: A SLIGHT TAPER). CHISEL OUT THE MORTICE 1/4" DEEP. THE FEMALE DOVETAILS ARE ROUGHLY CHISELLED TO A 60° ANGLE.

A MORE PRECISE FEMALE DOVETAIL MAY BE CUT WITH THE HELP OF A CHISEL GUIDE MADE FROM A BLOCK OF SCRAP ← WOOD

60°

AND FINISHED WITH A 3-CORNERED FILE, ONE SIDE OF WHICH HAS BEEN GROUND SAFE ←

60°

1/4"

1ST. HAVING DRAWN THE PATCH-BOX AREA ON THE SIDE OF THE BUTTSTOCK ACCORDING TO YOUR PATTERN, THIS AREA MUST BE FILED <u>PERFECTLY</u> FLAT. USE A T-SQUARE.

3RD: A block OF WOOD IS SELECTED FOR THE MALE BASE, CUT TO SHAPE, AND THE BOTTOM PLANED, FILED, SANDED PERFECTLY FLAT. IT IS GRADUALLY AND GENTLY FILE-FITTED TO THE FEMALE MORTICE. USE TYPEWRITER CARBON PAPER FOR TRANSFER COLOUR.

4TH: AFTER THE MALE BASE HAS BEEN FITTED TO THE FEMALE MORTICE, IT IS CAREFULLY FILE FLAT AND FLUSH WITH THE SURFACE. A PIECE OF WOOD, SELECTED CAREFULLY FOR GRAIN AND FIGURE DIRECTION IS CHOSEN FOR THE LID, BROUGHT TO SHAPE, PERFECTLY FLATTENED ON THE BOTTOM, AND GLUED TO THE MALE BASE, ACCORDING TO GUIDELINES

5TH: SLIDE THE LID BACK 1/16" (THE THICKNESS OF THE BRASS END PLATE, CLAMP, AND FILE THE END FLUSH WITH THE BUTT PLATE.

FILE ←

1/16"

THE LATCH

AND ITS MORTICE IN THE BOTTOM OF THE LID

WITH THE LID FINISHED AND FITTING, THE PATCHBOX CAVITY CAN BE BROUGHT TO FULL DEPTH. WITH THE LATCH INSTALLED, FILE THE NOTCH TO CATCH ON THE INNER SIDE OF THE BUTTPLATE, AS EXPLAINED IN THE TEXT.

6TH: ROUGH SHAPE THE END PLATE OF 1/16" THICK BRASS OR STEEL, GLUE TO THE END OF THE LID, DRILL AND INSTALL TWO WOOD SCREWS. CAREFULLY FILE TO FINAL FIT.

1/16"

IN CROSS-SECTION, SHOWING THE LATCH NOTCH

7TH: SHAPE AND DECORATE THE LID

Next, prepare the stock for the female dovetail. Draw in the limits of the dovetail on each side, which also are the limits of the patchbox cavity, and draw in the front end, which can be a straight cut, or a semi-circular cut. The width of the dovetail should be about 1/16 inch less at the front than at the butt-plate, which helps keep the lid from jamming if the wood swells in damp weather. If the taper is much more than this, the lid may fall out when slid back only a little distance. The depth of the dovetail may be between 5/32 and ¼ inch, and in part is dependent upon the amount of inner butt-plate surface lying in contact with the wood in the region of the cut. If the contact zone is but 1/8 inch wide, then a cut to ¼ inch depth would expose a gap or hole. This could, of course, be filled with a brass shim soldered to the inside of the butt-plate. The dovetail angle can be anywhere between 45° and 70°, and although a 45° angle is often used today, a 60° angle probably is preferable, and easier to make.

Though it is possible to cut the patchbox cavity first, and then the dovetails, it is easier to cut the cavity first, only to the depth of the dovetails, then cut the dovetails. The flat surface of the shallow cavity serves as a guide for the undercutting. If a 60° dovetail angle is used, the cut can easily be trued up with the aid of the triangular file with one surface ground flat that was prepared for the barrel loop work. For added strength, make a transverse dovetail at the front, connecting the two side cuts.

With the dovetail in the stock prepared, the patchbox cavity can be deepened to its desired depth. A total depth of 1 inch is adequate. Leave about ½ inch of wood next to the butt-plate. It is possible to do the initial cutting with a brace and bit, as was done in the old days. This can provide rounded ends for the cavity. However, the bits used for such work always had a very small centering spike at their front ends, rather than the large screw usually present on modern bits. But, the cavity can be cut with chisels. On old American rifles the cavity almost always was made with a flat bottom, and the work was neatly done. In contrast, patchbox cavities on 18th century rifles usually had curved bottoms, and on even the finest pieces the workmanship was casual and crude.

The patchbox lid can be made from one piece of wood, or two pieces glued together. Both methods were used in the old days. The two-piece lid is easier to make, and in general provides a better fitting dovetail joint. Quarter-sawn wood is preferable for both parts, as it will minimize warping problems.

To make a two-piece lid, first make the dovetail base, using a piece of wood about ¼ inch thicker than the depth of the dovetail in the stock. Plane one side flat and finish to a smooth surface with fine sandpaper. The upper surface can be left rough, as it will be trimmed away later. Make the base about ½ inch longer at the rear than the length of the dovetail slots. Start with the width of the base a little greater than the width of the mortise. Gradually work the base into the mortise by cut-and-try. Thin carbon paper placed in the joints may help locate high spots.

When the base is finally installed, carefully scribe around it, and cut away the excess wood lying above the level of the stock. This can be done most easily with the base held in the stock, but great care must be taken to avoid cutting the flat surface of the stock surrounding the base piece. A single layer of masking tape is a help in protecting the wood from accidental cuts. For the final fitting, the top surface of the base should be flush with and in the same plane as the flat surface of stock that surrounds it.

Having chosen an appropriate piece of wood for the top of the lid, cut it to be a slab about ½ inch thick, with reasonably smooth surfaces. Lay out the pattern of the lid, and then cut it out, keeping the cut line about 1/8 inch outside the pattern line. Leave about 1 inch of extra wood at the rear end. Then smooth the bottom to a fine finish.

To fasten the pieces together, first mark centerlines on both pieces, and guide lines to determine relative fore-and-aft positioning. To help the glue hold on the finely sanded surfaces, score both surfaces in the area of contact by making a series of light transverse cuts with a sharp knife. Then apply glue, spreading it evenly over the entire surface of the base, and clamp together, being sure that the guide lines match up. Epoxy glue may be used, and also Titebond® II glue. In the 18th century, hide glue was used for purposes such as this, and it has stood the test of two or three hundred years, so it must be suitable also if one can buy the equivalent today. When the glue is dry, cut away excess glue squeezed out at the edge of the joint, and make any small adjustments needed for a
final fit of the lid to the mortise.

The rear face of the lid is normally backed by a piece of brass which should be comparable in thickness to that of the butt-plate near its edge, i.e. about 1/16 inch, so use a piece of 1/16 inch sheet brass. With the lid in the stock and full forward, carefully cut off the tail of the lid flush with the surface of the butt-plate. Then slide the lid out exactly 1/16 inch, so use a piece of 1/16 inch sheet brass. With the lid in the stock and full forward, carefully cut off the tail of the lid flush with the surface of the butt-plate. Then slide the lid out exactly 1/16 inch and clamp it in place, and trim the rear end again, to be flush with the surface of the butt-plate. Remove the lid, and cut out a piece of the brass the same shape as the end, but about 1/16 inch oversize all around. Make certain that the surface of the brass fits tightly to the wood around its edges. With some 5-minute epoxy, glue the plate to the wood. Drill and countersink for two # 4 steel wood screws. Heat the end plate a little, and knock it off. Scrape away the epoxy and fasten it in place again with the screws. Adjust the screws or the counter-sinking so that the screw slots end up parallel with the base plane of the lid. File away excess metal so that the end plate fits snugly in its cut-out in the butt-plate, and trim the top to conform with the wood. File the surface of the plate so that it conforms with the surrounding part of the butt-plate.

The next operation is to shape the top surface of the lid. Most lids are thicker at the rear end than at the front. The thickness at the rear, excluding the dovetail base, may be as much as 7/16 inch, though this probably is thicker than necessary, and 3/8 or possibly even 5/16 may be better. The thick-ness of the lid near the front end, just ahead of the dovetail base, should be at least 3/16 inch, and pref-erably about ¼ inch thick. Wood that is too thin here is subject to breakage, and practicality must pre-cede aesthetics. If the lid is to have lengthwise moulding, beads, or flutes, work these in, though final finishing of them will have to be done after the metal end plate is installed. The excess wood at the rear of the lid will aid in keeping these linear elements straight at the rear end of the lid.

The latch is next made. This is a piece of steel, preferably spring stock, 1/8 inch thick, ¼ inch wide, and 1 ½ to 2 ½ inches long. However, at the rear end there is extra width needed to form the up-turned head that extends outside of the lid, so the metal there should be about 5/16 inch wide for the last ¼ inch. First, forge the turned-up head by placing the strip in the vise so that the widened end protrudes about ¼ inch, heat with a torch, and peen over for a 90° bend. Heat again and peen out the edges to end up with a blob about 7/16 inch wide, ¼ inch high, and 3/32 inch thick, which is large enough for any head. Shape the head however you wish, but leave it as wide as possible along the bottom edge for the finger to grab.

Next, heat the front end of the piece and peen it to reduce the thickness in a tapering fashion to about 1/16 inch. Drill and countersink the end for a # 4 flat-head wood screw, and trim the width back to ¼ inch except around the screw where a bit of extra metal is needed.

Fasten the spring to the underside of the lid with a screw, and then with the knife cut around the edges to begin the inletting. Let the spring in so that its surface is flush with the surface of the wood. A notch will have to be cut in the underside of the end plate about 1/16 inch deep, and the spring in this region can be reduced to 1/16 inch thickness by cutting away the underside to 1/16 inch thickness. The aim is to end up with a step on the underside of the spring that is 1/16 inch high, which catches on the edge of the butt-plate to hold the lid securely in place. The problem is to end up with the step in exactly the right place.

One solution is to deepen the mortise for the spring and to deepen the notch in the end plate, then determine where the edge of the butt-plate comes by coating the underside of the spring with transfer color and slowly pushing the lid into position in the stock. This is fine if the head is sufficiently high to hide the notch. As an alternative, the end plate could be removed temporarily. A small amount of wood will have to be removed on the stock between the butt-plate and the cavity, to allow for the latch. File the spring carefully, to end up with a latch that drops sharply over the edge of the butt-plate. There really is no need to heat-treat the spring as it has very little travel.

With the latch completed, the finishing details of the lid may be completed. Usually a sliding wood lid has a recess of some sort near the rear end to give the thumb a hold when the lid is to be re-moved. A touch of decorative carving could be in order, but it should be very simple and restrained.

When final finishing of the stock is being done, seal the lid and the female dovetails with two coats of sealer. Remove excess sealer from the dovetail slots with an old toothbrush. Keeping in mind that wood swells in humid weather, you may want to scrape or file the sides of the dovetails until there is a little bit of clearance between the mating parts. If the finished rifle is merely to be hung on the wall for admiration, you may want to provide a little clearance between the front end of the lid and the stock, so that the lid does not scrape off stock finish. On the other hand, if the rifle is to be carried through grass, brush, and trees while hunting, a tight fit at the front of the lid will minimize the catching of growing things there.

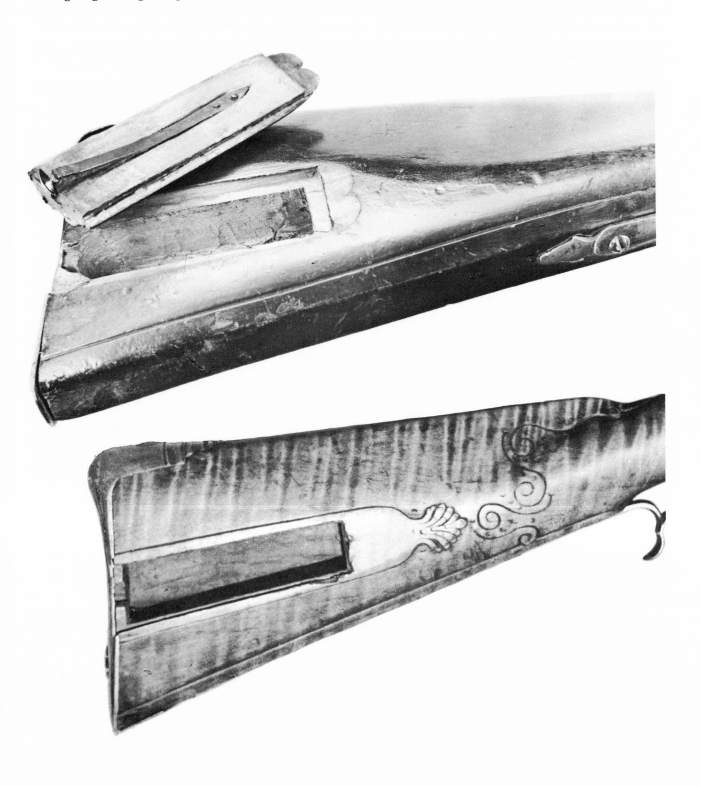

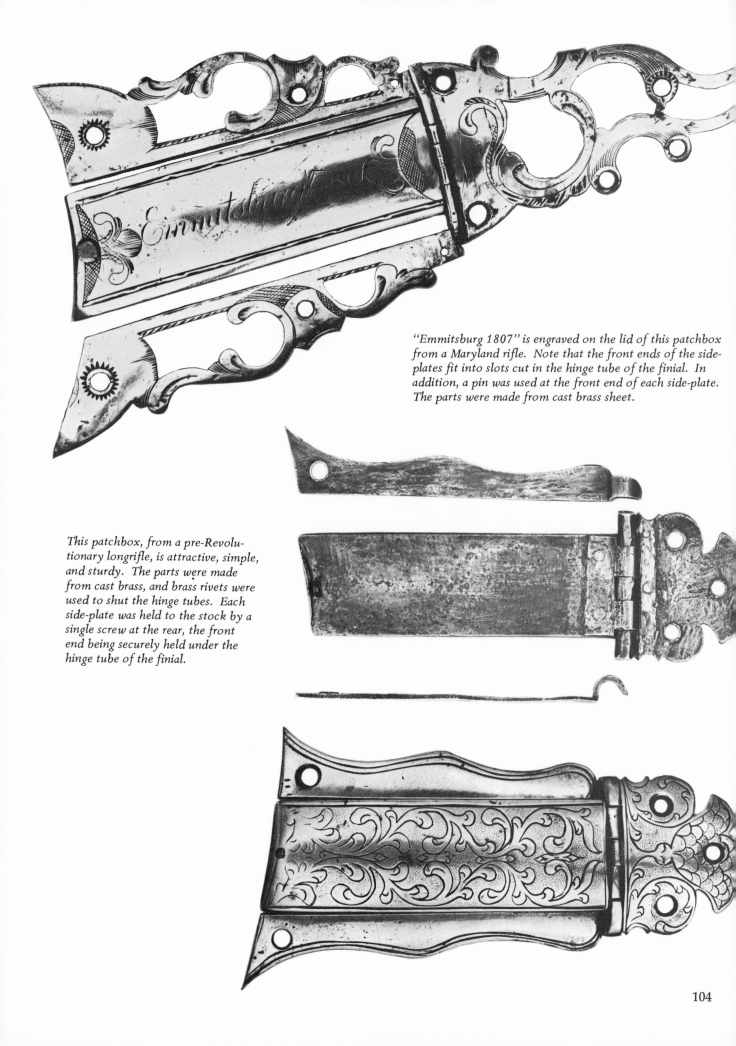

"Emmitsburg 1807" is engraved on the lid of this patchbox from a Maryland rifle. Note that the front ends of the side-plates fit into slots cut in the hinge tube of the finial. In addition, a pin was used at the front end of each side-plate. The parts were made from cast brass sheet.

This patchbox, from a pre-Revolutionary longrifle, is attractive, simple, and sturdy. The parts were made from cast brass, and brass rivets were used to shut the hinge tubes. Each side-plate was held to the stock by a single screw at the rear, the front end being securely held under the hinge tube of the finial.

CHAPTER 24

METAL PATCHBOX

The metal patchbox, with its hinged lid, appears to be primarily an American development. The sliding wood patchbox lid was used by gun stockers in the German lands through to the end of the percussion era. However, an extremely elaborately decorated garniture of arms made in the 1740s at Suhl in Germany by J. C. Stockmar includes a flintlock rifle with a side-opening metal patchbox lid. Other exceptions doubtless exist. In England in the late 18th century English-pattern trade rifles were made with hinged brass patchbox lids, but these were special products intended for the American market. And in the decades following the American Revolutionary War, a few English sporting arms were made with metal patchboxes.

The American metal patchbox came into use before the Revolutionary War, but it is not known where, when, or by whom it first was made. Sheet brass was not readily available, so the brass patchbox parts were made as sand castings, with a net thickness after smoothing and finishing of between 1/16 and 3/32 inch. Even the daisy finial patchboxes made in Birmingham, England, for use on trade rifles in the first quarter of the 19th century were made from castings. In the decades following the Revolution, sheet brass from Europe became available, and gunsmiths lost little time putting it to use, along with sheet silver, and then, during the 1830s, German silver. Today's rifle builder probably will use sheet brass for patchboxes, though one manufacturer introduced cast plates intended for patchbox use to the market in 1983, with a choice of yellow brass, or yellow bronze.

It is evident that the metal patchbox evolved from the wooden patchbox lid, for some of the earlier brass patchbox lids have domed surfaces resembling the wooden lid in size and shape. These patchboxes have a great deal of charm, and offer lots of opportunity for creativity. The high domed lids of early patchboxes were made as castings, the original pattern being carved out of wood or possibly hammered out of sheet lead.

From the design standpoint, the rectangular patchbox lid, with its prominent transverse hinge line at its front edge, is most awkward, and it is incompatible with all the other lines and designs of the rifle. And mechanically, it is not the best either. The side-opening patchbox, with its long hinge along the lower edge of the lid has a great design advantage over the standard rectangular lid. First of all, its sides can taper to conform with the profile of the butt. Secondly, the side-opening lid can have a rounded or curved front end which can be tied into a rococo design much more easily than the rectangular lid. But the side-opening patchboxes were mainly used by gunsmiths of northern Bucks County, Pennsylvania, near the southern edge of the Lehigh Valley, and occasionally in nearby regions. The well-known Lancaster, Pa. Gunsmith, Jacob Dickert, made a fine side-opening patchbox for one of his rifles, and so did the York County, Pa. Gunsmith, J. Lowmaster. The long hinge on the lower edge of the side-opening lid is tedious to make. But in spite of the design difficulties, the rectangular lid, hinged at the forward end, prevailed, and many very attractive patchboxes were made using them.

The traditional brass patchbox consists of four parts, the lid, the finial, the upper side-plate, and the lower side-plate. Patchboxes on many rifles from the Lehigh Valley of eastern Pennsylvania were made without side plates, but as far as lid, finial, hinge, and release are concerned, they are similar to the same parts on four-piece boxes.

A whole book could be written about the design of patchboxes, and many possibilities are shown in books illustrating old rifles. There is no room here to delve into the subject, and it is assumed that with paper, pencil, and the help of reference books, a suitable design can be worked out. Paper is cheap, and it is only reasonable to cut out patterns and try them on the stock. When a suitable overall design is achieved, work out all of the details, including the limits of the lid, the hinge, and the positions of the screws, which must be worked in with the engraved designs, and the engraving itself. If carved decoration is planned for the right side of the stock in front of the patchbox, design it while designing the patchbox.

The width of the lid and its hinge must be considered while designing the patchbox. For any

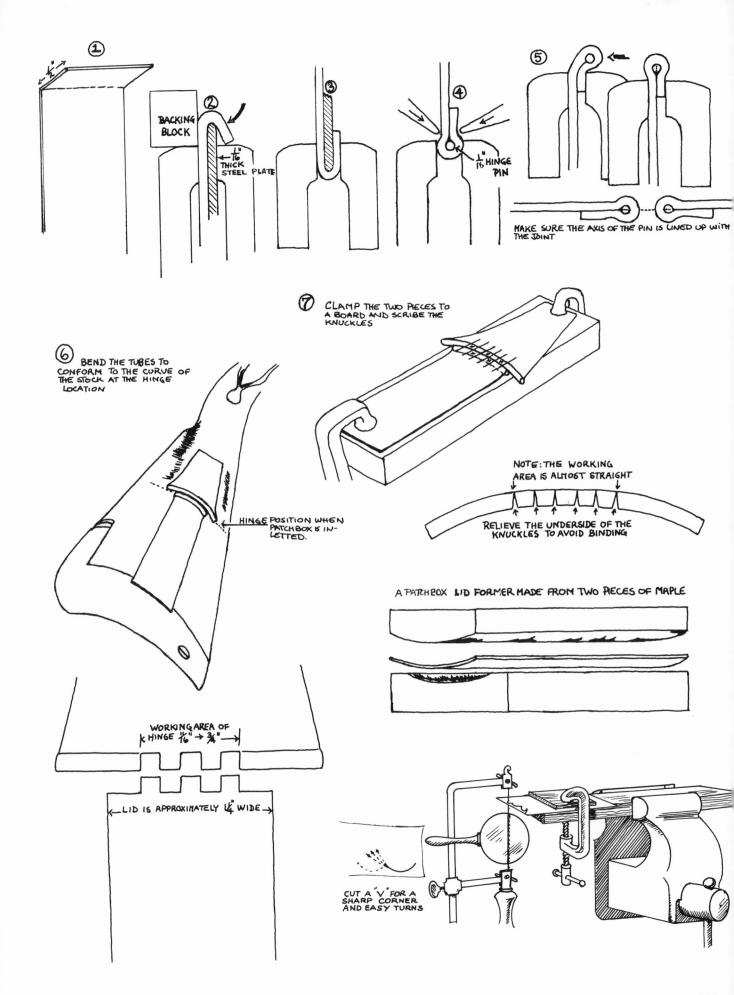

①

② BACKING BLOCK $\frac{1}{16}$" THICK STEEL PLATE

③

④ $\frac{1}{16}$" HINGE PIN

⑤ MAKE SURE THE AXIS OF THE PIN IS LINED UP WITH THE JOINT

⑥ BEND THE TUBES TO CONFORM TO THE CURVE OF THE STOCK AT THE HINGE LOCATION

HINGE POSITION WHEN PATCHBOX IS IN-LETTED.

WORKING AREA OF HINGE $\frac{7}{16}$" → $\frac{3}{4}$"

LID IS APPROXIMATELY $\frac{1}{4}$" WIDE

⑦ CLAMP THE TWO PIECES TO A BOARD AND SCRIBE THE KNUCKLES

NOTE: THE WORKING AREA IS ALMOST STRAIGHT

RELIEVE THE UNDERSIDE OF THE KNUCKLES TO AVOID BINDING

A PATCHBOX LID FORMER MADE FROM TWO PIECES OF MAPLE

CUT A "V" FOR A SHARP CORNER AND EASY TURNS

hinge to work properly, the axis of the pin must be straight. But the side of the stock where the patch-box is to be installed is curved. Somehow the hinge must be bent to fit the curved surface of the stock yet allow the hinge to function, so the working portion of the hinge must be kept as narrow as possible, and within this portion the hinge is straight. Traditional lids rarely exceed 1 ¼ inch width. If the hinge is planned so that it has no knuckles at its corners, and 2 or, at the most, 3 knuckles near its center, the working portion is reduced to about ¾ inch. The finial has 1 or 2 small knuckles at or near the center, bordered by 2 relatively long knuckles on either side which serve to hold the ends of the pin, but have no direct effect on the working portion of the hinge. Hence the traditional patchbox has 5 or 7 knuckles The 5-knuckle patchbox has 2 on the lid and 3 on the finial, while the 7-knuckle patchbox had 3 on the lid and 4 on the finial. The 7-knuckle patchbox takes more work but can make a neater job.

It is recommended that brass 1/16 inch thick be used for the lid and for the finial. The side plates can be made from stock 0.040 inch thick. Sheet brass usually has a minor "grain" as a result of the rolling process that produced it. If possible, lay out the designs with their long dimensions parallel with the grain. Cut out the lid, somewhat oversize, leaving lots of extra metal around the pattern out-line, and ½ inch of extra metal for the hinge tab. Do not bother cutting the outline of the pattern, just in case the hinge making turns out poorly and it becomes necessary to shift the pattern and start over. Anneal both parts.

The patchbox hinge requires care in its construction. The process consists of making a tube on one end of both lid and finial by bending over the ½ inch long tabs, and shutting the joints with silver solder. First, scribe a line ½ inch from the end of each piece to mark the bend lines. On the reverse side use fine abrasive paper to help prepare the surface to take the silver solder. Place each ½ inch long tab in the vise and bend to a 90° angle. To complete the bending, take a rectangular piece of steel about 1 x 2 inches in size and 1/16 inch thick, and round off one long edge to a semicircular profile. Clamp the steel piece tightly into the corner of the 90° bend, using the vise, and with a hammer and a metal backing block, bend the tab down all the way, using the vise jaws to complete the job.

The hinge pin is best made from a piece of 1/16 inch drill rod. Make a working pin from this drill rod that is about 2 inches longer than the length of the hinge. Remove the steel bending plate, and re-place it with the hinge pin. Clamp the assembly in the vise so that just the portion containing the pin is above the level of the jaws, forcing the jaws to close further around the pin. It may be necessary to remove the assembly from the vise, open the vise jaws to about 3/16 inch, and with the tube laid in the opening, close the joint further with the help of a dull cold chisel. After that, if necessary, with just the tube portion sticking out of the vise, hammer on one side or the other with a wood block placed against the brass, to line up the axis of the pin with the joint between the brass pieces. Now, remove the pin and shut the joint with silver solder. If the hole gets partially filled with solder, drill it out.

Old time gunsmiths often shut the hinge joints with small brass rivets, and sometimes used cop-per or even iron in place of brass. This certainly is an appropriate alternative to silver solder.

Next, remove the pin and, with a jeweler's saw, cut out the sections somewhat within the scribed lines. To fit the hinge together is a matter of using transfer color, needle files, and a great deal of pa-tience. When the two sides begin to mesh, try the hinge pin so that the slots are not cut too deep. A little oil on the pin will help. The job is done when the pin passes through the knuckles and the hinge works smoothly. If it tends to be stiff, remove the pin and relieve the underside of the knuckles. Any gaps in the top of the knuckles can be peened closed with light taps of a hammer. Finally, file the hinge smooth, and polish with abrasive paper. The neatness of the patchbox is a good test of your pa-tience and craftsmanship.

Now the finial may be brought to final shape, first by cutting out the paper pattern, and gluing it in place on the brass with white glue, then engraving close to the paper outline. The pattern is re-moved, and the brass brought to shape with jeweler's saw and needle files. Don't forget the small bevel on all edges.

Patchbox lids usually have a convex shape, which adds to their stiffness. A simple way to bend the lid to the desired shape is to make forms of hard maple, one convex and one concave, and to bend the brass to shape by clamping between them. The result is a lid free from kinks that otherwise might result if it were bent with simpler tools. However, if only one patchbox lid is to be made, a satisfactory result can be obtained by laying the brass on a piece of soft white pine or other wood, laying a piece of pipe 2 to 3 inches in diameter on top of the brass, and striking the pipe with a hammer.

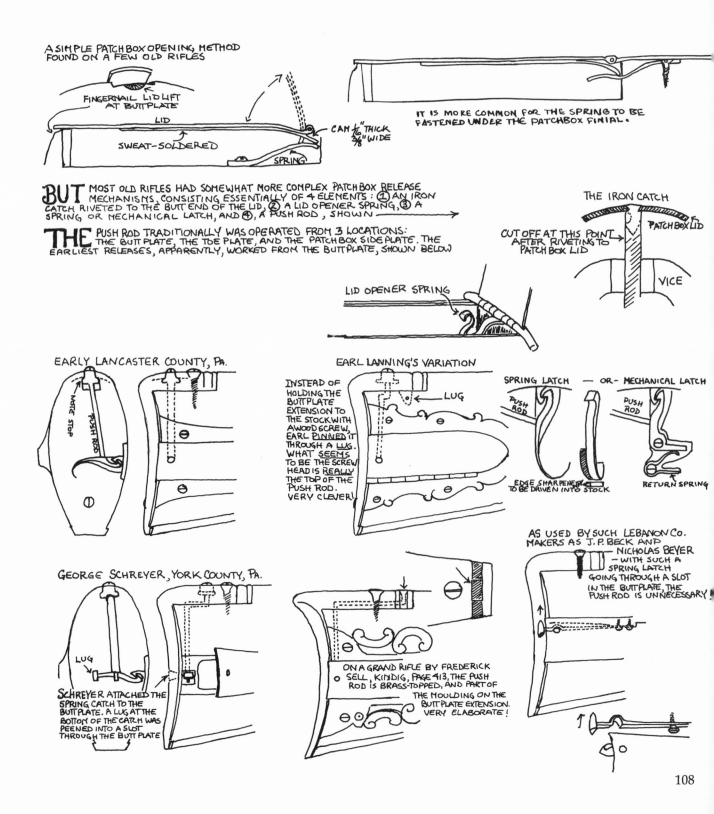

A SIMPLE PATCHBOX OPENING METHOD FOUND ON A FEW OLD RIFLES

FINGERNAIL LID LIFT AT BUTTPLATE

LID

SWEAT-SOLDERED

CAM 1/16" THICK 3/8" WIDE

SPRING

IT IS MORE COMMON FOR THE SPRING TO BE FASTENED UNDER THE PATCHBOX FINIAL.

BUT MOST OLD RIFLES HAD SOMEWHAT MORE COMPLEX PATCHBOX RELEASE MECHANISMS, CONSISTING ESSENTIALLY OF 4 ELEMENTS: ① AN IRON CATCH RIVETED TO THE BUTT END OF THE LID, ② A LID OPENER SPRING, ③ A SPRING OR MECHANICAL LATCH, AND ④, A PUSH ROD, SHOWN ⟶

THE PUSH ROD TRADITIONALLY WAS OPERATED FROM 3 LOCATIONS: THE BUTTPLATE, THE TOE PLATE, AND THE PATCHBOX SIDE PLATE. THE EARLIEST RELEASES, APPARENTLY, WORKED FROM THE BUTTPLATE, SHOWN BELOW

THE IRON CATCH

CUT OFF AT THIS POINT AFTER RIVETING TO PATCH BOX LID

PATCHBOX LID

VICE

LID OPENER SPRING

EARLY LANCASTER COUNTY, PA.

NOTE STOP

PUSH ROD

EARL LANNING'S VARIATION

INSTEAD OF HOLDING THE BUTTPLATE EXTENSION TO THE STOCK WITH A WOOD SCREW, EARL PINNED IT THROUGH A LUG. WHAT SEEMS TO BE THE SCREW HEAD IS REALLY THE TOP OF THE PUSH ROD. VERY CLEVER!

LUG

SPRING LATCH — OR- MECHANICAL LATCH

PUSH ROD

PUSH ROD

EDGE SHARPENED TO BE DRIVEN INTO STOCK

RETURN SPRING

GEORGE SCHREYER, YORK COUNTY, PA.

LUG

SCHREYER ATTACHED THE SPRING CATCH TO THE BUTTPLATE. A LUG AT THE BOTTOM OF THE CATCH WAS PEENED INTO A SLOT THROUGH THE BUTT PLATE

ON A GRAND RIFLE BY FREDERICK SELL, KINDIG, PAGE 413, THE PUSH ROD IS BRASS-TOPPED, AND PART OF THE MOULDING ON THE BUTT PLATE EXTENSION. VERY ELABORATE!

AS USED BY SUCH LEBANON Co. MAKERS AS J. P. BECK AND NICHOLAS BEYER — WITH SUCH A SPRING LATCH GOING THROUGH A SLOT IN THE BUTTPLATE, THE PUSH ROD IS UNNECESSARY!

CHAPTER 25

INSTALLING THE PATCHBOX AND RELEASE MECHANISM

A great variety of different patchbox lid catches and release mechanisms are found on old rifles, ranging from simple and adequate, to elaborate beyond necessity. Some schools of gunsmithing favored a particular method, and if your rifle were styled to one of these schools, it would be well to stick to tradition. But no matter what kind of mechanism is chosen, it must be planned out before the patchbox is installed, so that allowances can be made for it, if necessary. With catch and release mechanism planned out, the general procedure is to let in the finial and lid, make and install the side plates, and then install the catch and release mechanism.

Before starting the inletting of the patchbox, the butt-stock should be completely shaped, including all mouldings. The relief carving ahead of the finial, if there is to be any, also could be done before inletting the patchbox, but it can just as well be drawn in by pencil, and executed later. To begin the inletting, drill holes in the finial for the screws, and countersink partially. Use relatively small flat-head wood screws of steel, not brass. In the old days, all screws were hand made of iron, and no one even thought of using such a soft metal as brass for their production. Screws are the only really satisfactory method of holding the patchbox parts in place on a stock, though in the old days brass or iron pins or nails sometimes were used to advantage. Even under the best circumstances, screw heads do not add to the appearance of the brass inlays, so it is desirable to keep the visible parts to a minimum size. Also, note that the machine-made flat-head screw of today is noticeably different in external appearance from the hand made screw, with its narrow slot and slightly domed exterior.

The screws initially used to hold the patchbox in place should be considered as try-screws. They will be turned in and removed many times before everything is done, so their surfaces may end up showing signs of much use, and the holes in the wood where they fit may end up a bit enlarged. If try-screws are used that are one size smaller than the intended finish screw, a tight fit will be assured. A ½ inch length is sufficient for both screws.

Screws ranging in size from # 2 to # 8 may be suitable for use on patchboxes. Some highly regarded old gunsmiths, like John Armstrong, and the real screw nut, George Eister, used different sizes of hand-made screws on the same patchboxes. However, these are not typical cases. It may work well to begin with a # 5 try-screw and to finish with a # 6 screw. However, be sure not to countersink the try-screw to full depth in the brass.

It is easy to alter the modern screw head to resemble the old screws. Chuck the screw in an electric drill, drill press, or lathe, and as it turns, file away the top of the head almost to the bottom of the slot, leaving the tip slightly domed. Polish the head with some fine abrasive paper, and remove from the chuck. Re-cut the slot, using a sharply V-shaped, or knife-edge needle file. Screw slots were made this way in the old days. To finish the screw later, it can be browned, dipped in cold blue, or colored by heating to redness with a propane torch. It is suggested that the heads of the try-screws be reduced in height slightly, but left flat, and that the slots in them be deepened slightly. This will allow them to be fitted flush with the metal surface while the patchbox is being worked on.

To start the inletting, position the patchbox on the stock, and draw the outline of the finial and lid on the stock. The wood area that will underlie the lid should first be made flat, from hinge line to butt-plate. Bend the finial to conform roughly to the curve of the stock. Mark the position of the forward screw hole, and drill it. This forward screw often lies on or close to the centerline of the patchbox, and it serves as a pivot point for establishing the final position of the patchbox. After making the final determination of position, snug down the forward screw and mark the position of the other two screws. Carefully make punch marks at the centers for the other screws, and drill them for the try-screws, being sure to drill the holes perpendicular to the plate at the location of the holes. Turn in the screws snugly.

The hinge at this stage prevents the finial and lid from lying on the surface of the stock. Carefully remove wood from under the hinge until the finial and lid lie on the surface of the wood. If necessary, bend the finial further, to better conform to the curve of the stock. Then scribe all around the finial with a very sharp knife, including all piercings, if any, making the initial cut at a slight angle, similar to the small bevel on the edge of the metal, or even a bit more. If this initial cut is made carefully, and reasonably deep, it will help insure a good finished job. Then with chisels and knives gradually let in the finial. Use lots of transfer color, and care. When the finial is inletted flush with the wood, or slightly below the surface, there may be small parts still too high. Additional bending may be necessary, but in any case, the whole finial can be filed flush with the surface of the wood.

The lid is inletted in the same manner as the tang of the rear ramrod pipe, by scribing and by removing no more wood than the lid touches as it drops into place. To save some work, the patchbox cavity can be cut out roughly at this point. Allow at least ¾ inch between the cavity and the butt-plate. The sides of the opening should be at least 1/8 inch inside the limits of the lid, though for now it would be best to allow ¼ inch there, assuming that the cavity will be rectangular in shape. A cavity depth of ¾ inch is sufficient. An excessively deep cavity would weaken the stock. Patchbox cavities on old rifles often were made with the help of a brace and bit, which gave nicely rounded ends to the cavity. However, the brace bits that were used had a very small spike at the center instead of a large screw, and the little knife-like fin at the outer edge of the cutting surface was very small also. It is possible to use a sharp spade bit in a drill press for this cutting, provided that the center spike is reduced to a small size. Practice on some blocks of scrap wood.

As inletting of the lid proceeds, eventually the lid will come to lie against the edge of the butt-plate. Furthermore, the domed lid will not lie in conformity with the edge of the butt-plate, which is only slightly curved. Lids traditionally overlap the edge of the butt-plate. There are two choices for fitting the lid to the butt-plate. One is to lightly hammer the end of the lid against the edge of the butt-plate until it conforms. In this case the overall width of the lid will have been increased slightly by the straightening, and it will have to be filed back to uniform width. The other choice is to file the edge of the butt-plate to match the shape of the lid. In either case, there is a notch in the butt-plate where the end of the lid lies. A well-domed lid might even have a fillet of brass fastened at the end with silver solder.

With the lid and finial inletted, the upper and lower side plates can be made and let in. Paper patterns, or sheet aluminum patterns will help. Make sure of a good fit against the side of the lid, and start with the pieces about 1/16 inch extra long on each end, to ensure a tight fit against butt-plate and hinge. As with the patchbox finial, the pattern is drawn with the piercings, if any, screw holes, and engraving. If a paper pattern is used, glue it to the sheet brass of 0.040 inch thickness, run the engraver around the edge of the pattern, and then cut out the brass with the jeweler's saw, and bring to final shape with files, including the small bevel on the outer edge for inletting.

To inlet the side plates, proceed as with any other inlay. Place the plate in position and drill the stock for the screws. Fasten the plates with try-screws. Mark the ends for trimming, remove the plates from the stock, and cut the ends for a good tight fit. A slight bit of bending will be necessary to make the plate conform to the curvature of the stock. With the plates lying on the stock, cut in the outlines and proceed with the inletting. Remember, however, that with the lid up the joint between metal and wood will be visible along the inner edges of the side plates, so it should be made with appropriate care.

The catch to hold the lid closed, and its release mechanism, are now installed. These lid mechanisms were made a number of different ways on old rifles, ranging from simple to unnecessarily complicated. One of the most complicated methods involves a push rod that runs beneath the upper side plate. It is activated by pushing the uppermost portion of the patchbox hinge toward the butt-plate. Actually this portion of the hinge is not part of the hinge at all, but it appears to be.

One of the simplest mechanisms of all, and one found on some old rifles, involves a cam that works against a spring to hold the lid closed, or open. The cam is a piece of steel about 1/16 inch thick and 3/8 inch wide, fastened under the lid by rivets of brass or iron, or with soft or silver solder. The other end of the piece projects under the hinge, where the wood is cut away for it. A simple flat spring of appropriate shape is screwed to the bottom of the cavity so that one end of it pushes against the cam. To aid in opening the lid, a small concavity is filed into the butt-plate where it is overlapped by the lid.

Simple and adequate though the above method is, old rifles more often have a more complicated mechanism. This involves an iron catch fastened to the inside of the lid about ¼ inch in front of the butt plate. A spring-loaded latch holds this in place until released by a push rod activated by a button in the toe-plate or by a button on the top of the stock in the extension or tang of the butt-plate. It was usual to have a spring mounted under the finial with an end protruding that worked against the lid and kept it partially open when the catch was released.

In another variation, often used by the gunsmiths of Lebanon, Pennsylvania, the catch was held in place by a spring fastened at one end to the stock, and having its other end terminate at a stud on the outside of the butt-plate. Old-time gunsmiths seemed to take delight in concealing the patchbox release mechanism, using ingenious schemes that provided outlets for creativity. The rear end of the upper side plate of the patchbox might press in to provide the release. A silver inlay set in the brass side plate might be a release button. Release buttons often appear in toe-plates, disguised as screws, or inlays. Or part of the toe plate may push in to make the release.

One of the release mechanisms widely used in the old days had a vertical push rod connected to a button that protruded through the butt-plate extension. A clever variation of this features a button on top of the butt-plate extension which has the appearance of being the screw that attaches the butt-plate to the stock. The butt-plate extension however, is held to the stock by means of a lug at its front end and a pin through the stock.

To make a catch and release mechanism involving a vertical push rod activated either from above or below, begin by making the catch and attaching it to the lid. The catch is made from a piece of ¼ inch diameter rod about 2 inches long. Turn the shank that will extend through the patchbox lid and be riveted in place. The latch usually is located along the centerline of the lid and the hole center is about ¼ or 5/16 inch in from the end of the lid. Clamp the lid shut, and with a 1/8 inch diameter drill, drill through the lid and into the wood below a sufficient distance for the catch. Lift the lid and enlarge the hole in the wood to ¼ inch diameter. Countersink the hole in the lid slightly, and rivet the catch to the lid, afterward filing the rivet flush with the surface of the lid. The patchbox will have to be removed from the stock for this riveting. After the riveting is done, the excess rod material can be cut off, leaving the catch initially about ¾ inch long.

The traditional latch is made from a piece of spring steel about ¼ inch wide, 3/16 inch thick, and about 2 inches long. One end is tapered to a thinness of about 1/32 inch and one edge is sharpened. This end is curled and it is driven into the wood to hold the latch in place. With the butt-plate removed, a mortise must be cut in the wood to accommodate the catch and latch combination. Before final installation, the spring must be polished, hardened, and tempered, like any spring.

The push rod merits some consideration. The button that protrudes through the butt-plate extension, or the toe-plate, may be a separate piece that pushes against the push rod, or it may be the end of the rod, or something fastened to the end of the rod. In any case, there has to be an enlarged portion of the rod behind the butt-plate or toe-plate, to keep the rod from falling out. The push rod can have a diameter between 1/8 inch and ¼ inch. The axis of the push rod does not lie along the central plane of the butt. It starts along the centerline of the butt-plate extension or toe-plate, but it goes off at an angle to meet the catch a short distance from the lid. Thus, if the push rod emerges from the butt-plate or toe-plate, it does so at an angle. If the end of the rod is used as the button, this emergence angle will not be noticed if the end of the button is domed and does not protrude very far. The hole in the stock for the push rod must be drilled with the aid of eye-ball alignment. It may be worthwhile to use a drill press for this work but this calls for being able to clamp the butt-stock at the appropriate angle.

To make notches in the latch and the catch that meet correctly, the notch is first made in the latch, and this must be done before the spring is hardened, tempered, and driven into place. With the butt plate removed it is possible to observe the relative position of the two pieces, and to file the notch in the catch accordingly. Alternatively, transfer color may be put on the catch, and the catch carefully pushed down so that the edge of the latch removes the color up to the point where the notch is to be made.

PUSH RODS IN THE TOE PLATE

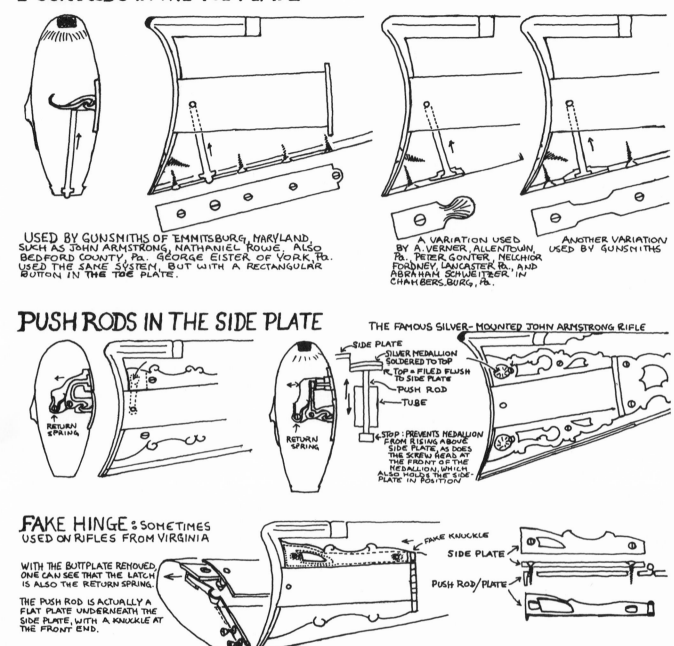

USED BY GUNSMITHS OF EMMITSBURG, MARYLAND, SUCH AS JOHN ARMSTRONG, NATHANIEL ROWE. ALSO BEDFORD COUNTY, Pa. GEORGE EISTER OF YORK, Pa. USED THE SAME SYSTEM, BUT WITH A RECTANGULAR BUTTON IN THE TOE PLATE.

A VARIATION USED BY A. VERNER, ALLENTOWN, Pa., PETER GONTER, MELCHIOR FORDNEY, LANCASTER Pa., AND ABRAHAM SCHWEITZER IN CHAMBERSBURG, Pa.

ANOTHER VARIATION USED BY GUNSMITHS

PUSH RODS IN THE SIDE PLATE

THE FAMOUS SILVER-MOUNTED JOHN ARMSTRONG RIFLE

RETURN SPRING

RETURN SPRING

SIDE PLATE
SILVER MEDALLION SOLDERED TO TOP
R TOP = FILED FLUSH TO SIDE PLATE
PUSH ROD
TUBE
STOP: PREVENTS MEDALLION FROM RISING ABOVE SIDE PLATE, AS DOES THE SCREW HEAD AT THE FRONT OF THE MEDALLION, WHICH ALSO HOLDS THE SIDE-PLATE IN POSITION

FAKE HINGE: SOMETIMES USED ON RIFLES FROM VIRGINIA

WITH THE BUTTPLATE REMOVED, ONE CAN SEE THAT THE LATCH IS ALSO THE RETURN SPRING.

THE PUSH ROD IS ACTUALLY A FLAT PLATE UNDERNEATH THE SIDE PLATE, WITH A KNUCKLE AT THE FRONT END.

FAKE KNUCKLE
SIDE PLATE
PUSH ROD/PLATE

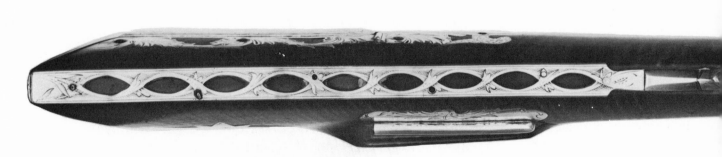

This beautiful toe-plate is on a rifle made in Salem, North Carolina, by John Vogler, who was a silversmith and gunsmith. All of the inlays on this rifle as well as the furniture are made of silver. This is an example of how far one can go with a toe-plate, and a piece this elaborate is not recommended for the beginner.

CHAPTER 26

TOE – PLATE

The toe-plate is a functional inlay that serves to protect the toe of the butt-stock, which is vulnerable to chipping and cracking as a result of blows on the toe of the butt-plate. It serves a secondary purpose in helping to protect the lower edge of the butt from being dented, and a tertiary purpose in being a place to locate the patchbox release button. It also serves as an attractive and decorative inlay, or it can be if designed with that in mind.

If a toe-plate really is to serve the first mentioned purpose, that of protecting the toe of the butt from chipping and cracking, then it must be made of heavy metal and fastened so that it can do its intended job. It should be made of brass about 1/8 inch thick, or steel 3/32 inch thick, with the rearmost fastening screw threaded into a metal lug silver-soldered to the toe of the butt-plate.

But toe-plates are not normally made and fastened this way. Typically, the toe-plate is made from sheet brass 1/16 inch thick. In its simplest form it extends forward of the butt-plate for about 2 inches, and has a square-cut front end. In its most elaborate form the toe-plate may extend the full length of the butt, ending at the rear trigger-guard finial. Some full length toe-plates on southern rifles feature piercings filled with silver. Typical toe-plates on Pennsylvania rifles are made of brass, have a length between 2 and 4 inches, carry a small amount of decorative engraving, and terminate in a decorative finial. Some finial designs were characteristic of particular schools of gunsmithing. In particular, the gunsmiths of Berks County, and the nearby Lehigh Valley of eastern Pennsylvania, often used toe-plate designs that somewhat resembled the patchbox finials used in their respective regions.

The toe-plate is a fine place for decoration, and the beginner can go to town here without being pretentious. Toe-plates can be fastened with pins, but screws are better, and more frequently used. Screws help if there is need to remove the toe-plate, such as a need to work on a patchbox release mechanism. Brass of 1/16 inch thickness is best to use, for anything thinner would be easily subject to denting on the edge. If the toe-plate is removable, it can be engraved off of the rifle, which is an advantage.

In making the toe-plate, cut a piece of brass at least 1/8 inch wider than the wood where it will fit. In fitting the toe-plate it is critical that the wood surface against which it lies is perfectly flat, and that the edges are good and sharp, for here the wood-to-metal fit will show. Ideally, one would like to make a good initial cut in the wood on the sides of the stock just a little less than 1/16 inch below the uncut surface of the underside of the stock. Why not do it? Make a cutting guide by soldering a straight-edged strip of brass or steel 1/16 inch thick and about ¼ inch wide at the edge of a larger piece of metal. Hold the guide firmly against the lower side of the stock and first make a very light test scratch, and then the cut. As an alternative, take a piece of steel about 1/8 inch thick and about 1 ½ by 2 inches in size, and with a single screw fasten a small cutter to one corner of the plate, the cutter being shaped or shimmed out so that the cutting edge is at the desired distance from the plate. An old Exacto knife blade with a re-shaped point could serve well.

The placement of the screws holding the toe-plate to the stock deserves some consideration. Be careful that the rear screw does not touch the toe of the butt-plate. If the push rod that releases the patchbox lid is to protrude through the toe-plate, its position already is determined, and the screws will have to be positioned on either side of it. Finally, it is a neat and traditional touch to have the slots of the screws aligned with the centerline of the butt. Steel flathead wood screws, # 4 size, work well.

Brass toe-plate on a rifle made by Jacob Kunz in Lehigh Valley (Pa.) style about 1810. Between the screws is a rectangular horn button that is the patchbox release.

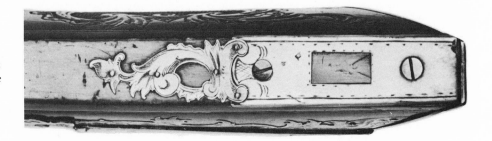

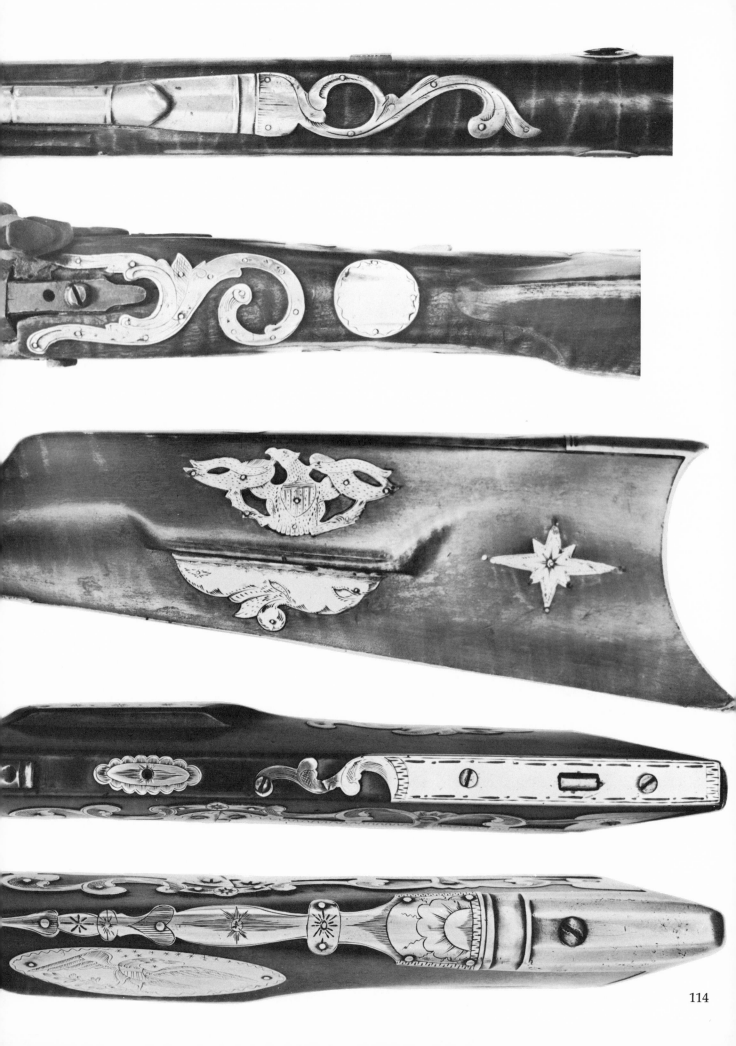

CHAPTER 27

INLAYS

Some inlays that are put on rifles serve no function other than as decoration. Others serve useful purposes, and their decorative purposes are secondary. The patchbox falls into the category of a functional inlay, but because of its size and complexity, has been treated separately. The side-plate opposite the lock is a functional inlay, as is the toe-plate. Fore-stock escutcheons for the barrel wedges are functional, as is an inlay under the cheek-piece if it is made to hold a touch-hole pick. And sometimes plates are put on the lower fore-stock between the rear ramrod pipe and the front of the trigger-guard finial, to protect the wood if it is thin, or broken. Most other inlays, including a thumb-piece atop the wrist, a cheek-piece inlay, and a comb-plate are not functional and serve only as decoration.

A rifle is not necessarily made more beautiful by the addition of inlays. In the old days, particularly in the twenty-year period following the American Revolution, many beautiful rifles were made with no decorative inlays, and with functional pieces such as side-plate, patchbox, and toe-plate kept to a minimum. It is the architecture –the flowing lines and curves which carry the eye from one region to another, from butt-plate to muzzle, that make a rifle beautiful. Inlays only enhance the beauty of the architecture. A stock of poor design and architecture cannot be improved with the addition of inlays. In one sense it might be advisable for the beginner to avoid decorative inlays on the first rifle. But on the other hand, by the time a beginner has installed the working parts of the rifle and the functional inlays, a decorative inlay or two should not be difficult to make and install.

To be effective as decoration, inlays need to be engraved. In the old days, most gunsmiths who used decorative inlays put engraving on them, at least in Pennsylvania where these gunsmiths usually went through some sort of apprenticeship that included training in engraving. The outstanding exception was in the upper Susquehanna River Valley, north of Harrisburg, where inlays without engraving were used in abundance. Unengraved inlays are fairly often found on rifles made in the 1830s, 1840s, and 1850s in the Mid-west. However, it can be stated as a general rule of longrifle making that all inlays should be engraved. This does not include the muzzle-cap, although some old gunsmiths did engrave or otherwise decorate their caps.

So, take a good critical look at your rifle at this stage and ask yourself just what inlays your rifle really needs to enhance your work so far. There is a traditional balance between rich and gaudy, which old Polonius explains to his son in Shakespeare's HAMLET. And there is a fine line between the two, which if followed, can lead toward classic works of art.

As with the functional inlays, design the inlays on paper, including pin holes for fastening, and engraving lines, and then make try patterns of stiff paper. Glue the pattern to the sheet stock, and with graver and chasing hammer, chase the outline of the pattern, including piercings if any, and then after removing the paper, cut out the design. File the edges to finished shape, putting on the usual slight bevel to help ensure a tight fit.

The main problem with inlays is holding them in place against the stock while cutting in the lines. Decorative inlays are usually pinned to the stock instead of being fastened with wood screws. And for the initial holding it is best to use some thin steel brads, smaller than the finished pins, preferably 18 or 20 gauge size.

Traditionally, decorative inlays chiefly were made from brass and silver, though occasionally iron and copper were used. In some situations other materials were used too, such as ivory, bone, mother-of-pearl, pewter, ebony, and other woods. Only in the 1830s did German silver, sometimes called electrum, appear on rifles. German silver is suitable for use on rifles styled to the very end of the flintlock period, i.e. the 1830s, and the percussion era, but it is completely inappropriate as a substitute for sterling or coin silver on a flintlock rifle of the Golden Age. Sterling silver is relatively inexpensive for the small quantities needed to make rifle inlays.

Usually inlays are made of sheet metal thin enough that bending the piece to fit the curve of the stock is not a problem. If the metal is too thin, however, it dents easily, and dimples when fastening pins are driven in to hold it in place. Furthermore, if a very thin inlay is further reduced in thickness as it is filed to lie flush with the stock, it may be too thin to engrave. In sheet silver, 22 gauge (0.029 inch thick) is a good minimum thickness to work with. The cost savings in using thinner material are not significant. Sheet brass is stronger than silver, but 22 gauge is a reasonable minimum thickness to use for this also.

The inletting of decorative inlays is little different from the inletting of the patchbox and side-plate, though the depth of the cut is less. Transfer color will help in locating high spots. Where the curvature of the wood is extreme, as on the top of the comb, under the fore-stock, or along the sides of the fore-stock, problems of lateral displacement arise. If the inlay is large, and particularly if it is pierced, it may be necessary to inlet it by cutting in the central portion first, and then gradually working toward the outer edges. In this case, the use of transfer color is essential.

A related problem arises in inletting barrel key escutcheons, because the key slot is not perpendicular to the side of the stock. Careful preparation of the escutcheons will help. First it must be realized that escutcheons are individually fit to each key. The keys are, of course, slightly tapered, and on most rifles, enter and exit from the left. As the key is 1/16 inch thick, two 1/16 inch holes are drilled in each escutcheon somewhat closer together than the width of the key, and joined into a slot with jeweler's saw and files. The keys, being left longer than necessary, are driven into the stock and scribed at wood level. The escutcheon slots are then filed to fit each key, just inside the scribed line on each key. Number the escutcheons on their inner side to avoid confusion. The slot in the escutcheon is then beveled to the inside to conform to the angle between key and escutcheon as the escutcheon lays on the surface of the stock. If the escutcheon binds or will not lie flat, when bent to conform to the surface of the stock, additional relieving of the inside of the slot will have to be done. When it seems right, tack it to the stock, and try the key. Some additional fitting may be needed. With the escutcheon held to the stock by the wedge and two tacks, the outline is cut in and the metal inletted. After inletting, the keys are trimmed and the heads formed and shaped.

On old rifles, inlays are held in place either by pins, or screws, and sometimes by a combination of both. Where screws are used they always are made of iron, and usually have rather narrow screwdriver slots. A single centered screw sometimes was used to hold the cheek-piece star in place. But in general, screws are inappropriate for decorative inlays.

Inlay pins on old rifles were made of iron or brass or silver. Sometimes iron or brass pins were used to hold silver inlays in place, though silver pins most often were used. Silver pins for brass inlays would be unusual, but not out of the question if the pins purposely were used as part of the design.

Brass escutcheon pins can be purchased through hardware dealers. Unfortunately, pins of 18 gauge are about as fine as can be obtained easily, and for inlay work these are about the maximum diameter that should be used. Pins of 20 or 22 gauge are more suitable. In any case, the commercial pin has a head that is flat on the bottom and rounded on top, whereas the head desired for inlay work is conical with a flat top, like a flat-head screw. The commercial pins can be modified by using a steel plate about 1/8 inch thick drilled to take the shank of the pin and having a countersunk upper end. The pin is driven into this to re-form the head. In buying escutcheon pins be sure to get real brass rather than brass-plated steel pins.

The possibility of installing inlays without having any external means of fastening may occur to the 20th century maker. If you are capable of turning out masterfully designed and engraved inlays of silver, and feel that the presence of neat silver pins is an affront to your design, then you may be justified in seeking other methods of installing them. For the most part, however, it smacks of gilding the lily.

There are exceptions, however. A silver thumb-piece could be soldered to a backing plate of brass with a threaded nut fastened below the brass. This could be held in place by a screw from below.

Epoxy cement can be used to fasten inlays in place so that pins are not needed, but a more secure inlay is achieved when pins are used in addition to the cement. If epoxy is used in addition to pins, it can serve a useful purpose in filling in low spots in the wood so that the inlay is evenly backed with solid material. Also, if brown colored epoxy is used, it can be laid in so as to squeeze out around the edge to fill up small gaps at the inlay edge. To color the epoxy, use a small amount of burnt umber paint pigment. Be sure to use only powdered pigment rather than a mixture containing oil. This pigment is a stable oxide and does not react with the epoxy. Avoid the quick-setting epoxy in favor of the 24-hour kind. To use the epoxy, prepare the back of the inlay by roughing it with medium sandpaper. Spread the tinted epoxy in the mortise and press the inlay into place. If necessary, provide a means of holding it down firmly. For installing key escutcheons, first lubricate the keys with Vaseline or oil so they will release. Pin the inlay in place with temporary pins. When the glue is dry, remove the pins from any inlay, and the keys from escutcheons, and with small flat files, working from wood to metal as far as it is possible, dress down the inlay to lie flush with the wood. The pin holes are now re-drilled, and slightly countersunk.

Relatively large silver pins can be made from wire 0.064 inch in diameter, or slightly smaller. Before cutting off a length of wire for a pin, make a point of sorts by filing a tapering flat on the end of the wire, extending about 5/16 inch up from the end of the wire. To help hold the pin in place, make a series of small transverse cuts on the flattened surface with a sharp knife. With the inlay held in place, drill through the preliminary pin holes and about 1/8 inch into the wood, using a drill as close as possible in size to the wire diameter. Then with a smaller drill, deepen the hole to about ½ inch total depth. With the point of a knife, countersink slightly the end of each hole in the inlay. Cut the pin to a length between 3/8 and ½ inch, and file the upper end square with the axis of the pin. With a small hammer tap the pin into the stock. The intent is to form a head on the pin before it reaches the inlay, which will happen if the wood resistance is sufficient. This same process can be used to make very small pins from silver wire of 22 or even 24 gauge. No matter what size of wire is used, it is necessary to practice first on scraps of wood cut from the stock blank. After the pin is set in place, the top is filed flush with the surface of the inlay. Brass pins have considerably more strength than silver pins, and it is necessary to form heads on them before setting them in place.

There are disadvantages to the use of epoxy as an aid in securing inlays. It certainly is not a traditional material, and some may question its use for this reason alone. But this argument stands questioning if the use of epoxy can result in a superior product. Much more important is the problem of differential movement between the inlay and the wood caused by differential thermal expansion between wood and metal, by shrinking of the wood as it gradually dries out, and by flexing and bending of the wood. An inlay fastened with pins alone can take up this differential movement, whereas an epoxy-fastened inlay cannot. The inlay could pop loose, or buckle. Epoxy is a great material in its place, and there are places on a longrifle where it can be used to advantage, sometimes, but it certainly is not the universal panacea.

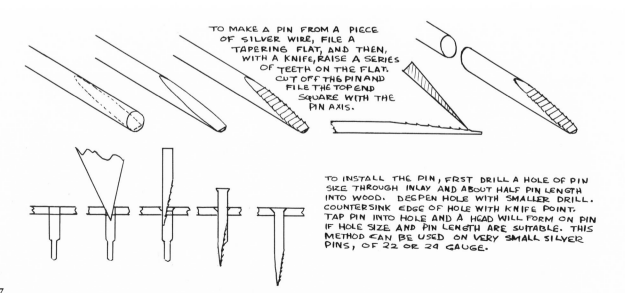

TO MAKE A PIN FROM A PIECE OF SILVER WIRE, FILE A TAPERING FLAT, AND THEN, WITH A KNIFE, RAISE A SERIES OF TEETH ON THE FLAT. CUT OFF THE PIN AND FILE THE TOP END SQUARE WITH THE PIN AXIS.

TO INSTALL THE PIN, FIRST DRILL A HOLE OF PIN SIZE THROUGH INLAY AND ABOUT HALF PIN LENGTH INTO WOOD. DEEPEN HOLE WITH SMALLER DRILL. COUNTERSINK EDGE OF HOLE WITH KNIFE POINT. TAP PIN INTO HOLE AND A HEAD WILL FORM ON PIN IF HOLE SIZE AND PIN LENGTH ARE SUITABLE. THIS METHOD CAN BE USED ON VERY SMALL SILVER PINS, OF 22 OR 24 GAUGE.

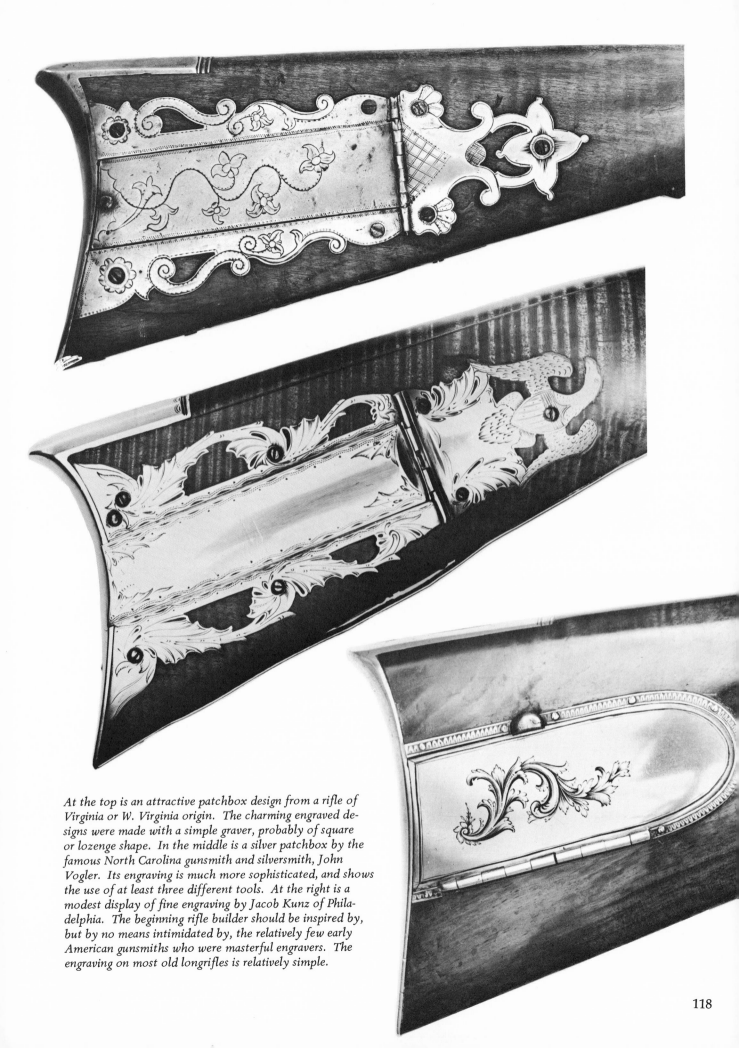

At the top is an attractive patchbox design from a rifle of
Virginia or W. Virginia origin. The charming engraved designs were made with a simple graver, probably of square
or lozenge shape. In the middle is a silver patchbox by the
famous North Carolina gunsmith and silversmith, John
Vogler. Its engraving is much more sophisticated, and shows
the use of at least three different tools. At the right is a
modest display of fine engraving by Jacob Kunz of Philadelphia. The beginning rifle builder should be inspired by,
but by no means intimidated by, the relatively few early
American gunsmiths who were masterful engravers. The
engraving on most old longrifles is relatively simple.

118

CHAPTER 28

ENGRAVING

It already has been mentioned that old rifles almost never carried patchboxes or other inlays that were not engraved. In the 18th century, engraving was a widely practiced art. Professionals in the larger cities of Europe could engrave with an amazing degree of skill. Engraving served not only as a means of decoration, but also as a useful means of putting letters and numbers on metal. Engraving also was the means by which copper plates were prepared for use in the printing of maps and illustrations. Gunsmiths often, but not always, learned engraving as part of the art and mystery of the trade. In old Europe, there was much more specialization within the gunmaking trade, so the European gun worker may or may not have done engraving. In early America, the gunsmith had to do everything, engraving included. The engraving learned and practiced by the American gunsmith often was not the sophisticated shade cut engraving of the silversmith, but a simpler form that can be termed simple line engraving.

Simple line engraving is a less formidable task than may appear at first. A beginner can achieve good results in a relatively short time using the chasing method in which the engraving tool is held in one hand and driven along slowly with a chasing hammer. The engraved design will never be any better than the design drawn up beforehand, of course, but still it is amazing how a few simple lines and curves can enhance and decorate an otherwise plain metal surface.

In the engraving process the specially sharpened engraving tool is pushed along the metal surface so that a chip or sequence of chips of metal are removed. The power to push the graver is supplied either by light taps with a hammer, or by a steady and firm push with the palm of the hand. Many of the engraving needs of the muzzle-loading rifle builder can be accomplished by either method, but each technique has its special uses and advantages that cannot be met by the other technique. Push-engraving works best on the softer metals – silver, copper, and soft brass, and has the advantage in allowing long sweeping curves to be made. In contrast, the relatively hard steels that are present in modern firearms are best engraved by the chasing technique.

In this chapter there is room to present no more than a brief introduction to the complex subject of engraving. Part of this brief introduction is to suggest that a favorable mental attitude is desirable. One need not have taken a formal course in engraving and be equipped with a set of regular engraving tools to start engraving. It is possible to begin with little more than an old and worn out triangular file, which can be ground to make an engraving tool either for chasing or for push engraving.

Three books exist which the beginning student of arms engraving can benefit from having read, and by having in his library for reference. James B. Meek's book, THE ART OF ENGRAVING: A BOOK OF INSTRUCTIONS, was specifically written to help people get started with gun engraving. Unfortunately, it makes no reference to the special needs of muzzle-loading rifle makers. Bowman and Hardy's book, THE JEWELRY ENGRAVERS MANUAL, is intended for those learning push engraving, and contains a lot of basic information, including much on lettering. A somewhat earlier book is A PRACTICAL COURSE IN JEWELRY ENGRAVING by A. A. Winter.

Engraving tools can be made or purchased in almost finished form. As mentioned above, old files can be made into engraving tools. However, regular hardened steel engraving tools in many different cross sectional shapes and sizes are available at modest cost from jewelry supply houses and from a good many of the dealers who sell muzzle-loading gunsmiths's supplies. The onglet, with v-shape cross section, and the graver of square cross section are the ones most frequently used for work on longrifles.

The engraving tool, as it comes from the supplier, typically has a blade about 4 inches long and a tang of 1 ½ inches, more or less. If it is to be used as a chasing tool, it is best left full length. If it is to be used for push engraving, then it is best to break off the front half of the blade before sharpening. For push engraving, small specially shaped wooden handles are available. For chasing work, this palm handle may be used, or a simple hardwood handle may be forced over the tang with the help of a drilled hole.

Proper shaping and sharpening of the end of the graver is essential, and gravers for both chasing and push engraving are treated the same way. First, grind the front end to an angle of about 45°. New tools frequently come with this angle already formed. If not, a medium or fine-grit motorized grinding wheel can be used, great care being taken to keep the graver from being overheated and losing its hardness. This is done by limiting the grinding time to about 1 or 1 ½ seconds, followed by a dip in cold water. Then grind away the excess metal at the upper corner of the graver so that the face area is reduced and hence easier to keep sharp.

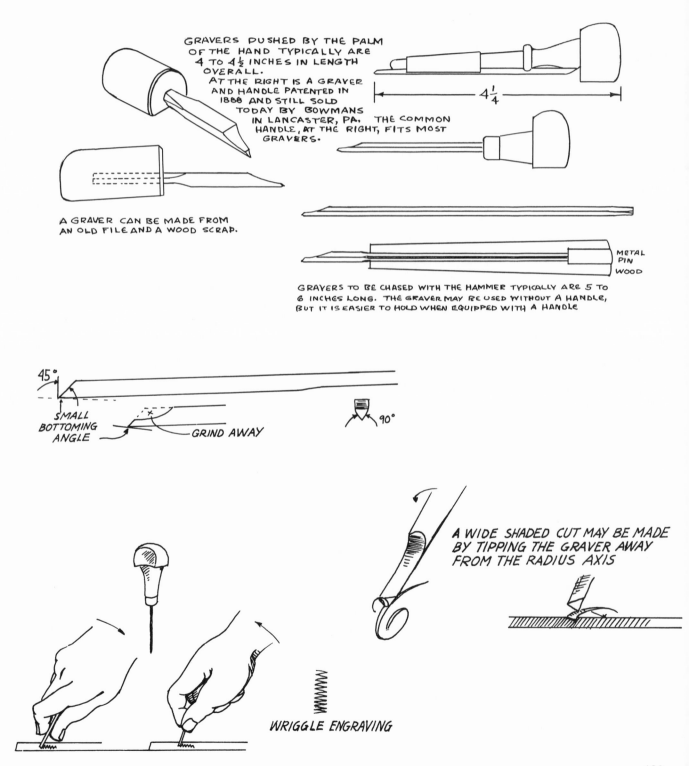

GRAVERS PUSHED BY THE PALM OF THE HAND TYPICALLY ARE 4 TO 4½ INCHES IN LENGTH OVERALL.
AT THE RIGHT IS A GRAVER AND HANDLE PATENTED IN 1888 AND STILL SOLD TODAY BY BOWMANS IN LANCASTER, PA. THE COMMON HANDLE, AT THE RIGHT, FITS MOST GRAVERS.

$4\frac{1}{4}$

A GRAVER CAN BE MADE FROM AN OLD FILE AND A WOOD SCRAP.

METAL
PIN
WOOD

GRAVERS TO BE CHASED WITH THE HAMMER TYPICALLY ARE 5 TO 6 INCHES LONG. THE GRAVER MAY BE USED WITHOUT A HANDLE, BUT IT IS EASIER TO HOLD WHEN EQUIPPED WITH A HANDLE

45°

SMALL BOTTOMING ANGLE

GRIND AWAY

90°

A WIDE SHADED CUT MAY BE MADE BY TIPPING THE GRAVER AWAY FROM THE RADIUS AXIS

WRIGGLE ENGRAVING

A small bottoming angle, or clearance angle, of about 15°, must be provided at the front end of the graver, to provide a fulcrum by which the depth of the cut can be controlled. This should extend back from the point about 3/32 inch. After the face of the graver is roughly shaped on the grinder, it is finished first on a fine-grit oil stone, and then on a fine Arkansas stone or equivalent. The two facets that are ground on the lower sides to provide the clearance angle are cut on these two stones, not the grinder.

Before attempting to do any engraving on inlays, practice on scraps of metal that are securely pinned, screwed, or glued to scraps of wood. It can be useful to practice by making identification tags to use on key rings, or other possessions.

In the chasing method of engraving, the graver is forced through the metal by many light taps of a hammer. Professional engravers use small metal hammers designed for this specific purpose. But a light wooden mallet works quite well also, and can be easily made. The technique is to hit the end of the graver with many light taps, to produce as smooth a cut as possible. Except in cutting straight lines, the rear end of the graver is in constant motion as it is swung around to produce curved cuts. Each tap of the hammer makes a cut that is essentially straight, so many light taps produce a smoother curve than fewer but heavier taps. Good, smooth engraving takes time, so avoid hurry. Rest often, for you probably will be gripping the graver in your left hand much too tightly at first, which will be stressful.

For right-handed people, the graver is held in the left hand, which controls the graver's depth of cut and direction. When going around a curve, tip the graver slightly toward the outer side of the curve, which will enable it to cut more smoothly. Good engraving can be done with a line of constant width, but better engraving uses lines of varying width. Certain parts of curves look best if they are wider than other parts. This lends a shaded effect to the overall design and gives it the feel of fine script writing done with a quill pen. Widening the curve is simply a matter of tipping the graver away from the center of the curve. At the end of each curved line, lower the butt of the graver to bring the tip out of the cut smoothly without leaving a butt.

In any design, the main lines are cut first, then all the secondary lines. With the chasing method it is possible to cut all the lines lightly, then go back over them, widening as necessary, or varying the width of the lines to provide shading effects.

After the engraving is completed, the surface of the metal at the edge of the cuts is raised in little fins and burrs. These must be knocked off with an old finely cut file, and then further rubbed with fine abrasive paper, then polished with # 0000 steel wool. At this point the cuts which looked quite deep when first made may appear shallower than intended. It is possible to go over them to add depth. Also, it is possible to see and correct minor errors, and to add cuts to improve the design. Further, it is possible to smooth any jagged cuts.

The designs that are to be engraved on metal gun parts are, of course, worked out first on paper patterns. To prepare the metal surface for drawing, it is convenient to use a material called China white. This is a white chalky substance usually bought as a small white cube or rectangular block. To use it, wet the tip of the finger with water or saliva, and rub on the China white block, then rub on the metal. This leaves a white film that may be drawn upon with a pencil. It also serves to cut down on the glare from the metal surface that comes from the bright light necessary for engraving. A cheap set of water-color paints can serve the purpose too.

It should be realized that really beautiful engraving is a fine art, and that those who do this work professionally, spend much of their lives at it. We who only occasionally make rifles cannot hope to equal their skill. But we can take heart in the knowledge that only a few of the early American gunsmiths were really good engravers. With practice and determination, we may execute an acceptable job, if not a pretty good one.

The relief carving on this rifle is particularly low, being of the order of 1/32 inch high. It looks higher, however, because there is a deep incised cut along the edges of the relief figures. From a rifle attributed to Peter White of Uniontown in western Pennsylvania, and probably made during the 1820's.

This design consists basically of two rococo C-scrolls face to face, elaborated with other scrolls. One scroll end is seen to overlap the upper main C-scroll. There is a cross-hatched background in the center of the figure. From a rifle made by John Noll of Chambersburg, Pa., probably in the period between 1795 and 1815.

The two major scrolls of this beautiful rococo design overlap each other in two places. The overlapping scrolls help to give a three-dimensional character to the very low relief figures. From a rifle made by Martin Shell of Harrisburg, Pennsylvania, probably in the period between 1795 and 1815.

122

CHAPTER 29

CARVING

One of the most pleasant aspects of building a fine rifle is doing the decorative carving. Actually, the carving could be done at any time after the stock is brought to final shape, but it is preferable to wait until after the inlays have been installed and engraved, not only because the finished and carved stock could be damaged if the inlays were put in afterward, but also because final decisions about the carving can best be made with the inlays in place.

If your rifle is to be relief carved, you must plan carefully, and be certain of what you want before you do it. By this time your rifle represents a considerable investment in time and money. In the Golden Age of rifle making, amateurs usually did not mess around making rifles, though there were no laws to prevent them from doing so. Almost invariably, if an old rifle has carving it has good carving. Today, alas, such is not the case. Many rifles are being turned out now with poorly designed and even more poorly executed carving that would have been better to leave off. This is not to discourage you from attempting carving, but rather to encourage you to be discriminating enough to be critical of your own efforts.

The designing of relief carving is a sophisticated problem in art. Rococo art forms are the basis for almost all of the designs carved on longrifles, and for the designs of inlays and their engraved decoration. Rifles of 18th century origin sometimes show remnants of baroque art also. To use these art forms calls for some understanding of both rococo and baroque art. Fortunately, there is such a wealth of this art on early American and European firearms that one can get pretty well educated by studying a number of the books listed in the Bibliography. It is well to bear in mind, however, that during the first four decades of the 19th century the Americanized rococo art found on American rifles underwent a gradual degradation. As the old masters of the 18th century died off, and the less well trained students of their less well trained students moved westward, the principals of rococo decoration were forgotten and then lost.

Baroque art was the principal art form of Europe from the mid-17th century until the second quarter of the 18th century. One author on baroque art suggests that the word "movement" best expresses what the art is all about, and notes that the word ended up meaning extravagant, deformed, abnormal, unusual, absurd, and irregular. As found on firearms of the early 18th century, baroque art often featured bilateral symmetry, and in its more complicated forms could leave the observer with an uneasy feeling of busy perfection.

Rococo art, on the other hand, avoids symmetry and emphasizes informality. Basically it is an expression of the growing plant forms found in nature, coupled with forms derived from the scallop shell. Some rococo art elements resemble the unfolding foliage of plants in the springtime. Flowers opening, leaves unfolding, and tendrils uncurling are what one predominantly sees in this art, though the forms are generalized, and no attempt is made to represent specific plants. However, representations of acanthus leaf foliage, very popular in the baroque period, were carried over into the rococo period. Good rococo art is rhythmic and causes the eye to move easily from one part to another without discontinuity. The C-scrolls and S-scrolls have a wave-like appearance, and in some applications can be thought of as representations of ocean waves.

One of the principal purposes of using rococo (or baroque) art on a rifle is simply to decorate an otherwise plain area. Another purpose, and by no means a secondary purpose, is to form a bridge across a discontinuity. For example, there is a discontinuity of stock surfaces where the cylindrical wrist joins the butt-stock. By having carved designs and relief steps in the zone where the surfaces meet, the distinctiveness of the separate surfaces is emphasized and the overall attractiveness increased.

C-scrolls and S-scrolls are basic building blocks of rococo art, and it is necessary to have some understanding of them before trying to use them, which is best done by studying how good artists have used them, and then going to work with paper and pencil. To avoid monotony, these scrolls should be of varying size and shape, cleverly connected with other lines and related forms. The width of the

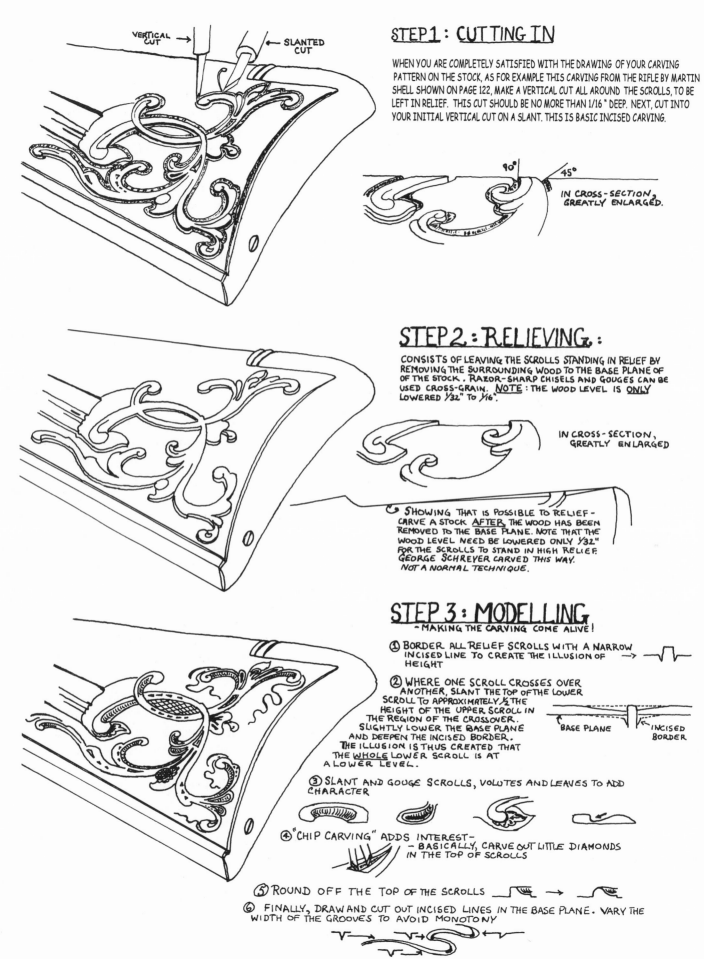

STEP 1 : CUTTING IN

WHEN YOU ARE COMPLETELY SATISFIED WITH THE DRAWING OF YOUR CARVING PATTERN ON THE STOCK, AS FOR EXAMPLE THIS CARVING FROM THE RIFLE BY MARTIN SHELL SHOWN ON PAGE 122, MAKE A VERTICAL CUT ALL AROUND THE SCROLLS, TO BE LEFT IN RELIEF. THIS CUT SHOULD BE NO MORE THAN 1/16" DEEP. NEXT, CUT INTO YOUR INITIAL VERTICAL CUT ON A SLANT. THIS IS BASIC INCISED CARVING.

VERTICAL CUT

SLANTED CUT

90°   45°

IN CROSS-SECTION, GREATLY ENLARGED.

STEP 2 : RELIEVING :

CONSISTS OF LEAVING THE SCROLLS STANDING IN RELIEF BY REMOVING THE SURROUNDING WOOD TO THE BASE PLANE OF OF THE STOCK. RAZOR-SHARP CHISELS AND GOUGES CAN BE USED CROSS-GRAIN. <u>NOTE</u> : THE WOOD LEVEL IS <u>ONLY</u> LOWERED 1/32" TO 1/16".

IN CROSS-SECTION, GREATLY ENLARGED

SHOWING THAT IS POSSIBLE TO RELIEF-CARVE A STOCK <u>AFTER</u> THE WOOD HAS BEEN REMOVED TO THE BASE PLANE. NOTE THAT THE WOOD LEVEL NEED BE LOWERED ONLY 1/32" FOR THE SCROLLS TO STAND IN HIGH RELIEF. GEORGE SCHREYER CARVED THIS WAY. NOT A NORMAL TECHNIQUE.

STEP 3 : MODELLING
~ MAKING THE CARVING COME ALIVE!

① BORDER ALL RELIEF SCROLLS WITH A NARROW INCISED LINE TO CREATE THE ILLUSION OF HEIGHT

② WHERE ONE SCROLL CROSSES OVER ANOTHER, SLANT THE TOP OF THE LOWER SCROLL TO APPROXIMATELY 1/2 THE HEIGHT OF THE UPPER SCROLL IN THE REGION OF THE CROSSOVER. SLIGHTLY LOWER THE BASE PLANE AND DEEPEN THE INCISED BORDER. THE ILLUSION IS THUS CREATED THAT THE <u>WHOLE</u> LOWER SCROLL IS AT A LOWER LEVEL.

BASE PLANE   INCISED BORDER

③ SLANT AND GOUGE SCROLLS, VOLUTES AND LEAVES TO ADD CHARACTER

④ "CHIP CARVING" ADDS INTEREST—
— BASICALLY, CARVE OUT LITTLE DIAMONDS IN THE TOP OF SCROLLS

⑤ ROUND OFF THE TOP OF THE SCROLLS

⑥ FINALLY, DRAW AND CUT OUT INCISED LINES IN THE BASE PLANE. VARY THE WIDTH OF THE GROOVES TO AVOID MONOTONY body of the scroll should never be uniform, with parallel edges, but rather should be constantly changing. The ends of these scrolls call for special study; on American rifles these scroll ends usually have a small secondary lobe on the inside of the main scroll, giving somewhat the appearance of a small child's mittened hand, with the fingers closed over the thumb. The scroll ends should not be portions of circles but instead show constantly changing radius of curvature.

Really good relief carving has a three-dimensional quality purposely planned and executed. On old rifles this is more frequently found on 18th century pieces and those of the early Golden Age than on pieces from the late flint period. In the late period not only the designing of carving but also its execution became somewhat degenerate, and this three-dimensional aspect disappeared. As a result, the carving on rifles such as those from Bedford County in Pennsylvania is somewhat monotonous compared with the work of the earlier masters such as George Schreyer, George Eister, Frederick Sell, and John Armstrong.

In preparation for carving, a good deal of time should be spent in drawing. For starting, it can be beneficial to try copying the designs on old rifles, as shown in books, sketching and sketching until they seem to be coming out your ears. Learn how to sketch a group of scrolls linked together, doing the work rapidly for overall effect, then go back and shape each scroll to perfection. Study the work of Henry Albright, who made his scrolls rapidly, without bringing them to perfection, yet managed to create impressive effects. In contrast, study the much more sophisticated scrolls of John Noll on his engraved inlays, and the carved scrolls of J. P. Beck.

The principal place for relief carved decoration on a rifle is in the area on the left side of the butt behind the cheek-piece. But there are a number of additional areas that traditionally carried carved decoration: surrounding the barrel tang and the top of the wrist immediately behind the tang; on the left side of the stock just ahead of the cheek-piece; on the right side of the stock, where wrist meets butt-stock; to the rear of the rear ramrod pipe. Carved decoration sometimes, but less frequently, was present on old rifles in front of the lock and side-plate panels, in front of the trigger-guard, and under the cheek-piece. Few, if any, old rifles have carved decoration in all of these places.

Relief carving rarely stands higher than 1/16 inch above the base level of the stock that surrounds it, and typically the carving lies between 1/16 and 3/64 inch high. It is easy to make carved decoration that stands up high, but one does not get awards for great elevation. The challenge is to keep the carving very low, yet to have it show a strong three-dimensional effect. So, if you have not already done so, reduce the elevation of the area to be carved to approximately 1/16 inch above the final base plane of the stock. These areas must now be sanded perfectly smooth.

Now transfer the design to the stock, being sure that it relates well with the physical boundaries of the area in which it will lie. It is perfectly reasonable to sketch and erase on the stock until the per-fected design is worked out.

The tools needed for carving are simple and basic. A cutting-in knife is essential, and this can be the same sharply pointed knife used for the inlay work and other cutting-in work. An Exacto knife is particularly good, and its factory-sharpened blades can be re-sharpened easily. Various small chisels and gouges ¼ inch wide or less are necessary also. The bevel angle of the sloping front faces should be ground back to about 10° to 15° for effective cutting and easy sharpening. The square upper cor-ners of the sloping faces of flat chisels can be stoned to be slightly rounded.

There are three steps to relief carving: cutting-in, relieving, and modeling. Cutting-in consists of making vertical cuts around the carved figures. Relieving consists of removing the wood that sur-rounds the figures to the base level of the stock. Modeling consists of giving the relief figures their desired three-dimensional shapes.

Cutting-in is a critical operation, for unlike the pencilled outline, once done it cannot easily be erased for another try. This fact can be intimidating to the beginning gunsmith, untrained at making smooth, curved, freehand cuts exactly where desired. One way to get around this problem is to prac-tice on scraps of wood until confidence is gained, and skill acquired. Another way is to make some templates out of thin sheet metal – brass, copper, old tin cans, or aluminum. Aluminum is recom-mended as it is readily available, inexpensive, and easily cut with scissors and brought to finished shape with files. It is not practical to make exact templates for every curve in a design, but it is practical to make templates for some of the larger curves, and to make a set of curve templates that can be used more or less in the way a draftsman uses French curves, to fit most of the curved parts of any design. No matter how it is brought about, the first outlining cuts should be relatively shallow, about 1/32 inch deep. Then sloping relief cuts are made to remove the first wood around the figure. After that the vertical cuts can be deepened, and further relieving done.

Now the wood surrounding the figures or design should be reduced to the base level of the stock. Long before this you will have discovered that curly maple is at times a miserable and unfortunate wood to work with, particularly in hard-to-get-at places. One must be constantly alert to curl and grain direction, for often, without warning, a part will break away, and usually at an unfortunate spot. Should this happen, it may be possible to alter the design to cover up the misfortune. In some situations, chips can be glued back into place, providing a second chance. In removing the wood outside the design to base level, it often is best to cut with chisels across the grain. After the initial cutting is done, the surfaces must be smoothed up with sandpaper, always backed with something firm or hard. One experienced gunsmith glues sandpaper to variously shaped pieces of rubber eraser. Another idea is to make use of the fingernail files made of stiff cardboard with abrasive grit glued on, cutting pieces to suitable shape for work in small areas. In any case, the base level of the stock should end up smooth, and free from humps and swales. A low-level oblique back light and a straight-edge piece of paper can help detect the flaws. After the base level of the stock around the designs is perfected, some of the carving may stand too high in relief. If so, reduce it with files, and sandpaper suitably backed.

Usually it is necessary to re-outline the scrolls and design outlines after the surrounding base level is completed. Cut all around them about 1/32 inch deeper than the base level. When the stock is stained, this cut will retain stain and help make the carving stand out. The dark outline will actually make the relief figures appear higher than they really are – one of the illusions of the longrifle.

Modeling, the third step in the process, consists of shaping the upper surfaces of the relief figures. Some parts of scrolls need to be convex, and other parts concave. Often in rococo design, scrolls or other design elements are made to overlap other scrolls. It is necessary, then, for the upper scroll to appear to stand higher that the lower part of the design. This effect is achieved by reducing the height of the lower scroll to about half the height of the upper scroll in the region of overlap. The incised border of the scrolls is deepened slightly in the region of overlap to enhance the illusion.

Incised carving often is used in combination with relief carving, at times in very clever ways. In the old days, incised carving often was used alone for rifle stock decoration. Today, however, it is rarely used alone. Incised carving basically consists of cutting a narrow v-shaped groove in the wood. Sometimes this is accomplished with a narrow veining tool, which is a small wood chisel with a v-shaped cross section. In practice, these veining tools often cut a groove too wide. The alternative is to use the cutting-in knife, and cut the lines of the design. Then the knife is used to make a slightly sloping cut parallel to the first line, so that a narrow v-shaped piece of wood is removed. Ideally, the v-groove should be narrow, and contain an angle of 10° to 15°. As with engraved lines, the incised line or groove should vary in width.

An important design element which was frequently made use of in the old days is the volute, or spiraled line. Baroque gun art made great use of volutes, and their use was carried over to 18th century American rifles. The volute was cleverly integrated into American rococo gun art during the Golden Age.

Volutes almost invariably are incised features, i.e. spiraled lines rather than being two-dimensional figures like rococo C-scrolls and S-scrolls. However, incised volutes sometimes are given a three-dimensional aspect by cutting a sloping step on one side of the curved line. Volutes come in a variety of shapes and size, and some that are found on old rifles are so small and so neatly done that it is difficult to believe that they were done freehand with a knife. It is possible to make a spiraled cutter or stamp by sharpening one edge of a small, thin, rectangular piece of steel, bending it into a spiral, and then fastening it to a shank with silver solder. But to use such a stamp creatively calls for having a number of others of various sizes, both left-hand and right-hand spirals. To use only one size of volute repeatedly on a rifle could lead to a mechanical appearance. It also is possible to make templates to guide a knife in making a volute.

In addition to rococo designs, American rifles sometimes were made in the old days with relief carving of animals such as lions, deer, griffins, etc. These were executed in rather low relief, in keeping with the rest of the relief carving. Furthermore, it should be noted that the carved representations of animals and birds on old rifles have a different visual flavor than the modern pictorial versions we sometimes see today engraved on modern firearms. So, if an animal is to be included in your design, study old examples to grasp the style.

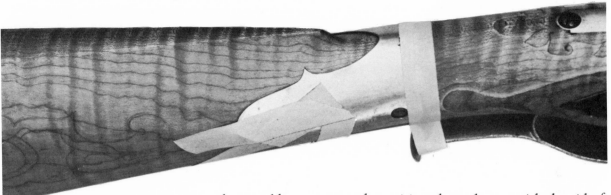

Smooth curved lines, accurately positioned, can be cut with the aid of sheet metal templates. The ones shown here are aluminum, though iron, steel or brass would serve. These are particularly helpful for cuts that must be the same on both sides of the stock, such as the lock panel mouldings. To reverse the pattern for the opposite side of the stock, the metal is bent in the opposite direction.

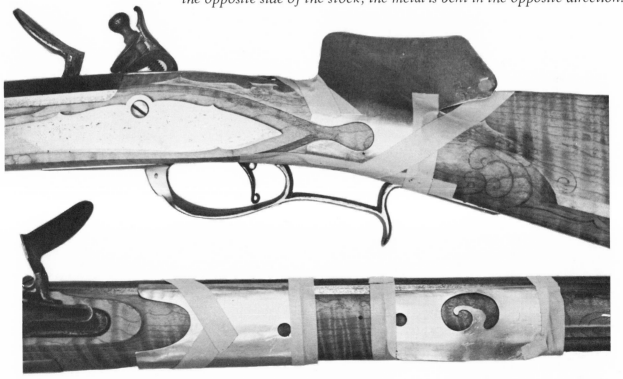

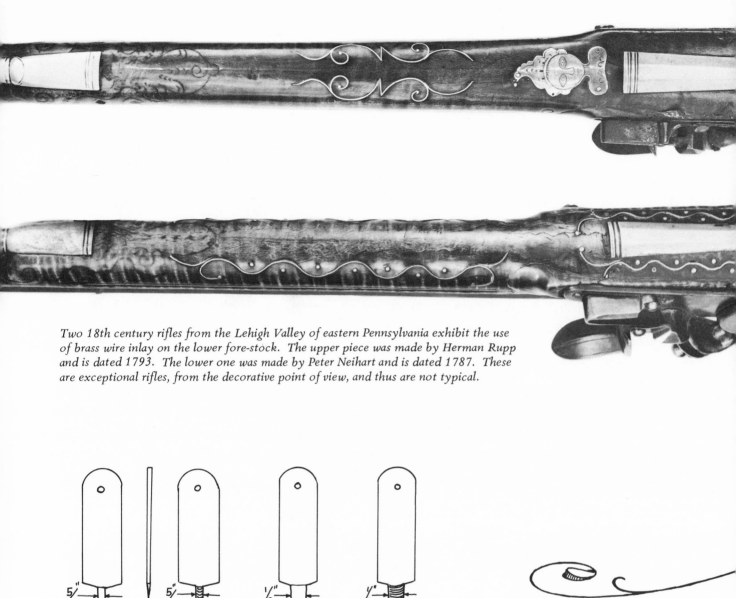

Two 18th century rifles from the Lehigh Valley of eastern Pennsylvania exhibit the use of brass wire inlay on the lower fore-stock. The upper piece was made by Herman Rupp and is dated 1793. The lower one was made by Peter Neihart and is dated 1787. These are exceptional rifles, from the decorative point of view, and thus are not typical.

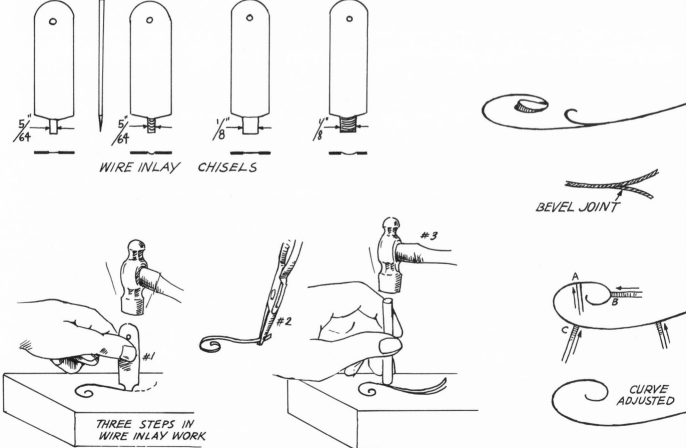

WIRE INLAY CHISELS

BEVEL JOINT

THREE STEPS IN WIRE INLAY WORK

CURVE ADJUSTED

128

CHAPTER 30

METAL RIBBON INLAY

Wire inlay, sparingly used, can be a charming addition to the rifle. It was used in old Europe by gun stockers in the 16th, 17th, and 18th centuries. Silver wire inlay was developed into a fine art by English gun stockers in the 18th century, and its influence was carried over to New England where it frequently was used on rifles and smoothbore guns in the late 18th and early 19th centuries. In small amounts, wire inlay was used on some of the earliest American longrifles.

First it must be made clear that what is called "wire inlay" does not involve round wire at all, but rather thin ribbons of silver or brass that are set on edge into cuts in the wood. When properly used, this form of inlay can produce beautiful effects, but the designing is more difficult than the execution. Wire inlay should not dominate the designs on a longrifle, but should be used to add continuity and rhythm to carving and inlays, or for other special purposes. To appreciate how effective this wire inlay can be at its best, it is good to study the work on fine European guns, particularly those of English origin, which readily can be seen in many books.

For use on American longrifles, it is recommended that wire ribbon about 0.010 inches thick be used. For silver wire, the minimum practical thickness is about 0.007 inches, but this is difficult to work with and may buckle when driven in. Metal much thicker than 0.010 inches is difficult to install and has a heavy look. Sheet silver 0.010 inches thick is readily available from jewelry supply houses, and sheet brass of this thickness can be bought as shim stock from auto parts dealers. One modern longrifle maker, Rudi Bahr, buys round silver wire, which then is flattened to appropriate thickness in a rolling machine. The advantage of this is that it leaves a rounded edge on the upper surface.

To prepare sheet silver or brass for making inlay wire, a bevel is filed along one edge of the sheet stock, to aid in driving the metal into the narrow cut in the wood. Then, with scissors or tin snips, a strip between 1/32 and 1/16 inch wide is cut off. Take a fine-toothed needle file and draw the strip across the file so that some of the teeth score the strip lengthwise. These score marks help the wire to be retained in the wood.

The inlay procedure is basically simple. A groove is cut in the wood and the ribbon is forced into the groove. The groove is merely a vertical cut somewhat deeper than the width of the wire. To make the cut in the wood some special tools are helpful. These are a set of grooving chisels made from pieces of discarded hacksaw blades. Depending on the blade, it may be necessary to remove the hardening by heating before grinding to shape, and then hardening again afterward. If a hardened blade breaks off when driven into the wood, drive the imbedded piece on into the wood, and proceed to lay the wire on top of it. The chisels are made in the manner shown in the drawing, some flat and some curved. Six chisels are sufficient for most work, but two very narrow ones could be added, plus some special curved ones for use on tight volute ends.

The groove is cut slightly deeper than the width of the ribbon. After the inlay line has been cut in the wood, a strip of ribbon is bent to the shape of the line. One end of the ribbon is placed in the end of the groove and tapped into place. Do not tap the ribbon directly with the hammer, but use a short section of ramrod or other dowel as a buffer between hammer and ribbon. Carefully tap the ribbon into the stock, moving slowly down its length. Where tight curls or volutes are present, it is best to start at the tightest part of the volute or curl, and work outward. If there are cross-overs in the design, one ribbon continues across the junction while the other is interrupted. At a cross-over, first cut the groove for the continuous wire, and tap this wire into place, then cut the groove for the discontinuous pieces. If two pieces of ribbon are to join at a small angle, it is necessary to make a bevel joint. One end of the ribbon is filed to a wedge shape by resting the end on a solid support, such as the rounded top of a vise.

One hazard that comes with this work is that a small circle of wood may break loose at the inside of a spiral or scroll. The only way to lessen the possibility of this happening is to use very narrow grooving tools, proceeding at a slow, nibbling pace, and cutting as shallowly as possible. These little circles of wood always will be a problem, and if you note that one is cracked when you are about to retract the chisel, you must hold it in place. If you do not, it may fall out and be lost, or when glued back into position you may find the grain direction changed.

After the wire is installed, some of the curves may not be as well shaped as desired. This can be corrected in part by tapping the top edge of the ribbon in the desired direction. Very slight changes can make a difference.

With the wire all in place and adjusted, it may be that in some places the top surface of the wire stands slightly above the level of the stock. Do not use a file, for in filing a thin silver ribbon, a burr is left that can never be removed. Instead, take a sharp chisel or knife and cut it off flush with the surface.

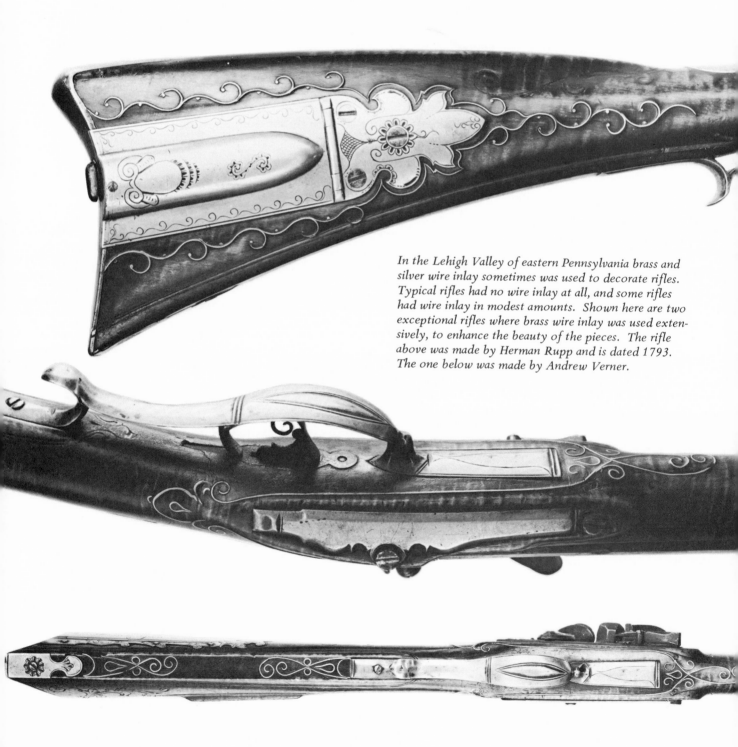

In the Lehigh Valley of eastern Pennsylvania brass and silver wire inlay sometimes was used to decorate rifles. Typical rifles had no wire inlay at all, and some rifles had wire inlay in modest amounts. Shown here are two exceptional rifles where brass wire inlay was used extensively, to enhance the beauty of the pieces. The rifle above was made by Herman Rupp and is dated 1793. The one below was made by Andrew Verner.

CHAPTER 31

WOOD FINISHING

With the work on the stock finished, it remains to stain the stock, put the sights on the barrel, blue or brown the barrel and lock, and make the ramrod. There is a general agreement among those who appreciate the beauty of the longrifle that in the finishing and staining of curly maple, nothing quite can compare with the mellow golden brown or reddish brown that many old rifles have acquired after having been around for 150 years. The word *patina* (with accent on first syllable) is used to refer to the combination of this mellowed color plus its over all finish. Patina is principally the result of chemical oxidation that takes place very slowly from natural causes, but other chemical reactions take place in the wood also. In addition, there are long-term effects of ultra-violet radiation and other radiation, the effects of oil, the accumulation of dirt, and abrasion from handling and use. To duplicate all of this in a very short time is impossible, but some approximation to it can be made.

Gun stock wood can be stained heavily or lightly in a variety of colors, and it also is possible to finish a stock without adding any color to the finish. The staining of the stock, like the shaping of the stock and the decoration of it, becomes a statement of the maker. Therefore it is well to have intentions in mind from the start. If the intention is to recreate an old rifle as it appears today, which is a most valid objective, then where does one stop as far as finish is concerned? Drying cracks, dings, dents, and the effects of abrasion and wear are part of the patina. Should these be added as part of the final finish? An alternative, and probably better objective, might be to try to finish the rifle as it might have been finished when originally made.

What about the surface finish? A good many longrifle makers, and longrifle buyers, today are hung up on the hand-rubbed linseed oil finish with its attractive soft gleam, which seems quite antique. But there are many fine old original rifles that still have their original varnish on the stock, for a varnish finish often was used in the old days and may have been the finish of choice. The hand-rubbed oil finish takes a lot of time, and the old gunsmith may not have had that time to spare. This train of thought suggests that many old guns initially had bright, shiny, varnish finishes, and that time, use, and oil rubbed on their surfaces over the years have changed them. This is not to suggest that one objective is right and another wrong, but merely that there are choices, and that it is good to have an objective.

WHISKERING

With the stock completed, there is a natural tendency to rush the finishing. With all the hard work done, the finishing would seem a simple matter of a few more hours work at the most. But the reality is that it may take a number of days, or even weeks, before the rifle is completed. First, the entire stock must have a final sanding, working down to 400-grit paper. At this time take a number of scraps of stock wood, smooth some surfaces on them, and also finish them with 400 grit paper, to use in testing stains. Sand with care and avoid rushing the work. Next use a vacuum cleaner with a soft brush attachment to pick up sanding dust from the stock. Be very thorough, and be certain that there is no dust left in the barrel channel, the lock mortise, and in incised cuts and checkering on the stock. Now thoroughly vacuum the entire workbench area. If the almost finished stock has acquired some dents, these probably can be removed by steaming, with the aid of a damp cloth and a hot iron.

With the sanding complete, the stock is not yet ready for stain. Even finely sanded wood has many small fiber ends that warp and curl upward if the stock wood is wetted with stain. Stains with a base of alcohol or other spirits may have less tendency to raise up the annoying little whiskers, but even so, it is desirable to whisker the stock, which actually is the process of de-whiskering the stock.

Water is applied to the stock surface by means of a well-wetted cloth or sponge. Do not apply too much water, only enough to dampen the outer surface of the stock. Then the wetted wood is moved back and forth over a moderate heat source, such as an electric hot plate or the burner of an electric stove. A propane torch can be used, but only with difficulty, as its intensive and directed heat is difficult to control. The purpose of the heat is to dry the wood and to induce the whiskers to curl up as much as they can. After applying the heat, the once smooth stock will seem quite rough. It must be sanded again with 400-grit paper. Repeat the whiskering process until there seem to be no more fibers to raise up, and then do it one more time. At this stage, some gunsmiths wear white cotton gloves, to prevent oil from their hands from getting onto the stock. At this final stage, it may seem desirable to touch up the carving in a few places. The final quality of the stock finish is directly related to the amount of time and care put into whiskering.

STAINING

From looking at a large number of old rifles and other guns, it is apparent that a wide range of stain coloring were applied to the stocks. Of course all of these have been modified somewhat by time and use, but nevertheless, the initial range of coloration cannot be denied. Typically these range from uncolored to very dark brown, through intermediate blends of yellow and brown. Reddish hues were added to the browns and yellows, particularly in the Lehigh Valley of eastern Pennsylvania during the 19th century, but elsewhere also. A half-stock percussion rifle from Pittsburgh in the 1840s or 1850s has been seen with its original stock little used or worn and of an intense red color; this is an unusual case, but it is for real. The point is that there is no correct or best color to aim for, nor is there any specific stain that can be concocted or purchased to give a "correct" color, but many give good colors.

The range of stain colorings on old stocks can only be appreciated by seeing a large number of old rifles and other guns. Of course time has produced its changes on all of them and we never can know exactly the color that any one of them appeared when originally made. Even so, we can get some pretty good ideas. Unfortunately, published books with good color illustrations of old longrifle stocks are not large in number. A few color illustrations have appeared in periodicals from time to time. The only book presently available is Merrill Lindsay's work titled THE KENTUCKY RIFLE, which is inexpensive, worthwhile having, and not to be confused with a number of other books of the same title.

In the old days a variety of substances were used to stain gun stocks, and today almost all of these exist for use if desired. But in addition, there are new stains available today that broaden the range of choice. The beginning gun maker does not have the time to try them all, and it is doubtful that most full-time rifle makers of today have given everything a try. The problem with the old stains is that the colors they produced were not very permanent, especially the reddish tones and colors. It is possible to purchase commercial products today that are designed specifically to stain wood and are much more light-fast. Some of these stains are designed specifically to match the appearance of firearms with years of patina.

Probably the best stains for the beginning rifle maker to work with are the commercial products made specifically for staining wood. The base or vehicle for these stains may be water, alcohol, mineral spirits, or some other type of solvent. Oil stains generally are not suited for use on gun stocks for they basically consist of finely ground oxides and other minerals suspended in an oil vehicle. They do not penetrate well and may leave a muddy appearance. Many of the other stains make use of aniline dyes as coloring agents. These penetrate well because the coloring agents are carried as solutions in the water or solvent. Some of these stains are bottled and sold for use on gun stocks.

A very good example is a series of stains manufactured by Laurel Mountain Forge. These stains are deep penetrating Metal Complexed dyes. They are very light-fast and easy to use. Since they are NGR (non-grain-raising) stains they will not swell wood grain. The solvents used with these stains are unique in that they can be mixed into most finishes to produce some unique transparent glazes. This is the same finishing/staining technique that was used on many of the original Allentown-Bethlehem rifles. The antique Wood stains from Laurel Mountain Forge are available in seven different colors that are very good matches to most of the original rifle colors.

Another source of stains are aniline dye type products sold for dyeing leather. The Tandy Leather company, for example, offers two or three shades of brown plus one or more orange or yellow dyes in convenient small bottles, and some very satisfactory results have been attained with them.

Among the old staining methods reported in the literature is the use of coal tar, such as one can find in the cracks of roads. Small pieces of this are dissolved in turpentine or mineral spirits, and the mixture rubbed into the stock. The use of tobacco juice also is reported.

Probably the most important old stock staining material is aqua fortis, which we know today as nitric acid. This was widely used in the flintlock period, and old gunsmith inventories often mention aqua fortis. The nitric acid is applied to the wood as a rather strong solution, and then immediately heated by being held near a suitable flame, electrically heated element, or forge-heated iron bar. The heat produces an immediate dark color. The action of the acid is stopped with a strong chemical base solution.

Carl Pippert, the dean of longrifle builders in the third quarter of the 20th century, used nitric acid successfully for many years. He claims that by using this acid for initial coloring, finishing off with oil containing burnt umber pigment, he can reproduce and match the color of almost any old gun stock, and the considerable amount of splendid restoration work he has done proves this point well.

Carl's procedure is to begin with a solution of one part concentrated nitric acid and one part water. The acid normally comes in concentrated form, and it is best to let a pharmacist prepare the solution. The acid is applied to the whole stock with a brush, or with a piece of cloth, the hand being protected with a rubber glove. The wetted stock then is immediately dried by being moved back and forth in the flame of a gas stove. Care is taken not to scorch the stock, only to dry the wood. In the process, the wood takes on a brown color, the darkness of which is controlled by the amount of heat applied. If some whiskers in the wood have been raised, they are removed with fine abrasive paper or with #0000 steel wool. Then the stock is rubbed with linseed oil to which some burnt umber pigment has been added. Contrary to the usual practice, Carl does not neutralize the acid with a base solution. To add a reddish brown tinge to the stock, some brown color Griffin shoe dye is applied. After that, further rubbings and oilings are in order.

Other chemicals have their uses as stock stains also. Medicinal iodine solutions can be purchased through veterinarians, and these work well for stock staining. A number of applications are necessary, as the first applications impart a yellow color to the stock. The stock takes on a mellow yellow-brown color with further applications. Sulfuric acid may be worth experimenting with also; acid from an auto battery applied to new white pine wood and allowed to sit overnight produces the kind of darkening that takes 100 years of oxidation in the air to produce.

When acid is used for stock coloring, remnants of the acid remain in the stock, and over a period of time can react further with the wood, to darken it more, and probably to weaken some of the wood fiber structure in a small way. The usual practice is to neutralize the acid by applying a strong base solution, such as bicarbonate of soda dissolved in water, and then to wash this off. In spite of the fact that Carl Pippert has been successful in not using a base solution after the acid application, it seems advisable to do so. Bicarbonate of soda is inexpensive and easy to apply.

Chromic acid, which is a solution of CrO_3 crystals in water, produces a good brown color on gun stocks, initially, but with time the acid converts to the divalent state and the brown-stained wood takes on a greenish cast. It is not recommended for stock staining. In the 1960s a Lancaster PA gunsmith died from too much exposure to this acid in his stock finishing.

If there is any impression to be gathered from the foregoing, it is to do a lot of experimenting with scraps of wood before working on the finished stock with stain or acid. No two samples of curly maple will appear exactly the same color after any particular stain has been applied.

SEALING AND FINISHING THE WOOD

After the staining has been done and the wood is dry, it remains to seal the wood and give a final finish to its surface. Ideally, three things need to be done:

1) The wood needs to be sealed at depth to keep out moisture.
2) Pores in the wood at or near the surface need to be filled.
3) An overall finish needs to be applied to the wood.

Ideal materials to do all of this have not yet been perfected, but in recent years some very important progress has been made.

The traditional old finish for a gun stock is boiled linseed oil, so the story goes. But linseed oil has its limitations. It is not particularly good as a deeply penetrating sealer. And it is not particularly good for filling surface pores as it does not readily harden, and when it does finally harden after much time has past, it cracks and shrinks. It certainly is not moisture-proof. And it is slow to use because it is so slow to dry. It can be loaded with dryers, but then tends to produce a hard shine rather than the soft gleam more desired. But it can be used as a surface finish after the pores have been filled.

Carl Pippert and a number of other experienced gunsmiths of today use linseed oil with good success. Ample time is allowed for each application to dry before the next coat is applied. For his final coats, Carl does a kind of French polish. He takes a piece of cheese cloth and folds it into a ball, which he then dips in linseed oil, and rubs thoroughly over a small portion of the stock. Then he dips the ball in some fresh shellac, and rubs the same area. As soon as this area begins to dry, he moves to the adjacent area, overlapping a bit. After the whole stock is treated in this fashion, he rubs on a thin coat of linseed oil with the palm of his hand.

After a day or two has passed and the oil is thoroughly dry, it is time for additional coats. Use uncut linseed oil. The oil should be applied with the fingertips, and thoroughly rubbed around to produce a thin film. Use an old toothbrush to clear the excess out of the carving. Puddled oil should not be allowed to dry on the stock. After each application, rub the stock lightly with fine steel wool. And rub some more with the hands and with a soft cloth. Linseed oil dries slowly. Never add another coat before the preceding one is thoroughly dry, or a gummy finish develops.

Various oils intended for use on gun stocks are available today, such as Linspeed and Birchwood Casey's Gunstock Oil. They dry quickly and produce hard shiny surfaces. This shine generally is avoided in finishing a longrifle, and if one of these oils is used, the shine can be cut by rubbing the finish with steel wool dipped in linseed oil or in a slurry of linseed oil and powdered pumice stone. However, there always are problems with the carving. Avoid getting Linspeed in the carving, and if you do, get it out immediately with a toothbrush.

Jim Chambers has developed an oil-type finish made from tung oil and linseed oil, with dryers added to speed up the drying and finishing time. He calls this Traditional Oil finish and it can be obtained from him (see listing of suppliers at back of book).

In the past quarter century of longrifle building not enough attention has been paid to the use of varnish finishes. A careful look at a lot of old rifles shows that varnish was the original finish on many of them. In the manuscript for his very thorough, but not yet published, book about the making of muzzle-loading rifles, ART OF THE FIRE-LOCK RIFLE, John Bivins points out that "Copal and dammar varnishes were particularly favored by early stockers because they were fast-drying and gave a hard and relatively waterproof finish, yet could be easily rubbed out to a lustrous sheen." He also points out that colorants commonly were added to the varnishes, such as derivatives from alkanet root, which produces a red tint over the base stain. The same effect can be obtained by adding small amounts of Laurel Mountain Forge's antique Wood Stain to a varnish finish.

John Bivins recommends the use of a urethane varnish system, Permalyn Sealer and Permalyn Gun Stock Finish, developed by fellow gunsmith Rick Schreiber. Bivins was so impressed with the product that for some time he re-marketed the product under his own label as Express Oil Sealer and Finish. John no longer sells the finish, but it still can be obtained from most Muzzle-Loading Suppliers or directly from Rick's company, Laurel Mountain Forge, P.O. Box 224, Romeo, MI 48065.

With varnish finishes of this type, the purpose of the "sealer" coat is to get it deep into the stock, to protect against moisture damage. The "finish" coat fills in the surface pores and develops the final surface finish.

The system Rick uses with his Permalyn is as follows. After staining the wood, the first coat of Permalyn Sealer is applied liberally, using a soft bristled brush, into the barrel channel and other inlet areas, and to the entire outside of the stock. Let this stand for 15 minutes, and wipe off any remaining excess, using an old toothbrush to get it out of depressions in the carving. Then let the whole stock stand and dry about 8 hours at normal room temperature.

After drying, apply a second of coat of Permalyn Sealer exactly as before. Allow this second coat of sealer to dry for three or four hours, or until the sealer is dry to the touch. Continue applying sealer and allowing to dry, until you first start to notice a slight gloss build up on the stock surface. This is your indication that the sealer has done its job and you are now ready to start applying finish. The number of coats of sealer it takes to get to this point is naturally dependent on the porosity of the wood. For typical hard maple stocks, only two or three coats of sealer are required.

After the last coat of sealer has dried, you are now ready to apply the finish coats. Apply the finish to a small area of the stock using a soft lint free cloth by daubing the finish evenly over the surface. The secret is to apply just the right amount. You are trying to build the finish up in the wood, not pile it up on the surface. Apply the finish to one side of the butt first. Distribute the finish by rubbing lightly with the fleshy part of the palm of your hand. Initially rub briskly, with moderate pressure, gradually relaxing the pressure as the finish warms and starts to "tack up". If you were to grab the stock at this point you would be able to mar the surface, so some care is required in handling. If you find you have marred the surface with a finger print, palm print or other type of surface damage, just add some additional finish to the damaged area. The damaged spot will be re-dissolved allowing the area to be smoothed again. Once you get an area covered, move on to an adjacent spot until the entire stock is finished in this manner. Remember that the finish is still tender at this point. Do not touch the surface until the stock has fully dried in about three or four hours.

Once the first coat of finish has dried, apply additional coats in the same manner, being careful to apply the coats as uniformly as possible. After about two coats of finish, most of the wood pores and sanding scratches will have been filled. At this point you will notice that the gloss is starting to build on the surface of the stock. From this point on, each additional coat of finish should be smoothed lightly between coats with #000 steel wool. This serves not only to level the surface and remove any imperfections, but also it enhances the adhesion between coats. After steel-wooling the stock, vacuum the surface carefully to remove all traces of the steel wool and the dust from the smoothed finish.

When applying a varnish finish coat such as Permalyn, be careful that the finish does not build in any of the checkered areas or next to relief carving. Using the same technique you used with the sealer, go over the area with a soft-bristled brush, to lightly smooth away any of the buildup. After brushing the area, re-smooth the surface with hand rubbing if necessary.

Once you have filled all the grain on the stock and you are satisfied with the overall appearance, you need only apply the final smoothing coat. This coat fills the remaining surface scratches left by the steel wool and gives you the final gloss. For the final coat, use a hand rubbed coat of Permalyn Sealer, as it dries a little slower and does not build as fast as the Permalyn Finish.

This varnish finish has stood the test of rough usage in all weather conditions far better than any linseed oil finish.

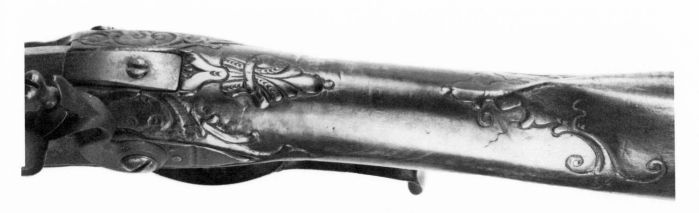

Relief-carved decoration on an 18th century rifle from the Lehigh Valley of Pennsylvania. See also p. 48.

This rear sight, present on a Pennsylvania smooth-rifle of the pre-Revolutionary period, is a very good one, with a wide top, adequate height above the top of the barrel, and a sloping rear surface.

A much more typical Pennsylvania rear sight is this one, which is barely adequate. Its top is not very wide and it is not very high. The rear surface is vertical.

Though the sight is typical, the long decorative finial is not.

Elaborate decorative sight finials are very rare on old rifles, being found on one out of perhaps 200 old rifles.

Decorated sight finials are authentic old details, but they certainly are not typical.

This elaborate sight finial is present on a rifle made in the South.

CHAPTER 32

SIGHTS

While the stock is being finished with patience, some attention can be paid to the barrel. The surface of the barrel needs to be finished smooth in preparation for browning or bluing, the sights need to be made and installed, and the touch-hole needs to be installed.

The barrel surface, as it came from the maker, probably was not completely finished. It is probable that the surfaces of the barrel flats were formed with a milling machine, and this process leaves irregularities that must be removed. Also, in the course of building the rifle, the barrel no doubt acquired a surprising number of small dings and dents. These barrel flats need to be made smooth, and the initial work is done with a file. A flat mill file with fine teeth, bastard cut, is best for this work. The usual method is to hold the file with one hand on either end and to draw it toward you along the barrel. This is the process of draw filing. The axis of the file is held at some angle to the axis of the barrel rather than being parallel to it or perpendicular to it. The particular angle is not critical and can best be judged by what seems to work well for the user. Use a file card to keep the teeth of the file clear, and wipe the barrel with a cloth to keep it free of cuttings. After filing, proceed to various grits of abrasive paper, always backing them with a wood block or other solid flat object. The final finish need not be put on the barrel, at this stage, for that should wait until just before the browning or bluing is done.

Two important facts must be acknowledged from the start about longrifle sights. The first is that old flintlock longrifles almost invariably were equipped with simple open sights. The only exception to this of any consequence is that late in the flintlock period some heavy-barreled bench rifles were equipped with original peep sights. The second fact is that you can shoot more accurately with peep sights. Whether to stick with tradition, or aim for accuracy, is a choice that you must make. It is not entirely out of the question to make a combination system that allows both kinds of sights to be used. Eighteenth century rifles from central Europe often were equipped with folding leaf open sights. Two realities of current usage help tilt the decision toward open sights. One of these is that those who establish rules for authenticity at muzzle-loader's gatherings often rather arbitrarily rule out the use of peep sights. The second is that Pennsylvania, the nation's leading deer hunting state, offers a special deer hunting season in which only flintlock rifles equipped with open sights can be used.

Open sights on old rifles often were set very low on the barrel. Front sight heights of 1/16 or 3/32 inch were not unusual. Both front and rear sights were ruggedly made and were rather immune to damage from rough or careless handling. For a shot at a deer in the shade of the forest they served adequately. But if the sun is present to beat upon the barrel, heated air immediately above the barrel renders such low sights useless for precision shooting, by refracting light as it passes through. The remedy for this is higher sights. Today's shooter will spend a lot more of his time shooting on the target range, and often in the sun, than he will in the shady forest glade. By making the front sight at least 3/16 inch high, and preferably about ¼ inch high, most of this undesirable heat wave distortion can be eliminated.

Front and rear sights are installed in dovetail slots in the same manner that barrel loops are installed. The front sight blade initially is made about 1/16 inch higher than the anticipated finished height will be, so that it can be filed away later to adjust for elevation. It is installed and left alone. Necessary adjustments in the lateral direction are made on the rear sight.

To make a front sight, first mark its position on the barrel. On old rifles this generally was centered on the vertical plane formed by the rear end of the muzzle cap. A dovetail slot, no more than ½ inch wide at the top, and 0.062 to 0.070 inch deep, is cut in the barrel. A piece of brass up to 1/8 inch thick is annealed, and then filed to fit into the dovetail. A few taps of the hammer on top will insure that it fits perfectly snugly into the dovetail. Leaving the ends long, file the top flush with the surface of the barrel. Scribe a centerline for the blade.

The blade can be either of brass or silver, which are the traditional metals for it. On late flintlocks, and percussion rifles. German silver sometimes was used. When the American Fur Company ordered English-Pattern trade rifles from the Henry factory in the late 1830s and early 1840s, it specified front sights of electrum, which was another name for German silver. German silver is stronger than Sterling silver, and makes a good blade even for a rifle of early styling. The width of the blade is a matter of choice. If it is too narrow, it becomes difficult to see, except under favorable conditions. However, for target shooting, a blade about as thick, visually, as the apparent width of the black bull of a 50-yard target (2 7/8 in. diameter) as viewed from 50 yards, is desirable, which is a relatively narrow blade, of the order of 1/16 inch thick. Blade widths between 1/16 and 1/8 inch are typical, and one that is 3/32 inch wide is a good choice with which to start. If this proves too wide, it can be narrowed with a file.

To make the blade, begin with a rectangular piece 7/16 inch wide, 1 or 1 ¼ inches long, and 3/32 inch thick. First, cut away most of the bottom of the blade, to leave a lug that will fasten it into the sight base. Note that the blade is not symmetrical in profile, and that the front end extends forward much more than the rear end extends backward from the sight base. Then cut out the profile of the sight. Scribe lines are made on the sight base to represent the limits of the sight blade, and the sight base then is removed from the barrel and drilled twice to begin the slot for the blade. The slot is finished up with files, and the inner corners are completed with small bevels. With the blade securely held upside down in the vise between protective jaws, the blade is peened or riveted to the sight base. Smooth and polish the sides of the blade, and file away any irregularities underneath the sight base from the fastening of the blade.

Now finish up the barrel in the region of the front sight, for when the sight is placed in the barrel, it need not be removed again. The sight is carefully tapped into place. The lower surface of the sight, which rests against the surface of the barrel must fit snugly, and may need to be filed carefully for a tight fit. This is how Rudi Bahr makes his front sights, and it is a good old traditional method.

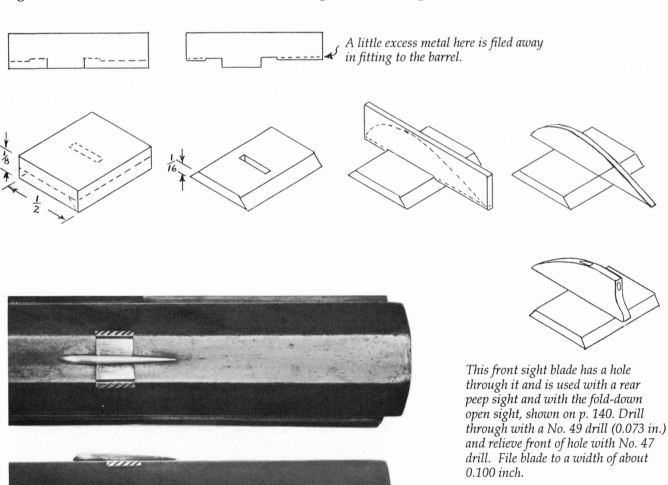

A little excess metal here is filed away in fitting to the barrel.

This front sight blade has a hole through it and is used with a rear peep sight and with the fold-down open sight, shown on p. 140. Drill through with a No. 49 drill (0.073 in.) and relieve front of hole with No. 47 drill. File blade to a width of about 0.100 inch.

Of course it is possible to use silver solder to fasten the two parts of the front sight together. Silver solder is strong enough that there is no need to make a lug to fit into a slot in the sight base. And even if Rudi's traditional method is followed, it could be helpful for purposes of strength to apply a very light touch of silver solder where the blade meets the base. A few old rifles are known that have long front sights fastened to the barrels with two separate dovetail bases. Dealers in muzzle-loading rifle supplies offer many kinds of ready-made front sights, and if one of suitable size and shape can be found there is nothing wrong in using it.

The rear sight is more of a problem to make than the front sight. In the old days it traditionally was made iron, and so today would be made from steel. Rear sights on old rifles range from low things of poor design that are just barely adequate for aiming a rifle, to rather sophisticated pieces that take the open sight about as far as it can go in practical design. The most sophisticated rear sights in the old days were those used on the long and heavy barreled chunk guns from the mountains of eastern Tennessee.

The location of the rear sight calls for consideration and experimentation. For accuracy, the front and rear sights should be as far apart as possible. But if the rear sight is too far back it is difficult to keep in focus with the eye while also looking at the front sight and the target. An additional consideration that seems to have escaped some old time gunsmiths as well as some modern ones is that it is a great pain-in-the-hand to carry around a rifle if the rear sight is located right at the balance point of the rifle. For a hunting rifle that is to be carried all day, this is not a matter to be taken lightly. In determining the location of the rear sight it is advisable to take a piece of tape about 3 to 4 inches long and put it on top of the barrel centered on the balance point of the rifle. By eliminating this region from consideration, the sight must end up in front of or behind the balance region. If a tapered-and-flared barrel is being used, the balance region probably will be far enough back that the sight will readily go in front of it.

The eyesight of the rifle user is another matter for consideration. Young eyes can tolerate a sight relatively close to the breech. Eyes of middle-age and beyond, call for a rear sight well down the barrel. To determine a good position for the rear sight, take a piece of tin can or other sheet metal and snip out a rear sight with a tab bent at right angles so that it can be fastened temporarily to the barrel with a piece of tape. Try this at different positions along the barrel and it will help solve the location problem. Also, with tin try-sights one can experiment with various sizes and shapes.

A wide range of shapes and sizes of rear sights were used in the old days, some just barely adequate, and some at the other extreme, rather sophisticated. Most sights were flat on top, but in the late flintlock and percussion periods, sights sometimes were turned upward at the sides, and in the more extreme cases became what are called buckhorn sights. Pennsylvania rifle makers almost always made their rear sights in an unsophisticated manner. The top was flat and of modest width, ½ to 5/8 inches wide being typical. The back face of the sight usually was vertical. Sights with concave profiles, of the buckhorn and semi-buckhorn types, are only rarely found on Pennsylvania rifles, but in Maryland, Virginia, and West Virginia, they are not unusual. The long-barreled match rifles of eastern Tennessee have the finest rear sights. They are almost always flat on top, and may be as much as an inch wide. Small ears sometimes are left at the extreme ends of the top flat, projecting upward 1/32 to 1/16 inch. These ears can be a useful visual aid in aiming. The back surface of a southern mountain rifle sight almost always has a slope to it to help keep it in the dark and to minimize the reflection of light from it.

From the optical point of view, the rear sight should be perfectly black and reflect no light. Ideally it should be of zero thickness at the notch so that there are no sides to reflect light and produce refraction at the edges. But to be practical the vertical blade of the sight should be at least 1/8 inch thick, and typically it is thicker. Therefore it is desirable to reduce the thickness of the sight in the vicinity of the notch. This can be done with the aid of a rotary file held in a drill press chuck or in a hand-held electric drill. It can be done with a milling machine with a small ball-end cutter. It also can be done, as it was in the old days, with a drill, if the metal is left thick enough at the start and then cut to its finished thickness after drilling. In the old days it also may have been done with a handmade rotary file held in a brace.

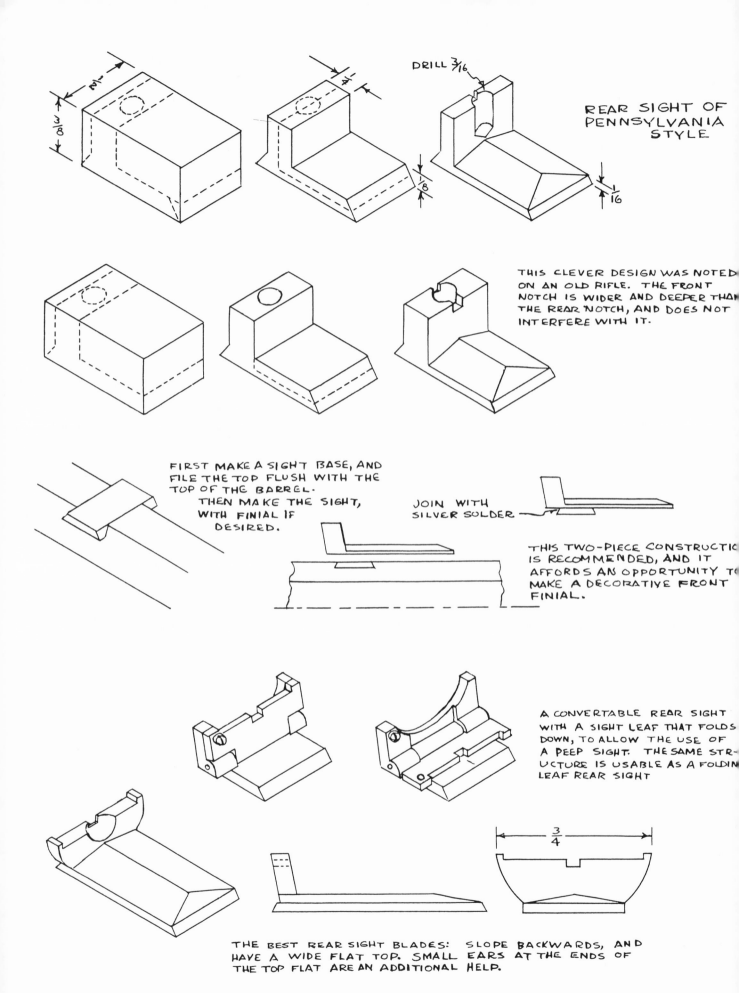

DRILL 3/16

REAR SIGHT OF
PENNSYLVANIA
STYLE

THIS CLEVER DESIGN WAS NOTED
ON AN OLD RIFLE. THE FRONT
NOTCH IS WIDER AND DEEPER THAN
THE REAR NOTCH, AND DOES NOT
INTERFERE WITH IT.

FIRST MAKE A SIGHT BASE, AND
FILE THE TOP FLUSH WITH THE
TOP OF THE BARREL.
    THEN MAKE THE SIGHT,
WITH FINIAL IF
DESIRED.

JOIN WITH
SILVER SOLDER

THIS TWO-PIECE CONSTRUCTION
IS RECOMMENDED, AND IT
AFFORDS AN OPPORTUNITY TO
MAKE A DECORATIVE FRONT
FINIAL.

A CONVERTABLE REAR SIGHT
WITH A SIGHT LEAF THAT FOLDS
DOWN, TO ALLOW THE USE OF
A PEEP SIGHT. THE SAME STR-
UCTURE IS USABLE AS A FOLDIN
LEAF REAR SIGHT

3/4

THE BEST REAR SIGHT BLADES: SLOPE BACKWARDS, AND
HAVE A WIDE FLAT TOP. SMALL EARS AT THE ENDS OF
THE TOP FLAT ARE AN ADDITIONAL HELP.

One old method of making a rear sight has considerable merit from the optical point of view as well as being easy to make. The finished sight blade is about ¼ inch thick. A hole of about 3/16 inch diameter is drilled downward into it at the center. The rear surface of the sight then is filed to the point where the wall between it and the hole is 1/32 inch thick at the most, and possibly as thin as 1/64 inch. The top surface of the sight is filed to slope forward, so that there are no reflections from it. When notching time comes, there are two vertical walls to notch out. The front wall is notched deeper and wider than the rear wall so that there is no possibility of reflections or diffractions from it. For optimum results the two faces of the sight as well as the hole should have a slope instead of being vertical.

A rear sight is easily made from a small block of mild steel ½ inch thick. First, the dovetail is cut into the barrel, and the male dovetail cut into the block, and the block fitted into the slot. The base of the sight, which lies along the top of the barrel, need be no more than 1/8 inch thick. A vertical hole 1/16 inch in diameter is drilled vertically, or sloping, near the rear end of the sight, so that at least 1/16 inch of metal is left behind it, and no deeper than the top of the base will be. With a hacksaw cut away the excess material and finish the sight to suit. Decorative mouldings can be filed in the base.

On some fine old rifles, particularly those of 18th century origin, rear sights sometimes are found with decorative front finials, which is a carry-over from 18th century German rifles. A front finial should present no particular problem, as it is only necessary to make provision for it when roughly shaping the sight. It also is possible to make the sight out of two pieces of metal, with the dovetail base being a separate piece riveted or silver soldered to the main part of the sight. Jack Spotz used this method to make his sights, and it has been found on at least one old rifle.

For good shooting, the shape and size of the rear sight notch, and the profile of the front sight, as viewed from the rear, are of considerable importance. The old rifle basically was a deer and small-game rifle, intended to be used in the forest and field. For this purpose the polished and rounded front sight of silver or brass worked well. But today, out on the target range, it is a different matter. The old barley corn front sight, and v-notched rear sight are not well suited for aiming at a small black bullseye. Much better for target work are the partridge-type sights, where the rear sight is rectangular in shape and the front sight appears as a post with a square-cut top.

Though final adjustments for elevation and windage must be made on the rear sight through testing on the range, it is possible to make the sights to approximately the correct size before then. On a typical barrel with no taper, the rear sight stands about 1/16 inch higher to begin with than the estimated height of the finished sight. This will allow ample room for adjustment of the elevation out on the range.

There are a variety of front and rear sights available today from dealers in muzzle-loading rifle supplies. Some are milled to basic dimensions and left in the rough for finishing to suit the maker. Others are made as investment castings. In using a rear sight casting, care must be taken to get the dovetail slot in the barrel cut to exactly the right depth, and in the long run it might prove easier to grind away the dovetail base and make a separate base piece. Sights traditionally are driven in from the left side of the barrel, and the dovetail slot may be very slightly tapered.

It is not to be denied that for good target work, peep sights are considerably better than open sights. For hunting also, the peep sight serves as well as, and, in many cases, better than open sights. The problem is that commercial peep sights which are adjustable for windage and elevation are bulky and detract from the appearance of a rifle. The situation can be compromised by making the sights by hand to be small and neat in design. For all but specialized target work, one wants to avoid the hooded front sight and the large micrometer rear sight.

The usual peep sight system for target work uses a front sight with a hole in it that appears to the shooter's eye just slightly larger than the standard black bullseye of a 50-yard target at 50 yards. A suitable front sight for a longrifle can be made with a blade about 5/16 inch high and 0.100 inches wide with a hole drilled in it. If this hole is made with a # 49 drill (0.073 inch diameter) it will be of correct size for a barrel of about 42 inches length. The rear sight is simply a small vertical projection fastened to the barrel tang beside the hammer, where it is most unobtrusive. An aperture of 1/16 inch diameter or larger is used. The design of such a rear sight offers possibilities for something with a decorative touch, in keeping with the rest of the rifle. It can be entirely handmade.

One antique rifle, made by Nathaniel Rowe of Emmitsburg, Maryland, has both a normal open rear sight, and a peep sight, original to the rifle. The peep sight was made in such a way that the open rear sight also could be used. This kind of dual sight system can be made quite easily, giving the best of two worlds. Also, the peep sight can be removed easily for matches which require open sights only.

Many surviving German jaeger rifles of the 18th century are equipped with a small brass fitting with a rectangular hole in it set in the wood on top of the wrist near the comb, or at the front end of the comb. This was to hold a diopter, i.e. a disc perhaps ¾ in. in diameter with a small central hole through it with which the shooter looked at the open sights and the target. These fittings on 18th century jaeger rifles typically appear to be 19th century additions, for shooting match use. But they are not peep sights, and one might be of help, especially to older shooters.

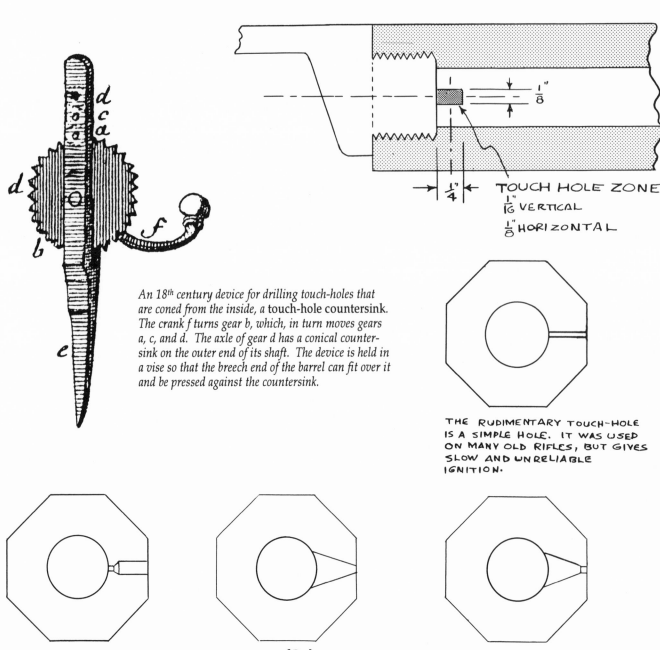

An 18th century device for drilling touch-holes that are coned from the inside, a touch-hole countersink. The crank f turns gear b, which, in turn moves gears a, c, and d. The axle of gear d has a conical countersink on the outer end of its shaft. The device is held in a vise so that the breech end of the barrel can fit over it and be pressed against the countersink.

TOUCH HOLE ZONE
1/16" VERTICAL
1/8" HORIZONTAL

THE RUDIMENTARY TOUCH-HOLE IS A SIMPLE HOLE. IT WAS USED ON MANY OLD RIFLES, BUT GIVES SLOW AND UNRELIABLE IGNITION.

IGNITION SPEED AND RELIABILITY CAN BE IMPROVED BY ENLARGING THE OUTER END OF THE TOUCH-HOLE

THE IDEAL (??) TOUCH-HOLE MAY BE OF THIS TYPE, BUT IN TIME IT WOULD BURN OUT TO A LARGER SIZE.

THE ALMOST IDEAL TOUCH-HOLE COULD BE PRACTICAL — BUT HOW COULD IT BE MADE?

CHAPTER 33

TOUCH-HOLE

With the stock finished, or essentially finished, it is time to make the touch-hole in the barrel. This could have been done earlier in the rifle making process, though there is no particular advantage in it.

For reliable and fast ignition, a well made touch-hole is necessary. A simple hole drilled through the side of the barrel can be adequate, and in the old days most rifle barrels in America had nothing more elaborate. Longrifles frequently saw so much service over so many years that the simple hole in the iron barrel became enlarged to the point of being useless. Then it became necessary to put in a bushing. The corroded hole was enlarged with a drill and then a tap was run in. A short piece of threaded rod was screwed in place and a new hole was drilled.

Fine European guns of the wheellock and flintlock periods often were equipped with more so-phisticated vents. Touch-holes coned out on the inside were used on wheellocks in the 17th century. Bushed holes were common, and often the interior portion of the bushing was made cone-shaped to bring the powder nearer to the touch-hole. To eliminate the problem of corrosion at the vent, inserts of gold or platinum were used on the better grade of guns.

Good ignition is so important to the shooting of a flintlock rifle or gun that it does not make any sense for the rifle maker of today to be satisfied with a simple drilled hole. In making a touch-hole, the problem is to eliminate the long, small-diameter hole that would exist if the main powder charge and the flash pan are merely connected by such a hole. One method is to enlarge the hole at its outer end, leaving the small vent near the powder charge. The second method is to enlarge the inside of the con-necting hole by coning or by drilling it to a larger diameter than the small vent that will be at the outer surface of the barrel. The first method is much better than a long narrow hole. The second method is best of all, and was used on German rifles in the 18th century, and in colonial America too. An 18th century German tool for coning touch-holes from the inside is illustrated on the opposite page. The gunmakers at Colonial Williamsburg have made a similar tool and use it with success.

The size of the touch-hole to be used is partly a matter of personal choice and partly a matter of intended rifle use. For a heavy bench-rest target rifle, shooting powder of FFF grain size, a hole of about 1/16 inch diameter (0.0625), or one made with a # 52 drill (0.063) may be suitable. For off-hand sporting and hunting rifles, shooting powder of FF grain size, a somewhat larger hole is desirable. It is the area of the touch hole that is significant, and to double the area of a hole one increases the radius or diameter by a factor of 1.414, which is the square root of 2. Thus to increase the area of a hole 1/16 inch in diameter (0.0625) to one of double the area, the calculation 0.0625 x 1.414 = 0.088375 shows that a # 43 drill (0.089) would be appropriate to use. The larger hole adds both to ignition reliability and to speed of ignition. The lower limit for hole diameter is about 1/16 inch, and the upper limit is about 1/10 inch (0.100). A hunting rifle touch-hole made with a # 40 drill (0.098) has given fine results. Some powder grains of FF size may come out a hole of this size at loading, but once they are packed in place they do not. A hole of this size has an area 2.56 times that of a hole 1/16 inch in diameter. However, it probably is best to begin with a hole 1/16 inch in diameter, and then to experiment with enlargements. It also is impressive to experience the changes in ignition as hole size is increased.

Most rifles in use today have bushed touch-holes, but it certainly is possible to make a touch-hole without one to get a rifle into use, with the realization that a bushing can be added later. The simplest touch-hole, of course, is a simple hole drilled straight through the side wall of the barrel. Here a hole of 1/16 inch diameter will not be adequate if the barrel diameter at the breech is, say 15/16 inch or larger. However, for a very slender barrel, 13/16 inch across the flats, a 1/16 inch diameter hole may serve well, particularly if the bore is of small caliber and FFF powder is used. Ignition time can be im-proved, however, by enlarging the outer portion of the hole. This can be done by drilling about half way through the barrel wall from the outside with a drill of 1/8 inch diameter, or by using a 60° coun-tersink to make a conical hole. The vent should be somewhat larger than 1/16 inch diameter, and a 5/64 inch diameter hole would be good to start. The possibility also exists of improving the inner end of the hole. With breech plug removed, it may be possible to open up the inner end of the hole some-what with the use of a ball-end rotary file. It also is possible to go a large step further and, after extending the touch-hole through the left side wall of the barrel, and enlarging the hole, to enlarge or even cone out the inner end of the hole. After the work is done, the large hole in the left side wall must be threaded and plugged with a threaded piece of steel. This process was used on some old European arms, and perhaps it was used on a lot more of them than we know about.

However, it is simpler and better to use a touch-hole liner. These liners or bushings are available commercially in a number of sizes, and they can be made relatively easily. One of the easiest bushed holes to make involves the use of an Allen-type set screw, which can be acquired in stainless steel in ¼ -20 or ¼ -28 thread size. The barrel wall is drilled to suitable size for tapping threads, and the threads are not fully cut all the way through the barrel wall, by working with a starting tap. This provides a good tight fit for the Allen screw. An ordinary, non-stainless, screw can be used temporarily if a stainless one cannot be located.

A touch-hole liner can be made from a piece of stainless steel rod ¼ or 5/16 inch in diameter. With the aid of a lathe, if possible, a center hole is drilled, and the inner end of the hole is enlarged with a drill, or coned, or both. The rod is threaded, and as with the Allen screw, seated in a threaded hole in the barrel wall with the threads not fully cut to ensure a tight fit. One can elaborate on the liner by making a small counterbore on the outside of the barrel and a corresponding shoulder on the liner. This ensures that the threads are drawn up tight and may slightly improve the appearance.

Many kinds of touch-hole liners or bushings can be purchased from dealers in muzzle-loading rifle supplies. These are made both in stainless steel and in a hard copper alloy called Ampco. Thread sizes of ¼ -20, ¼ -28, 5/16 – 24, and 3/8 – 24 are available. Some of these are made extra long on the outer end so that they can be tightened with a wrench, cut off, and filed flush with the barrel flat. Some are made with a screwdriver slot on the outer face, so that they can be turned in, and when de-sired, removed. But the slot must end up in line with the barrel so that there is no possibility for pow-der getting behind the lock-plate. Also, if a touch-hole clamp is used as an aid in cleaning the rifle, the screwdriver slot may make it difficult to seal the vent.

It is critical to have the touch-hole correctly located in the side of the barrel for best operation. The powder charge can be ignited with the touch-hole located almost anywhere, as long as it leads to the powder, but for best results it should lie within a certain zone. There is not one exact and precise spot where the touch-hole has to be, but rather a zone where it ought to be. With the barrel held hori-zontally, and viewed from the right side, the touch-hole zone can be defined as the region within the limits +/- 1/16 inch vertical from the center, and from the face of the breech plug forward a distance of ¼ inch. These limits are rather arbitrarily stated as a generalization, suitable to a .50 caliber rifle, and if necessary, could be expanded somewhat for a large-caliber (.58 or .69) rifle or smoothbore gun. Like-wise, for a .30 caliber rifle the zone would be a little smaller.

Many early American rifles had touch-holes located behind the front face of the breech plug. This called for part of the threaded plug to be cut away, and gave the exploding powder charge direct ac-cess to the breech threads. There appears to be no advantage to locating the vent so far back except that it often is required to allow the vent to be centered on the pan while the rear of the fence on the pan lines up with the rear end of the barrel. The modern viewpoint is that it is best to have a touch-hole that in no way interferes with the breech threads.

The ideal place for the touch-hole, in the vertical plane, is such that it intersects the axis of the bore. For bores of .45 caliber or larger it can be as much as 1/16 inch above or below the centerline, if pan location calls for such deviation. For bores of .40 caliber or less it is best to keep the vent on the centerline. The ideal location of the vent in the fore-and-aft direction involves other considerations. The powder charge is restricted to a space that basically is cylindrical in shape, and apparently it is not very critical where along the side of this cylinder the vent is located. Practicality suggests that the vent should enter near the face of the breech plug, but sufficiently far ahead of it that nothing connected with the vent interferes with the breech plug threads. A touch-hole liner of ¼ inch diameter has a ra-dius of 1/8 inch, so it would be favorable to locate the center of the hole slightly more than 1/8 inch in front of the breech plug face, perhaps 9/64 inch or 5/32 inch. For liners of 5/16 or 3/8 inch diameter, additional space is needed.

With barrel and lock installed in the rifle, now is the time to locate the touch-hole exactly. When the lock was installed, an indicator mark was punched lightly in the side of the barrel, to help locate the lock. But during the course of inletting, the lock may have moved somewhat from the intended position. With the hammer on half-cock, and the frizzen open, scribe the location of the bolster and the pan on the side of the barrel. Remove the barrel from the stock and extend the line of the bolster across the top of the pan recess. Scribe a vertical line marking the center of the pan recess. The intersection of these two lines is the ideal touch-hole location. The actual location may have to be slightly different. In any case, avoid locating the vent near the intersection of the pan recess and the barrel, for this gives slow and unreliable ignition.

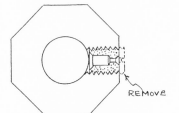

Commercial liners often are of this type. After installation, the outer portion with the screw slot is filed off, and the hole slightly coned.

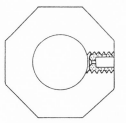

A good liner can be made from an Allen screw of ¼ -20, ¼ -28, 5/16-18, or 5/16-24 thread size. Stainless steel screws are best.

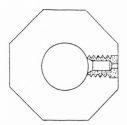

A very neat liner can be made from ¼ inch dia. stainless steel rod. At the outer end the liner is not threaded.

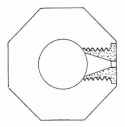

A liner with a shoulder on the end fitting in a counter-bored seat makes a fine touch-hole installation.

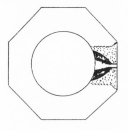

The Chambers liner, of stainless steel, fits against a 45° conical seat in the barrel.

Photos of the Chambers liner, include one cut in half to show shape of inner cavity and the touch-hole.

Jim Chambers offers for sale a well-designed touch-hole liner of stainless steel, available in two sizes. The larger is for barrels 1 1/16 in. across the flats at the breech, or larger. A slightly smaller one is for barrels of 7/8 in. across the flats or larger.

To install a Chambers touch-hole liner for a barrel 1 1/16 in., or larger, across the flats at the breech: (1) Clamp the barrel to the drill press table and drill a hole through the barrel wall using a drill of letter Q size (0.332 in. diameter). (2) Use a 45° countersink to make a seat for the liner at the outer edge of the touch-hole location. (3) Using a 3/8- 32 tap, cut threads in the hole. Keep the tap vertical by using a piece of rod with a pointed end in the drill chuck to hold the top end of the tap wrench in line. The rod fits in the center hole on the top of the wrench. (4) Screw the insert into the barrel, but put some heavy grease on the threads before doing so, and a touch of powdered graphite could be helpful also, but is not necessary. These lubricants might help keep water out of the threads at barrel-cleaning time. (5) With care, use a hack-saw to cut off the outer part of the liner, and then carefully file the outer end of the liner flush with the flat of the barrel.

If the smaller liner is to be used, a drill of size I (0.272 in. diameter) is used for the hole in the barrel wall. This hole is tapped for a 5/16-32 thread.

A unique touch-hole liner in stainless steel is offered by Keith Casteel. It screws into a hole in the barrel tapped for a 5/16 -24 thread. This liner has two separate holes leading from the pan, and it works very effectively.

145

CHAPTER 34

BLUING OR BROWNING THE BARREL

In the old days of longrifle building, barrels were finished on the exterior in one of three ways – polished bright, browned, or blued. The polished-bright surfaces, in the "white," were the easiest to produce, of course, and the most troublesome to care for.

The appearance of old barrel surfaces today usually is that of rusted iron, and one tends to conclude that generally they were finished by a browning process. But careful observations, particularly by the gunsmiths at Colonial Williamsburg, have shown that many old longrifle barrels originally were finished by bluing, which over long periods of time – 150 years or more – often have aged to appear as if originally browned. These observations are supported by early published accounts. For example, in the 1 May 1781 issue of the Philadelphia newspaper, the *Pennsylvania Gazette,* an advertisement by the gunsmiths Perkin and Coutty stated that, "They also blue and brown Gun Barrels in the neatest manner." The publication mentioned at the top of the next page quotes an advertisement in the *Virginia Gazette* of 1751 by the gunsmiths David and William Geddy of Williamsburg that describes "Barrels blued, bored, and rifled …"

PREPARING THE BARREL

Whether the barrel is to be finished bright, blued, or browned, its exterior surface needs to be prepared for the finish. The same procedure is used for all of these finishes, and it is simply a matter of making all the exterior surfaces very smooth. Begin by using a finely cut flat mill file, working on one barrel flat at a time. Hold the file on the barrel flat with its axis at about 45° to the axis of the barrel. Draw it toward yourself (draw filing), or push it away from you, removing machine marks plus scratches and dents that have developed during the stocking process. Be thorough, and smooth off all eight flats.

If you are working with an octagonal-to-round barrel, treat the round section as if it is a curved "flat," using lengthwise strokes. For all the filing, use a file card to keep the cutting surfaces clear.

With the initial filing complete, use emery cloth of 180 grit size, double in thickness, backed by a flat file. Work until all file marks and any remaining scratches are gone. Progress to 200 grit, then 320 grit, and finally 400 grit emery paper. Resist the temptation to use 600 grit paper if bluing or browning is to follow, for the surface must not be too smooth. However, if you intend to finish the barrel by fire bluing, or to leave it bright, the extra smooth surface provided by 600 grit paper is beneficial.

If you intend to put your name and the date of completion of your rifle on the barrel, now is the time to do it. The location should be between the breech end of the barrel and the rear sight, but closer to the sight. German jaeger rifles traditionally had barrel signatures that read from the right side, i.e. the side with the lock. American rifles generally followed this rule, but there were exceptions.

The bluing or browning procedures now follow, and cleanliness is important. Attack the workbench top and shop floor with a vacuum cleaner. Cover the workbench top with a cloth. Have clean cotton gloves, or latex gloves, available to use when handling the cleaned barrel from this point on, for oil from your hands on the metal can affect the finish.

In preparation for either bluing or browning, all the metal surfaces must be thoroughly degreased. Common spot remover (perchchlorethylene) works well, and is cheap. The breech-plug should be removed from the barrel and the threads on both parts also should be cleaned thoroughly.

FIRE-BLUING

The bluing of the surface of iron and steel by the application of heat goes far back in time – thousands of years. It was extensively used in the decoration of both arms and armor in the centuries preceding the development of firearms. This can be called fire-bluing. For steel or iron objects heated in a forge for the purpose of forging or tempering, the term "temper blue" can be applied.

A rifle barrel can be fire-blued by the application of an oxyacetylene torch to its surface. This can be done easily. Rest the breech end of the barrel on a workbench surface, on top of something that will not burn. Hold it in one hand below the mid-point, with the muzzle up, and play the flame back and forth across the barrel until the light-blue color appears. Then chase it to the muzzle. After the barrel has cooled enough to handle, reverse it, with muzzle down, and treat the rear portion.

Fire bluing is easy to do, but an evenness of color is not easy to achieve, and the finish is thin and not very durable. Also, it can not be used with soldered-on lugs or sights.

CHARCOAL BLUING

A more durable blued finish on iron and steel can be provided by baking the metal parts in a bed of charcoal. The charcoal is held in a metal trough and the metal parts are imbedded in it. Heat is applied to the outside of the trough and the charcoal within it is heated almost to the temperature of combustion. Oxidation of the metal surfaces takes place within the special environment provided by the heated charcoal surrounding them. This system was worked out in the gun shop at Colonial Williamsburg by Wallace Gusler, George Suiter, Gary Brumfield, Dave Wagner, and Jon Laubach during the 1990s. Details of this research were described and illustrated in a paper by James Anderson titled "Charcoal Bluing of Rifle Barrels," published in the JOURNAL OF HISTORICAL ARMSMAKING TECHNOLOGY, Vol. 5, June 1993, available from the N.M.L.R.A., P.O. Box 67, Friendship, IN 47021. Further work at Williamsburg since 1993 has added to knowledge of the process and made it a reliable one.

A trough of heavy steel sheet metal, 3/32 to 3/16 inch thick must be made. Sheet metal 1/16 inch thick can be used if angle iron is fastened to the long upper edges. The trough can be 54 in. long for most longrifle barrels, 8 in. wide, and 6 in. deep. Working outside, on the ground, provide supports for each end of the trough about 10 or 12 in. above the ground, using concrete blocks, bricks, or rocks.

Charcoal is the key ingredient in this process, and it must be good, pure hardwood charcoal. Common charcoal briquettes, as used for food preparation, typically are not pure charcoal and, if used, could supply unwanted chemicals to the environment surrounding the barrel. Pure hardwood charcoal in 25-pound bags may be purchased from Imperial Bricket Corp., P.O. Box 28365, St. Louis, MO 63146.

The charcoal, as purchased, will work best if the larger pieces are broken into pieces between ½ inch and 1 inch in length, and some of it should be broken down further, into smaller pieces and powder. This finer material is placed closest to the barrel, under and above it. The empty trough first is filled about 2 inches deep with the charcoal, and then a layer of the finer material is placed on top of that. Then the barrel and breech-plug are laid in place, and the top covered first with more of the fine material, then with the larger pieces.

The trough, on its supports, is heated from below and from the sides by an active wood fire burning the entire length of the trough. A substantial supply of wood of appropriate size must be available, on the site, at the start of this process. Pieces about 1 inch across, or 1 to 1 ½ inches in diameter, and 12 to 20 inches in length would be appropriate. Two logs, each about 4 ft. long, placed on either side of the trough supports, would help to confine the fire area.

Through trial and error the Williamsburg gunsmiths learned that the bluing process proceeds best when the charcoal visible on the top of the trough is hot enough to begin to burn spontaneously. This could be seen by the formation of white ash on the corners of charcoal pieces. Once the charcoal in the trough was up to this heated condition, it was maintained for a time between one and two hours. They also learned that pencil-sized pieces of pine wood about 8 inches long, when one end was pushed into the charcoal near the barrel, and left for a minute, would be smoking when removed if the charcoal at that location was suitably hot. However, to help insure even treatment of the barrel, it was removed from the charcoal bed halfway through the process, and replaced after being turned end for end. This was accomplished with

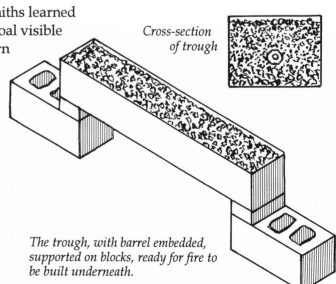

Cross-section of trough

The trough, with barrel embedded, supported on blocks, ready for fire to be built underneath.

the help of hooks bent at the ends of two iron rods. It also has proven helpful to rub the barrels with powdered lime (as used for gardening) every ten minutes, which helps to darken the color. Apply this with a piece of cotton cloth, for any synthetic cloth would melt into a mess.

Repeat the process until an even, dark blue, finish has been attained. Then remove the barrel and breech-plug and let cool. Let the barrel remain untouched for two or three days so that the oxidation scale on it will harden. Then re-heat the barrel and plug gently and wipe them with kerosene if you wish. The kerosene molecule is smaller than the water molecule, and is very healthy for all iron and steel parts. Use a piece of worn denim to rub off the excess. Then, with the aid of mild heat, coat the barrel exterior with beeswax.

CHEMICAL BLUING

Modern chemistry makes possible the bluing of iron and steel surfaces by much easier processes than fire bluing and charcoal bluing. We mention here two commercial products presently available. One is called Tru-Blue Cold Rust Blueing Reagent, developed by William Young of the Wahkon Bay Outfitting Co. of Wahkon, MN 56386. The other is Birchwood Casey's Perma Blue, available both as a liquid and as a paste.

To apply Perma Blue, first de-grease the barrel. Then apply the liquid or paste with a clean cotton pad. Use long smooth strokes. Wait five minutes, and then wash the barrel in cold water, and dry it. Use #0000 steel wool to "card" the barrel. Keep repeating the process until you are satisfied with the color. Then oil the barrel using kerosene or WD40.

BROWNING

The browning of steel and iron surfaces is simply controlled rusting. It was widely used on gun barrels and other parts in the 18th century, and was mentioned in the 1781 advertisement quoted at the beginning of this chapter. Browning was particularly suited for use on military gun barrels because Mother Nature put her sweaty hands on all of them that got into the field, hence the British "Brown Bess" military muskets. In addition, gun parts originally blued, tended to acquire browning from atmospheric moisture over a period of time.

Commercial products are available today that make browning a relatively simple process. One of these is Birchwood Casey's Plum Brown Barrel Finish. Metal parts must be thoroughly cleaned with detergent and hot water, and then be treated with a de-greaser. Then the parts must be well heated when the finish is applied. Adequate instructions are provided with the finish. It is important to card off loose rust particles with #0000 steel wool after each application. This process is not recommended for barrels with lugs and front sights soft-soldered in place.

Browning solutions that do not require the application of heat are available also. One of these is Laurel Mountain Forge's Barrel Brown and De-greaser. It is, of course, best for the barrel to be cleaned and de-greased before applying any browning solution, but this material is a de-greaser in itself, and it will work right through grease, oil film, and fingerprints. It is applied to an un-heated barrel at three-hour intervals, and a typical barrel can be completed with four to six coats. The color of the barrel attained can range from a reddish brown to a dark chocolate. In addition, it is possible to produce a "rust blue" with a deep blue-black color.

The Wahkon Bay Outfitting Co. offers a cold browning solution that provides a finish of hydrated iron oxides that can be controlled and enhanced by the use of a humidity box to control the moisture in the air surrounding the barrel.

Natural browning, done without the use of commercial products can be done easily. A box of plywood or suitable boards is made, long enough to hold the barrel with breech-plug installed, and about 12 inches square, standing upright, and with a hinged door on one side. A light bulb socket with a 40 watt bulb is fastened inside at the top. At the bottom is a small pan of water. The metal parts are wiped with vinegar, or some other acidic solution, and placed in the box for 24 hours. They then are removed, rubbed with #0000 steel wool to remove loose surface rust particles, and placed back in the box. The procedure is repeated a number of times.

CHAPTER 35

RAMRODS

The ramrod is not simply a stick with which to load a rifle, though ramrods found in old rifles may give this impression. The ramrod is a tool with a number of purposes. Unfortunately, the ramrod is the most easily broken part of a rifle, and very few original ones have survived. The ramrods one finds in old guns today are often old, beyond a doubt, but they are not the original ones and often are hardly more than sticks.

In the old days the standard ramrod was equipped with a metal tip of 1 or 1 ½ inches in length, with a threaded hole in the end, or with a smaller diameter shank about ½ or 5/8 inches long that was threaded. An iron worm with a threaded end was screwed into the ramrod tip. This worm held tow, which was unspun flax fibers that come as a by-product in preparing flax for spinning. This tow served to clean out and swab the barrel after shooting. Sometimes a ball-pulling screw also was made with a threaded end that fit the end of the ramrod. Replacement ramrods made in the mid-19th century often lacked the metal tip, probably because the user on the farm made the ramrod himself and was not equipped with the tools or skill to replace the iron tip. Many old records of rifle purchases and contracts specify the worm as a part of the rifle equipment.

Today tow is not used for cleaning rifle bores, so there is no need for worms for that purpose. Instead there is need for a special ramrod tip, called a jag, that makes it possible to swab out a bore with a small circular or square cloth patch. The particular shooter today often runs a cloth patch down the bore after each shot. However, there are times when a cleaning patch gets lost down the bore, and then a worm is needed to remove the patch.

Another feature of old ramrods that we do not often see today, because of the scarcity of them, is the brass tip at the front end of the ramrod. This brass tip was equal in length with the muzzle cap, so that when the ramrod was in place in the stock, the two brass parts terminated at the same point.

The ramrod serves the following purposes:
1) to push a patched ball down the bore in loading,
2) to run a cloth patch down and up the bore in cleaning,
3) to pull a patched ball from the barrel for unloading or in the event that the ball was put down without powder behind it,
4) to remove a cleaning patch that came off the jag by mistake, by means of a worm on the end of the rod,
5) to use as a rest for holding the rifle in hunting when a long shot must be taken and no rocks, trees, or other natural support is available.

Good hickory ramrods are available today from dealers who handle muzzle-loading rifle supplies. Hickory is the traditional wood for making ramrods. Ash, locust, osage orange, oak, and other strong and flexible woods are suitable also. Maple is not good for this purpose, and it would be well to avoid the use of walnut. Dowels made of birch often are available in lumberyards, and these must be avoided also.

Before tips can be put on the ramrod, the diameter must be modified to whatever size is necessary for it to fit through the pipes and into the hole in the stock. This probably calls for tapering the end of the rod where it enters the stock. The rough cutting can be done by eye using a very sharp wood plane, or with rasps and files, or with semi-circular scraping tools of about the correct diameter, to be finished up with sandpaper.

A useful scraping tool can be made from a piece of steel 3 x 5 inches in size and 1/8 inch thick. Scribe a line lengthwise about 1 ½ inches from one long edge, i.e. down the middle of the piece. Mark the center of the line with a punch, and also make punch marks along the line 1 ½ inches on either side of the center. Drill through the plate at the center with a 3/8 inch diameter drill, and use a 5/16 and a 7/16 inch drill for the other two holes. Make a tapered slot connecting each hole to one long edge of the plate. The 5/16 inch hole should be connected to the plate edge with a slot 3/8 inch wide at the edge.

Original iron ramrod tip with threaded end.

RIGHT – ANTIQUE IRON WORM AS IT FITS ON IRON RAMROD TIP.

ABOVE – ANTIQUE LONG SHANKED WORM THAT LEFT RAMROD STICKING OUT A FEW INCHES.

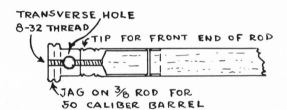

RIGHT – ANTIQUE IRON BALL PULLER IN BRASS RAMROD TIP, WITH SCREW-ON BRASS CAP. PROBABLY FROM A PERCUSSION RIFLE.

BALL PULLER   BRASS CAP

IDEAS FOR MODERN RAMROD TIPS

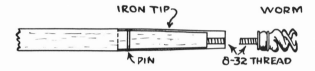

TRANSVERSE HOLE
8-32 THREAD
TIP FOR FRONT END OF ROD

JAG ON 3/8 ROD FOR 50 CALIBER BARREL

TIP FOR REAR END OF ROD

THREADED HOLE FOR WORM
CONCAVE END FOR PUSHING BALL
TRANSVERSE HOLE FOR NAIL TO HELP
PULL TIGHT CLEANING PATCH.

COMMERCIAL JAGS – SHORT & LONG

STEEL BALL-
PULLING SCREW
WITH BRASS
COLLAR
NEAR BORE
DIAMETER

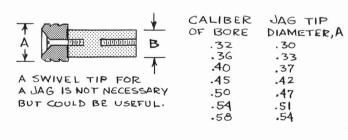

A SWIVEL TIP FOR A JAG IS NOT NECESSARY BUT COULD BE USEFUL.

CALIBER OF BORE	JAG TIP DIAMETER, A
.32	.30
.36	.33
.40	.37
.45	.42
.50	.47
.54	.51
.58	.54

WHEN A JAG IS IN USE, THE CLEANING PATCH BUNCHES UP AROUND THE SHANK. THE SHANK DIAMETER, B, MUST BE ADJUSTED TO THE CLOTH SIZE AND THICKNESS. WITH TYPICAL SQUARE GI PATCHES AND A .50 CALIBER BORE, THE SHANK DIAMETER, B, CAN BE 3/8 INCH.

Likewise the 3/8 hole slot should be 7/16 inch wide at the edge of the plate, and the 7/16 inch hole slot should be ½ inch wide at the edge of the plate. Cut the slots out roughly with a hacksaw, and carefully true up the slots with files. While doing this, give the edges of the slots a bevel so that sharp corners are left to scrape the ramrod. The bevel should continue around the remaining part of the hole. If a piece of carbon steel is used, it can be hardened, but this is not necessary. To use this tool, place it in a vise with the cutting edges away from you. Place a ramrod in the appropriate slot and pull gently on the rod to shave off the wood. The rod can be tapered, or portions of it can be cut to uniform diameter. It is necessary to watch for unfavorable grain direction, and at times reverse the rod in the slot.

To sand a rod smooth and round, the sandpaper can be clamped around the rod with the ends held in the vise. The rod is turned by hand and pulled lengthwise. Also, it can be beneficial to make semi-circular grooves the full length of a piece of wood about 8 inches long. Sandpaper placed in these grooves will effectively help to round a ramrod worked lengthwise in a groove.

The well-equipped ramrod has a metal tip at either end, and today they might as well both be made of brass. The tips can most easily be made on a lathe, though they can be worked out by hand if necessary. Also, they can be purchased ready-made. The outside diameter of the tips should be the same as the outside diameter of the rod where they join it, and the wood should extend into the tip for about ¾ inch. It is absolutely necessary that the tips be fastened with transverse pins that run through the wood and brass, and are riveted. A brass escutcheon pin of 18 gauge is good for this purpose. Epoxy glue helps.

The tip for the front end of the ramrod is basically the same as that for the other end. However, at the front end of the ramrod it is most useful to have a jag for use in running cloth patches down the bore. The physical dimensions of this jag will depend on the relative size of the bore and the rod or of the shank of the jag, and also on the size of the patches used and the thickness of the patch cloth. The end of a jag is reasonably near bore diameter, with enough clearance for the cloth that surrounds it. The shank of the jag must be smaller to provide room for the cloth that gathers around it.

At this point some problems arise concerning the length of the ramrod. Usually a ramrod is made so that it does not project beyond the muzzle of the barrel. If the trigger-guard was made in the traditional way, with the front end held into the stock by means of a lug, this necessarily limits the length of the ramrod to about the length of the barrel. When such a rod is stuck into the barrel it sticks out about the length of the breech plug, which is about ½ inch. But this is not enough to provide very much to grasp if the rod sticks in the barrel when a cleaning patch is pushed down. This may call for a pair of pliers, or a special rod end gripper that can be purchased today. One aid to the removal of a stuck rod is a transverse hole drilled through the tip of the rod, permitting a nail or small rod to be put through to grab. Another aid is a handle that will screw into the end of the rod to grasp for pulling.

In any case, it would be well to consider any possible ways to make the ramrod hole longer. Even eighths of an inch can be of help. By eliminating that fastening lug at the front end of the trigger-guard, the hole can be lengthened by at least ½ inch and possibly more.

One good solution to this problem is to have a cleaning jag which is an extension about 4 or 5 inches long, with a threaded shank that screws into the end of the rod. This can be kept in the patchbox, or in the hunting pouch when not in use. However, if the nature of the rifle bore and its rifling calls for a cleaning patch to be run down the bore after each shot, it becomes a great chore to screw this extension on and then remove it time after time.

It would be well to make or purchase a ball-pulling screw to have available when needed. It still is possible to find old 19th century military ball-pulling screws, though it may be necessary to turn down the outside diameter of the base. These are best because the threads were designed for their special purpose of being pushed into lead. Reproductions of these are offered for sale today, but the large diameter shoulder may need to be turned down to fit the bore size. The rear ends of these screws carry standard machine screw threads of 8-32 or 10-32 size for fastening to the ramrod tip.

Ball-pulling screws made with a threaded front end like a wood screw also are available, and probably are more suited to longrifle use. These have shanks threaded either 8-32 or 10-32 size, and brass discs screwed on the shanks for centering in the bore.

The patchbox is an ideal place to keep the ball-puller, and the jag extension, if one is to be used, though it would be folly to leave them there loose. A threaded piece of metal can be fastened inside the patchbox to hold the two pieces.

Occasionally an old ramrod is found with a ball-pulling screw concealed in the brass tip at the front end of the rod. This is a great idea, but it has to be integrated into the rest of the ramrod complex.

After the tips have been installed on the ramrod, treat it just like the stock, sanding and whiskering until it is perfectly smooth. Toward the middle of the 19th century it became popular in some regions to stain ramrods with a spiral configuration. Where this idea originated, and exactly when, is not known. The spirally strained ramrod may have its place on half-stock percussion rifles, but it definitely is out of place on a carved and decorated longrifle styled to an earlier period. The best thing is to stain the rod a uniform dark brown, and then to seal it well. The ramrod will get lots of wear in the course of use, and will acquire its own color, a mixture of stain color, oxidation color, and black gunpowder residues.

In addition to the ramrod made for the rifle, it is a decided advantage to have a long and sturdy rod made of steel, or some other material guaranteed not to abraid the bore. If a ball must be pulled, the wooden rod may not be up to the task if the ball is well stuck. Of course this special rod does not go everywhere that you and your rifle may go. And if by chance the hickory rod should break in use, you smile because you were clever enough to make up a second rod when the first was being made.

A device for turning down, and for tapering ramrods, has been developed by Michael Lea of Columbus, Ohio. This consists of a hand-held shaving tool that is moved along the ramrod as the rod is turned in an electric drill check. The drill is clamped so that its axis is horizontal.

This tool is a useful time-saver for those making many rifles, but the beginning rifle maker certainly can do without, as did the gunsmiths of old. Additionally, the beginner at rifle-building needs the experience of making a few with plane, rasp, file and sandpaper, and the tool illustrated here.

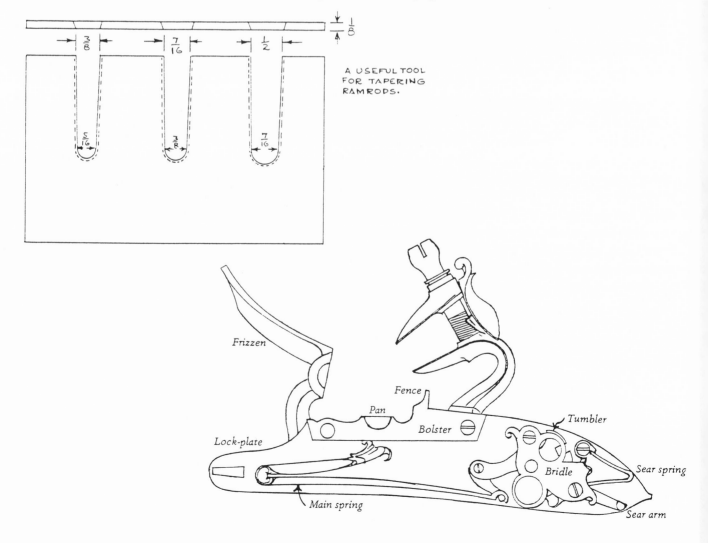

A USEFUL TOOL
FOR TAPERING
RAMRODS.

Frizzen

Fence

Pan

Bolster

Tumbler

Lock-plate

Bridle

Sear spring

Main spring

Sear arm

CHAPTER 36

LOCK NOTES

A flintlock is a spark-making machine that can range from very good to useless, depending on how well it is designed and made and used. Anybody who takes the trouble to build a rifle, or who shoots one very much, almost of necessity learns a good deal about the lock and some of its problems. Even the best of locks, if heavily used, require attention from time to time.

A good many different patterns of locks are available for purchase today, and many of these are available either as finished products or as kits to be finished by a gun maker. Most of the parts for all of these locks are made by the investment casting process. Some have springs made by other methods, but most springs also are made from investment castings. The various locks differ in quality of finish and assembly. Those made abroad are cheaper in cost and of lesser quality as a mechanism. In addition, most of the foreign-made locks are based upon old locks of cheap construction and poor design.

Because all locks are made from investment castings, and are finished more or less in the same way, there is no single "best" lock to buy. Most of the American-made locks are of good quality, but there are differences, and some are not so hot. If you insist on buying "the best," and cost is not a matter of concern, there are a few skilled gunsmiths who will make a lock from scratch for you, to whatever design you specify. Everyone else probably can find one of the better quality investment-cast locks to use. Some well-designed locks are available either as kits to be assembled, or as complete working mechanisms.

The design or style of a lock is of considerable importance. Not only does it affect the appearance of the rifle greatly, but it also affects the way the rifle shoots and functions. Though any lock may throw sparks and fire a gun, the different styles and designs of locks do it differently. Some are more efficient than others. The locks of today are designed or styled after the locks produced in Europe during the second half of the 18th century and the first third of the 19th century. Most locks used on old longrifles were either of German styling and made in continental Europe, or of English styling and principally made in Birmingham and Liverpool. It is desirable, of course, that in recreating a longrifle today, a lock of suitable styling is chosen.

A number of different locks of 18th century German styling are available today. The well-known lock produced by C. E. Siler in recent years and known as the "Siler Lock," no longer is made by him. But both Jim Chambers and Track of the Wolf have carried on, producing locks of the same or very similar design. They go well on rifles showing German heritage in design. Locks of similar design are offered by most suppliers of muzzle-loading rifle parts. These locks are particularly appropriate on guns styled to the last third or last quarter of the 18th century, and their use on pieces styled up to about 1810 is not inappropriate.

Many American longrifles, dating from as early as the 1750s to as late as the 1850s, had locks of English origin. A number of good English-style locks are available today. The better ones are styled after locks on guns of high quality by makers such as Durs Egg, John Twigg, John Bailes and John Manton, and also from quality locks of Birmingham or London manufacture.

When shopping for a flintlock, take a good flint and a piece of leather, a couple of screwdrivers, and a mainspring vise. Your dealer should allow you to test out the lock of interest. First, see how it sparks. You should get a shower that falls into the center of the pan. Observe the action inside. Does the sear click into place crisply in both notches? When the action is set off, does the frizzen open smoothly and quickly? With the aid of the mainspring vise, remove the frizzen spring. Cock and set off the lock again. There should be a shower of sparks even without the spring, for its basic purpose is to hold the pan closed. Target shooters with bench rifles sometimes remove the frizzen spring when in competition. With the spring removed, check the amount of play in the frizzen. If it wobbles from side to side, and has enough play to slide back and forth on the screw shank that holds it in place, it is too loose and will have to be shimmed and possibly even bushed.

Remove the sear spring, and check to see that the lock stays on full cock without its help. If it does

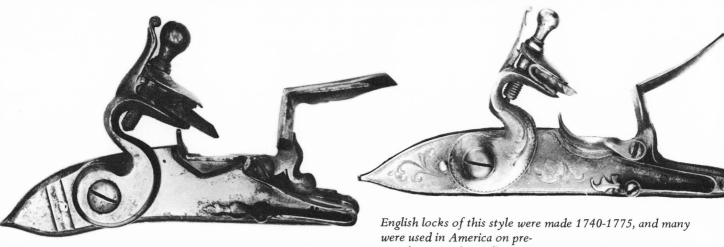

German lock of the 1730-1770 period. Lock-plate length 5¾ inches. Suitable for use on longrifles of pre-Revolutionary styling.

English locks of this style were made 1740-1775, and many were used in America on pre-Revolutionary longrifles. Plate 6 inches long.

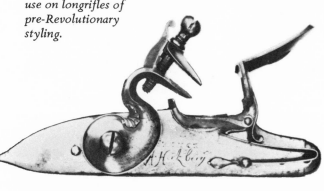

A German lock of the 1740's or 1750's by C. J. Franck. The plate is 5¼ inches long with a gently rounded surface. The water-proof pan is of English style.

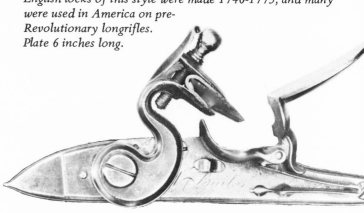

English flat-faced lock-plates also were made in the mid-18th century. This lock, 6 1/8 inches long, is on a gun of 1759. It could be a very good rifle lock.

German lock with rounded plate face, from the second half of the 18th century. The relatively small plate is 4 5/8 inches long. Suitable for use on longrifles of the period 1750-1810.

This particularly sturdy lock, 6 inches long, was made in London by H. W. Mortimer, probably in the 1790's. It is equipped with a good slide safety mechanism, and would make a fine longrifle lock.

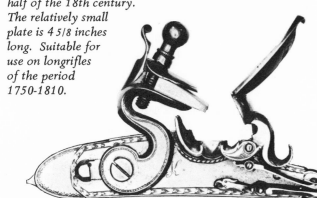

Styled after English pieces of the 1790-1810 period, this lock was made about 1810 by Jacob Kunz who used it on a longrifle of Lehigh Valley style.

Probably of Birmingham origin, this lock bears the name of P.A. & S. Small, a York, Pa., hardware firm still in business today. It is from the late flintlock period, i.e. the 1820's and 1830's. The lock-plate is 5 5/8 inches long.

not, the full cock notch is improperly set in the tumbler, and must be worked on. With the spring back in place, check to see if the hammer will stay on full cock while the back of the hammer is tapped lightly.

Remove the mainspring using the mainspring vise, and the hammer. Unscrew the bridle, and check the fit of the tumbler through its hole in the plate. If it is sloppy, reject the lock. Does the tumbler have a fly, also called a détente? This is essential for use with double set triggers, and may help in the operation of the lock. But its absence is no detriment if the lock is to be used with a simple trigger, and its absence does not indicate a lock of inferior quality.

Check the finish on the inside of the lock plate. All moving parts should be polished to a gleaming finish, but if they are not, it can be done as part of the process of tuning the lock. Lay a straight edge against the inside of the plate to insure that it is not warped.

Reassemble the lock. With the hammer full forward, compress the mainspring slightly with the mainspring vise and remove the hammer. Release the spring tension to see how much farther forward the tumbler will rotate without the hammer in place. Ideally the rotation of the tumbler should be stopped simultaneously by the tumbler meeting the bridle and by the stop on the back of the hammer meeting top edge of the lock-plate.

Perfect locks cannot ordinarily be purchased except from gunsmiths who build them piece by piece. Well designed and well made commercial locks can be tuned to work very well. In buying one of them, it is well to know their minor faults beforehand.

With a particular lock or lock kit decided upon, and purchased, the external appearance needs to be looked at carefully, with the idea that minor alterations could be made to improve it. There is nothing sacred about the exact shape of the lock-plate as it comes from the manufacturer. It may be possible to re-shape it slightly without affecting its function. Be sure not to remove too much metal on the lower edge of the plate, so that the moving parts extend below the plate. For special purposes it may be desirable to make a new plate, as, for example in reproducing a rifle of the style made by John Armstrong.

The flintlock hammer is the first part that catches the eye when looking at a flintlock. The hammer can be graceful and beautiful if carefully designed. Unfortunately, a good many hammers on old locks, as well as on new ones, are not designed as well as they should be. But there is nothing wrong with re-shaping the hammer on a commercial lock if it has enough metal to work with. It is well first to look at illustrations of a lot of old locks and thereby to develop a discriminating eye that distinguishes between the fine and the mediocre.

The shape and size of the jaw screw and its head have an effect on the appearance of the rifle that is far from negligible, yet few realize this or pay much attention to it. Jaw screws are easily made on a lathe, and it is well worthwhile playing with modifications of design if appearance is of concern. Locks of the mid 18th century and on into the Revolutionary period tended to have jaw screws that stood up higher above the top of the top jaw than those on later locks. On the practical side, it is a convenience to have a transverse hole drilled through the head of the jaw screw into which a nail or other piece of metal can be put to open or close the jaws. The screwdriver slot in the tip of the screw head should be wedge-shaped for best appearance rather than having parallel sides. A needle file with a sharp v-shaped cross section can be used to re-shape and deepen the slot. Threads on a jaw screw usually are 12-24 NC or 12-28 NF for small locks, and ¼ –20 or ¼ -28 for larger locks.

Lock parts made by investment casting usually have parting lines left on their surfaces. It is essential that all such lines are filed away. The outside of the lock-plate can be left as it is, after parting lines and other defects are filed away, if a rough browned finish is desired for the lock. But if a beautiful smooth finish is desired, then the plate must be filed and sanded smooth so that all parts gleam. After all that work, the lock can be browned, or blued, or left in the white with the screw heads blued. Another external finish for the lock is beading, a process by which tiny glass beads are thrown against the metal at high velocity, leaving the surface with a nicely matted surface that takes browning well.

Most locks need a little tuning to insure smooth and reliable operation. First check the action of the frizzen. On a good lock the frizzen usually throws open after a rotation of about 25°, or about 1/3 of its full travel. One design of flintlock widely used today, and in most respects well designed, has a frizzen that does not open until it has rotated about 40° or 45°. This causes problems that can be cured

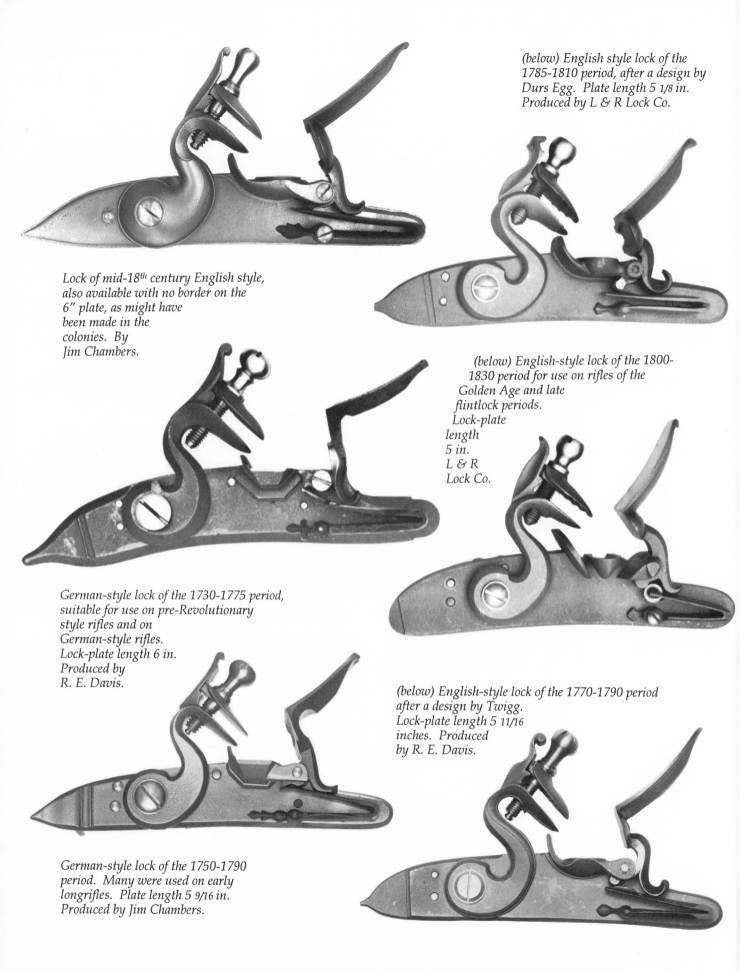

(below) English style lock of the 1785-1810 period, after a design by Durs Egg. Plate length 5 1/8 in. Produced by L & R Lock Co.

Lock of mid-18th century English style, also available with no border on the 6" plate, as might have been made in the colonies. By Jim Chambers.

(below) English-style lock of the 1800-1830 period for use on rifles of the Golden Age and late flintlock periods. Lock-plate length 5 in. L & R Lock Co.

German-style lock of the 1730-1775 period, suitable for use on pre-Revolutionary style rifles and on German-style rifles. Lock-plate length 6 in. Produced by R. E. Davis.

(below) English-style lock of the 1770-1790 period after a design by Twigg. Lock-plate length 5 11/16 inches. Produced by R. E. Davis.

German-style lock of the 1750-1790 period. Many were used on early longrifles. Plate length 5 9/16 in. Produced by Jim Chambers.

The locks shown here are representative of the well-designed and well-made products available today. Other locks for both flint and percussion ignition that are comparably good are available also.

only partially by tuning. Fortunately, another dealer offers an alternative frizzen for this lock with a cam of better design.

Sometimes, because of one problem or another, a frizzen will not open completely when the flint strikes against it, and the two parts come to rest against each other. No sparks get to the pan, and the gun does not fire. There are a number of possible causes for the problem. The flint may be of incorrect length, though with a well designed mechanism the length of the flint should not be critical. The mainspring may be too weak, which can be remedied by heating and re-tempering, or by replacing with a stronger spring. The frizzen spring may be too stiff. Most often, however, the problem arises from the shape of the end of the frizzen spring and its relationship to the cam on the bottom of the frizzen.

Assuming that the problem arises from the relationship between spring and cam, it is possible to make some changes to improve the operation. First, thin the top arm of the frizzen spring by grinding it very carefully, in order not to harm the temper. Polish it partially and try the action. When the operation seems to be improved, polish the newly ground surface carefully and thoroughly to remove scratches that might lead to breakage later.

On many locks the cam on the frizzen points too far forward. If there is enough metal to work with, carefully grind and re-shape the cam so that it does not contact the spring so far forward. Polish it well. As a last resort it may help to put a downward bend in the end of the frizzen spring, beginning where the cam meets the spring when the frizzen is closed. By holding the body of the spring in the vise, with the end projecting upward, it is possible to heat the spring with an acetylene torch at the bend point, and to bend it, without ruining the temper of the rest of the spring.

Long ago, in the middle of the 18th century, if not earlier, the problem of getting the frizzen open was greatly improved upon by the introduction of a roller either on the frizzen cam or on the end of the frizzen spring. A roller on the frizzen has been noted on an English lock dating to 1762. From this time on, and perhaps a little time earlier too, English locks of better quality often had roller frizzens. German lock design remained static during the second half of the 18th century, and rollers were not in use, though doubtless there are exceptions. However, if a lock of German style is to be used today it might not be a great travesty of tradition to make a frizzen with a roller. If the cam is relatively large, a roller only slightly larger in size can be placed within it so that the roller is scarcely visible.

With the frizzen operating to satisfaction, the fit of the frizzen to the pan needs attention. For hunting purposes the fit should be tight, more to keep the powder in than to keep the water out. The frizzen is hardened and usually cannot be filed. However, the bottom of the frizzen should be flat and free from irregularities. Check it on a flat surface such as a piece of glass. And if it needs touching up, put some fine abrasive paper on top of the glass and move the frizzen across it. With the frizzen fastened back in place, put some transfer color on the bottom and press it against the pan. Carefully file away the high spots until a perfect fit ensues.

The inside edge of the bolster, which rests against the barrel, must be perfectly straight, and the fit of it to the barrel should be good and tight. One very important reason for this is to prevent priming powder from falling down the crack, if there is one, to build up and eventually explode. Make sure that when the lock is firmly in place the inner edge of the frizzen does not scrape against the side of the barrel as it opens.

Inside the lock, with the lock-plate straight and polished, make sure that the lower arm of the mainspring does not come into contact with the plate anywhere in the course of its travel. The sear should not contact the plate anywhere except in the region of the pivot. Likewise, the upper side of the sear should be free from contact with the bridle except at the pivot.

The tumbler normally is equipped with half-cock and full-cock notches. First make sure that the front or nose of the sear falls easily into the half-cock notch. This is essential for safety, though a flintlock at half-cock is never completely safe no matter how well the sear fits in the notch. With the hammer at half-cock it is possible that the arm of the sear hangs a little below the edge of the lock-plate. By holding the main part of the sear in a vise, it is possible to heat the arm and bend it upward without doing damage to the hardening of the main part of the sear.

For a smooth and reliable release of the hammer, when the sear leaves the full-cock notch, it is necessary that the edge of the sear and the face of the notch are parallel. The face of the notch on the tumbler should lie in a plane passing through the axis of the tumbler. The curved surface of the tumbler should meet face of the notch at a 90° angle. If this is correctly made, the sear will hold even without a sear spring, and a good test of the mechanism is to remove the sear spring and try the mechanism.

Most locks made today have a fly in the tumbler, so there is no need to describe here how to add one. It can be done, though. When a lock comes with a fly, it is good to make sure that the contact surfaces between fly and tumbler, and the outer surface of the fly also, are good and smooth.

It may happen that the sear is difficult to release even when the notch and sear face are correctly made. The sear spring may be unnecessarily stiff. Thinning the spring is one way of weakening it. Also, it may be too hard. If it is too hard to file it may be too hard to work well. It could be re-heated to red color, quenched, and then drawn back to blue color.

With the mechanism operating smoothly, the hammer may need some attention. Considering the surface of the pan as a horizontal reference plane, the inner surfaces of the hammer jaws typically lie at an angle of about 40° from this plane, when the hammer is down at rest. Ideally, the edge of the flint should be pointed toward the centerline of the pan when the hammer is down. This helps to insure that the incandescent pieces of steel scraped off the frizzen by the flint end up in the priming powder. It may be necessary to heat the neck of the hammer and bend it slightly so that it drops the sparks properly. Be careful not to distort the hammer jaw screw hole.

Many hammers are poorly designed in the jaws. The jaws may be so short that they will hold only the smallest of flints. Another defect is having the top surface of the upper jaw made to be parallel with the lower surface. A better configuration has long jaws, a screw well back, and the upper surface of the top jaw slanted backward so that when the screw is tightened the front of the jaw more effectively clamps on the flint. Some lock manufacturers provide little ridges on the inside surfaces of the jaws to help hold the leather well. A better method, and one frequently found in old locks, is to use a graver and turn up some small teeth pointing backward on both jaws.

Many different sizes and types of gun flints are available today. The traditional flints were, and still are, chipped by hand. However, the few remaining flint knappers in England are leaving the trade for one reason or another. Hand knapped flints may grow scarcer in the future. Flints cut by diamond saw are coming to take their place. These saw-cut flints have the ideal parallel upper and lower surfaces and well shaped leading edges. They are expensive but work very well. Any sharp flint is fine for making sparks in a lock provided that it is of suitable size.

Sheet lead was used to hold the flint in the jaws of old military guns, but the rifle shooter of today almost always uses leather. One of the few good uses for the upper parts of old shoes is leather for flints. The beveled front edge of a flint may lead the newcomer to wonder which side of the flint is put up in the jaws. The geometry of the lock suggests that the bevel should be up, and probably it is best to try the flint this way first. But with the bevel down the flint may tend to sharpen itself a bit with each firing. Either way is fine if it works well.

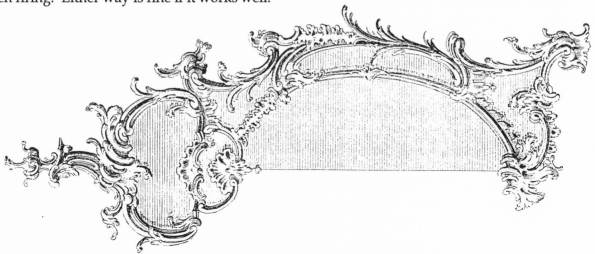

CHAPTER 37

SLING SWIVELS AND SLING

Eighteenth century German hunting rifles very often were equipped with slings. Early American longrifles almost never were equipped with slings, except when they were pressed into military service during the Revolutionary War. The contrast is extreme. Old German gun makers and gun users knew just about everything that was needed to be known about rifles and their use, and hunting rifles were equipped with slings to aid the users in carrying them. For all the rifle toting that was done during the settlement and development of early America, it is truly remarkable that the sling was not put to use. There is no rational reason for it. Looking back from today, the most reasonable explanation seems to be that a tradition got started in colonial America, and was carried on without change.

In spite of the facts of past tradition, a sling can be a useful addition to a longrifle if it is to be carried all day, for more days than one, while hunting. And if the hunter is successful, he finds it helpful to have three or four hands at one time while dragging a deer out of the forest, one at least to carry the rifle.

A longrifle sling is simply a strap, or in its simplest form, a rope, that is fastened at a point part way along the fore-stock and the other end of which is fastened to the underside of the butt-stock about half way between the rear end of the trigger-guard and the butt-plate. Some very early American rifles, of Revolutionary War vintage, have a hole drilled transversely through the front end of the trigger-guard. Apparently a sling swivel was fastened there. Military flintlock arms often have the rear sling swivel fastened just ahead of the trigger-guard. And some German rifles had the rear swivel there also. However, experience in the field while hunting shows that it is far better to have the rear swivel right where most old German rifles have it, about 6 or 7 inches forward of the toe of the butt. One very practical reason for this is that it allows the rifle to be carried under the right arm, upside down, with the sling over the shoulder. In this position the lock is well protected from the rain, sleet, and snow that so frequently are part of the hunting environment.

The traditional fastening for the front end of the sling is a U-shaped swivel fastened to the fore-stock in such a way that it does not fall into the path of the ramrod pipe when the rifle is held vertical for loading, and the rod is being returned to its groove. The best place for this swivel is about ¼ or 1/8 inch ahead of the front end of the middle ramrod pipe. In this position the swivel falls against the ramrod pipe when the gun is held vertical. This swivel can be removed easily when not needed.

One muzzle-loading gun parts manufacturer offers a small and neat front sling swivel made by the investment casting process. In cross section it is semi-circular, with the curved side inward. The screw for it passes through one side of the swivel, the fore-stock wood on one side, a thick metal lug, the fore-stock wood on the other side, and then threads into the head of the swivel. A screw threaded 10-32 probably is best for this. The screw must pass through a metal lug that is securely fastened to the barrel. This calls for adding a lug under the barrel similar to a barrel loop. But the lug should be wide, at least ¼ inch, and possibly 5/16 or even 3/8 inch. This width is necessary so that the screw that passes through it to hold the swivel cannot wiggle in its hole, to damage the wood of the stock.

Many old longrifles are equipped with a small metal inlay located along the lower side of the butt about midway between the rear end of the trigger-guard and the toe of the butt. Often this inlay is pierced with a hole that seems to serve no particular purpose, though collectors often state that this was to hold a feather for cleaning the touch-hole, but most of these holes are small and not deep enough to hold a feather or to serve any other apparent purpose. A few old rifles have a special touch-hole pick screwed into this hole. The hole, or inlay and hole remain an unsolved mystery of the long-rifle. It helps to preserve the curious old tradition of this inlay and its hole to put one on a rifle made today. It is most reasonable to make the hole useful as a threaded hole to hold the rear swivel.

The sling can be anything that suits the fancy of the user. It need not be large and bulky, and it affords the opportunity to add one more touch of color to the rifle if made of hand-woven material, flat braided macramé string, or fabric enhanced with embroidered designs. It can be made of leather. At the minimum, it could be a piece of nylon parachute shroud tied on only when needed for hunting.

The forward sling swivel is mounted slightly ahead of a ramrod pipe, so that when the rifle is held vertical, the loop falls against the pipe and does not block the ramrod channel.

The rear sling swivel can be small and easily removable. The one shown here screws into a piece of steel imbedded in the stock under the small brass inlay.

CHAPTER 38

PISTOL MAKING NOTES

In general, the same techniques used to make a rifle apply to making a pistol. The only real problem lies in holding the piece while working on it. Some consideration therefore should be given to the order of operations, so that the piece can be held in the vise as long as possible.

An important difference between rifle and pistol making comes in laying out the trigger location. A pistol that does not fit the hand well is difficult to shoot well. For layout, first shape the profile of the pistol butt. Some preliminary rounding of this area can be done after drawing a centerline completely around the butt. The objective is to have a pistol butt that the user can hold, and hands do vary considerably in size. With the pistol stock in hand, mark the position of the trigger where the trigger finger naturally falls, assuming that the stock is sufficiently rounded in this region to give a reasonable feel for the hand and finger. Now locate the lock position on the stock such that the sear bar will be ¼ inch behind the trigger. Note and mark the position of the center of the pan. The breech end of the barrel will go 5/8 inch to the rear of this point. This method could be useful in laying out a rifle also. With these basic measurements determined, proceed to inlet the barrel, run in the ramrod groove and hole, and all the other operations common to both rifle and pistol.

The pistol butt also can present a problem or two. One problem that does not arise is that of cast off or cast on. If there is to be a cap on the butt it should be inlet after the barrel and lock are in place. Assuming that a cast brass cap will be used, it first must be filed smooth and the edges trued up. The cap is slowly let into place, proceeding by cutting and trying. Usually the cap is fastened at the bottom by a large wood screw. It may be beneficial to drill the cap for the screw, and after some preliminary inletting is done, drill the wood for the screw, so that the screw can be used as a guide for settling the cap into place.

With the cap in place, the final profile of the pistol can be determined and the wood brought to shape. The trigger, trigger plate, and tang screw are now installed. A problem may arise in inletting the rear end of the trigger-guard because it is a curbed piece. First an opening is made in the stock to accommodate the fastening lug at the front end, then the guard is placed in the correct position and the wood marked for inletting the forward extension. Then this is let in. Next go to work on the rear portion of the guard, first marking its position carefully with respect to the centerline. But make the layout short by about 1/8 inch at the end. Then inlet. Cut a spur on the end of the guard and undercut the wood to take the spur. Be careful here because the wood can break easily due to the unfavorable wood grain direction. Then force the spur into the inlet and bring the forward end of the guard down for a trial fit. If it will not go in its mortise a little more wood may have to be removed at the spur end. With the trigger-guard in place, wait until the ramrod pipes have been inlet before shaping the lock panels and rounding and shaping the rest of the stock.

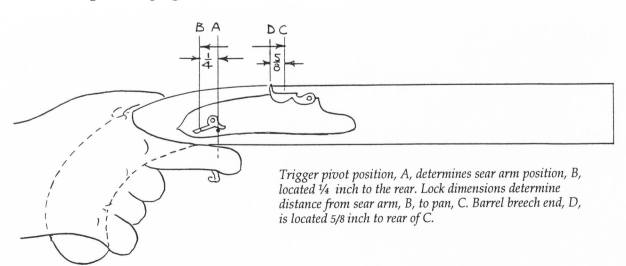

Trigger pivot position, A, determines sear arm position, B, located ¼ inch to the rear. Lock dimensions determine distance from sear arm, B, to pan, C. Barrel breech end, D, is located 5/8 inch to rear of C.

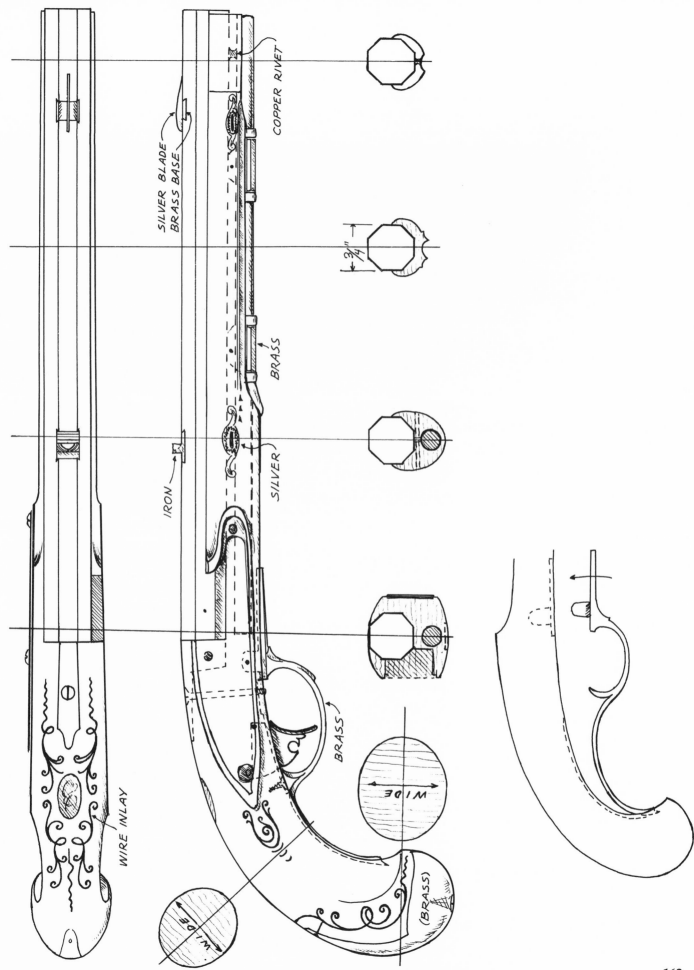

SILVER BLADE

BRASS BASE

COPPER RIVET

3/4"

BRASS

IRON

SILVER

WIRE INLAY

WIDE

WIDE

BRASS

(BRASS)

REFERENCE BOOKS FOR THE MUZZLE-LOADING ARMS MAKER

The titles listed below are of particular importance to anyone interested in building muzzle-loading arms. They contain insights and information not found in this book, and we encourage readers to examine these texts also.

BUILDING LONGRIFLES WITH THE GUNSMITH OF GRENVILLE COUNTY   by Peter Alexander   Scurlock Publishing. Co.
The author's many articles on rifle building as published in *MUZZLELOADER* magazine are reprinted here.

THE ART OF BUILDING THE PENNSYLVANIA LONGRIFLE   by Dixon, Ehrig & Miller   Dixon Muzzleloading Shop
This heavily illustrated book can be a very useful aid and guide for the rifle-maker, and it provides techniques, insights, and instructions not found in RECREATING THE AMERICAN LONGRIFLE.

BUILDING THE KENTUCKY RIFLE   by James R. Johnston   Golden Age Arms Co.
By means of 21 full-size drawings, this book guides the reader through the step-by-step procedure of rifle building.

BUILDING THE KENTUCKY PISTOL   by James R. Johnston   Golden Age Arms Co.
By means of 21 full-size drawings, this book guides the reader through the step-by-step procedure of building a pistol.

BOOKS ABOUT ANTIQUE AMERICAN MUZZLE-LOADING ARMS

The titles listed below are of principal importance to anyone involved in building or recreating muzzle-loading rifles and pistols.

RIFLES OF COLONIAL AMERICA, VOL.I & II Second Edition   by George Shumway   G. Shumway Publisher
An extensive photographic study of longrifles made in the colonial period and the post-Revolutionary years before the Federal Period. For each of the more than 150 rifles or guns treated here there are at least ten detailed photographs, plus an account of the piece and its dimensions.

THOUGHTS ON THE KENTUCKY RIFLE IN ITS GOLDEN AGE Third Edition   G. Shumway Publisher
by Joe Kindig, Jr., and George Shumway
American flintlock rifles from Pennsylvania and northern Maryland, in their Golden Age, from the revolutionary years to the late flintlock period, are described in detail and illustrated. This new edition to be published in 2000. Previous editions available in the used book marketplace.

KENTUCKY RIFLES AND PISTOLS 1750 – 1850   by James R. Johnston   Golden Age Arms Co.
Valued for its illustrations, this shows more than 650 photos of antique rifles, about 175 photos of antique pistols, and 14 accoutrement photos.

THE PENNSYLVANIA-KENTUCKY RIFLE   by Henry J. Kauffman   Bonanza Books
A valuable source of information about the guns and gunsmiths of old Pennsylvania, with many illustrations of rifles and other guns.

THE KENTUCKY RIFLE   by Capt. John. G. W. Dillin   G. Shumway Publisher
This classic work was first published in 1924. It contains overall views of many rifles and a lot of valuable information.

THE MUZZLE-LOADING CAP-LOCK RIFLE   by Ned H. Roberts   G. Shumway Publisher
A classic reference to rifles and shooting in the percussion period, with many illustrations of cap-lock rifles.

PENNSYLVANIA LONGRIFLES OF NOTE   by George Shumway   G. Shumway Publisher
The longrifle as a work of art is treated here with 100 photographs showing pieces from most of Pennsylvania's important schools of gunsmithing.

THE BEDFORD COUNTY RIFLE AND ITS MAKERS   by Calvin Hetrick   G. Shumway Publisher
A small and inexpensive book illustrating many graceful longrifles made in Bedford County, PA.

LONGRIFLES OF PENNSYLVANIA, Vol. I JEFFERSON, CLARION & ELK COUNTIES   G. Shumway Publisher
by Russell E. Harriger
Illustrations of many rifles from this region plus much biographical information about the makers.

THE KENTUCKY RIFLE   by Merrill Lindsay   Arma Press & The Historical Soc. of York Co., PA
The only book ever produced to date showing color illustrations of many fine longrifles, mostly from Pennsylvania
and Maryland. o.p.

THE KENTUCKY RIFLE AND ME   by Edith G. Cooper   Edith G. Cooper Publisher
This work is profusely illustrated with photos of rifles from the upper Susquehanna Valley of Pennsylvania. o.p.

THE KENTUCKY RIFLE – A TRUE AMERICAN HERITAGE IN PICTURE anonymous   The Kentucky Rifle Assoc.
Published in 1967 and now out of print, this book has particularly fine illustrations showing three views each of 100
longrifles plus 19 pistol illustrations.   o.p.

THOUGHTS ON THE AMERICAN FLINTLOCK PISTOL   by Samuel E. Dyke   G. Shumway Publisher
This modest book has 125 illustrations of flintlock pistols.

MARYLAND LONGRIFLES   by Daniel D. Hartzler & James Bisher Whisker   Old Bedford Village Press
Much information about Maryland longrifles and their makers, over 200 pages of longrifle illustrations.

Additional titles produced by James B. Whisker, Ph.D.
GUNSMITHS OF BEDFORD, SOMERSET & FULTON COUNTIES,   GUNSMITHS OF WEST VIRGINIA
PENNSYLVANIA   GUNSMITHS OF VIRGINIA (Second Edition)
GUNSMITHS OF ADAMS, FRANKLIN, CUMBERLAND   LONG RIFLES OF VIRGINIA
COUNTIES, PENNSYLVANIA   BEHOLD THE LONGRIFLE
GUNSMITHS OF WESTERN PENNSYLVANIA   BEHOLD THE LONGRIFLE AGAIN
ARMS MAKERS OF WESTERN PENNSYLVANIA   GUNSMITHS OF THE CAROLINAS
ARMS MAKERS OF LANCASTER CO., PA   OHIO LONGRIFLES (V. I &II)
GUNSMITHS OF YORK COUNTY (PA)

OHIO GUNSMITHS & ALLIED TRADESMEN 1750 – 1950   by Donald A. Hutslar   Assoc. of Ohio Longrifle Collectors
A county-by-county study of the gunmakers who worked in Ohio, with many illustrations of the muzzle-loading
arms they produced.

LONGRIFLES OF NORTH CAROLINA Second Edition   by John Bivins, Jr.   G. Shumway Publisher
A study of North Carolina rifles and the gunsmiths who made them, with 162 halftone illustrations of rifles.   o.p.

NOTES ON SOUTHERN LONGRIFLES   by Jerry Noble   J. Noble Publisher
Longrifle makers of Tennessee, Mississippi, Alabama, and Georgia, are listed together with brief biographical
information and 42 pages of rifle illustrations.

Additional Titles:
MAINE MADE GUNS AND THEIR MAKERS   by Dwight B. Demeritt, Jr.   Maine State Museum
RHODE ISLAND ARMS MAKERS & GUNSMITHS 1643 – 1883   by Wm. O. Achtermier   Man At Arms Publisher
CALIFORNIA GUNSMITHS   by Lawrence P. Shelton   distributed by G. Shumway Publisher

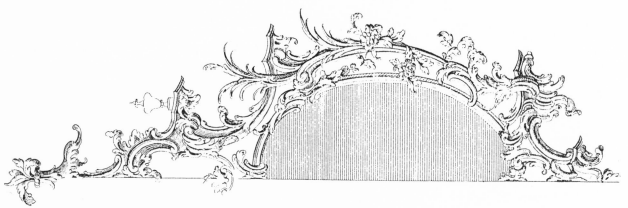

AMERICAN PIONEER VIDEO – This company specializes in producing videos concerning many aspects of longrifle building, and use for hunting and trekking. PO Box 50049, Bowling Green, KY 42101. Brochure free

BROWNELLS, INC. – This well-known company has been in business for over fifty years supplying a great variety of tools, equipment, and supplies to the gun world. 106 S. Front St., Montezuma, Iowa 50171. Catalog $3.75

ROBERT L. BAXTER - A large variety of parts and supplies for rifle builders. 1207 Nettie Dr., Miamisburg, Ohio 45342. Catalog $2.00

JIM CHAMBERS FLINTLOCKS LTD. – A variety of fine flint and percussion locks, assembled, or as unassembled parts. Rt. 1, Box 513-A, Chandler, NC 28715. Catalog free

HOMER L. DANGLER– This professional builder of muzzle-loading rifles also produces and sells videos concerning rifle building. PO Box 254, Addison, MI 49220. Brochure free

R. E. DAVIS COMPANY – Rifle and pistol barrels, Davis flint and percussion locks, rifle furniture, other assorted supplies. 3105 Lancaster-Circleville Rd., Lancaster, Ohio 43130. Catalog $5.00

DIXIE GUN WORKS, INC. – A very large catalog full of offerings of parts, supplies, and tools. Gun Powder Lane, PO Box 130, Union City, TN 38281. Catalog $5.00

DIXON'S MUZZLELOADING SHOP – Suppliers of parts and supplies for building muzzle-loading rifles and guns. Dixon's hosts the well-known Gunmakers Fair held the last weekend in July since 1979. 9952 Kunkels Mill Rd., Kempton, PA 19529. Catalog $5.00

DUNLAP WOODCRAFTS– Suppliers of a large variety of gunstock wood blanks. 1415 Wolftrap Run Rd., Vienna, VA 22182. Brochure free

DON EADS MUZZLELOADER BUILDERS SUPPLY – A catalog of parts and supplies for the muzzle-loader. 16075 Hwy. 22N, Lexington, TN 38351. Catalog $4.00

GETZ BARREL CO. – Manufacturers of premium barrels for the muzzle-loader. PO Box 88, Beavertown, PA 17813. Brochure free

GOLDEN AGE ARMS CO. – Muzzle-loading rifles and guns, shooting supplies, parts for building rifles, books, etc. 115 E. High St., PO Box 366, Ashley, Ohio 43003. Catalog $4.00

L & R LOCK CO. – Manufacturers of a variety of flint and percussion locks, and a variety of trigger mechanisms also. 1137 Pocalla Rd., Sumter, SC 29150-7558. Catalog $5.00

LOG CABIN SHOP – A catalog full of parts, supplies, tools, books and services for the muzzleloading rifle builder and shooter. 8010 Lafayette Rd., Lodi, Ohio 44254. Catalog $5.00

MANHATTAN SUPPLY CO. – This company specializes in selling machine tools and related supplies, including a large variety of drills, counterbores, taps, etc. Prices often are particularly favorable. MSC Industrial Supply Co., 151 Sunnyside Blvd., Plainview, NY 11803-9915. Catalog free

MOUNTAIN STATE MUZZLELOADING SUPPLIES, INC. – A large catalog of parts, tools, supplies, books, etc. for the muzzle-loader. #1 Muzzleloading Place, Dept. N, Williamstown, WV 26187. Catalog $8.00

TENNESSEE VALLEY MANUFACTURING – Flint and percussion locks, sights, furniture, and other parts for rifle building. Rt. 8, Box 440, Corinth, Mississippi 38834. Catalog $3.00

TRACK OF THE WOLF, INC. – A large and particularly attractive catalog full of everything for the muzzleloading rifle maker and shooter. Gun locks and furniture illustrated full size. PO Box 130, Osseo, MN 55369. Catalog $7.00

BOOKS AND TAPES ON MUZZLE-LOADER GUNSMITHING

FIREARMS BLUEING AND BROWNING   by R. H. Angier   Stackpole Books
The standard basic reference to rust-type gun blueing and browning.

JOURNAL OF HISTORICAL ARMS MAKING TECHNOLOGY – VOL. I – V   National Muzzleloading Rifle Assoc.
Volume V, June 1993, contains James Anderson article "Charcoal Bluing of Rifle Barrels."

BLACKPOWDER HOBBY GUNSMITHING   by Sam Fadala and Dale Storey
A wide range of topics covered in this 256-page book.

HAND RIFLING A MUZZLE LOADING RIFLE BARREL AT HOME   by Mark Wagner
Explains rifling of barrels with a hand-powered machine, with many illustrations of the machine and instructions on making one.

THE BASICS OF FIREARMS ENGRAVING   by Neil Hartliep
A manual used in the NRA schools' program to teach hammer-driven chisel techniques.

THE ART OF ENGRAVING   by James B. Meek
A classic reference to hammer-driven chisel work, that also deals with design and design layout on gun surfaces.

ENGRAVING ON PRECIOUS METALS   by A. Britain, S. Wolpert, P. Morton   Arco Publishing Co.
A text on hand engraving on the softer metals plus ivory.

HANDBOOK OF ORNAMENT   by Franz S. Meyer
Presents a great variety of illustrations for reference use in designing gun ornament.

MASTER FRENCH GUNSMITH'S DESIGNS OF THE XVII – XIX CENTURIES   by Stephen Grancsay
A great source for French, and some German designs, from the baroque period through the nineteenth centuries, but with no rococo designs. Out of print.

THE JEWELER'S SAW   by Alan Gutchess
A pamphlet showing how to make use of the jeweler's saw for gunsmithing work.

INSTRUCTIONS & HINTS FOR ASSEMBLING PIPE TOMAHAWKS   by Gerald and Alan Gutchess
A small book that tells a great deal about tomahawk assembly.

Instructional videos showing longrifle building procedures are offered by Homer L. Dangler of P.O. Box 254, Addison, MI 49220.

Instructional videos showing longrifle building procedures are offered by American Pioneer Video, P.O. Box 50049, Bowling Green, KY 42101.

This design, and those on pages 158, 164, 167, 168, are from Thomas Chippendale's book of 1762: THE GENTLEMAN & CABINET MAKER'S DIRECTOR

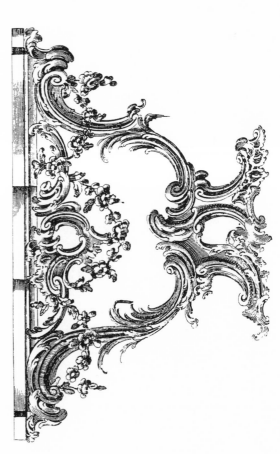

Frames for e Marble Slabs.

Published according to Act of Parliament 1750.

167

Fin

Designs   *for Sheilds.*

Publish'd according to Act of Parliament. 1761.